OTHER BOOKS BY ALEXANDER KING:

Mine Enemy Grows Older
May This House Be Safe from Tigers
Peter Altenberg's Evocations of Love

MY RIVAL

I SHOULD HAVE KISSED HER MORE

by Alexander King

1961

SIMON AND SCHUSTER
NEW YORK

Second Printing

LIBRARY OF CONGRESS CATALOG CARD NUMBER: 61–15125
MANUFACTURED IN THE UNITED STATES OF AMERICA
BY H. WOLFF, NEW YORK

To Margie,
with many silent prayers

CHAPTER ONE

I T RAINED VERY HARD on the day of my funeral, and, I must say, this pleased me enormously. From my earliest childhood on, I had always loved rain, because I was frequently ill during my boyhood in Vienna, and when I used to awaken in the morning and the weather seemed threatening, I realized with satisfaction that all the other children in the city would also have to spend their day indoors. It made the whole world equal; it muted the usual racket in the streets outside and reduced all human activities to a proper decorum. This early partiality to rain had remained with me all through my life.

The funeral parlor in the East Eighties was crowded with people, most of whom I had never known and whom I would most certainly never have wanted to know. There were a score or so of my friends there, too, of course, and I noticed that they eyed each other rather furtively, like a group of uneasy conspirators who were generally in the habit of meeting only after sundown but who had suddenly, by some incalculable mischance, been brought together by the cold light of day.

Also, let us confess it, each of them felt a certain twinge of guilty triumph that he had somehow successfully managed to outlive me. Since a good many of them had been standing around for quite a while in the phony, refrigerated refinement of the mortuary establishment, almost everyone present was simply dying for a hot cup of coffee. Actually this seems to be the basic need of the human heart in nearly every great crisis—a good hot cup of coffee.

They'd have to wait quite a while yet.

Although it had been clearly stipulated that there was to be no religious service of any sort, there was sure to be some kind of ceremonial rigmarole or the funerary functionaries wouldn't feel that they had properly earned their exorbitant fees. Perhaps they didn't even really care about this at all, but they were certainly anxious to make a decent impression on the assembled company. After all, every one of those present was destined to land in their hands sooner or later (theirs or their competitors'), so it was just as well to be a little somberly ritualistic—to display the proper seriousness of the firm and to demonstrate its full capacity to cope with the gruesomely inevitable on smooth and handsome terms, no matter how difficult the occasion.

I wondered whether some of the people in that room carried credit cards for just such exigencies. Maybe not yet, but it was surely coming.

Poor Margie had had to buy a coffin for me, despite the fact that I was only about to be cremated. There is some kind of a law about that. You've got to buy a coffin. Believe me, nobody, no matter how bewildered and annoyed by this piece of idiocy, is ever likely to put up much of an argument about it while the body of their dearly beloved is lying within hearing distance of the dispute. Although most people don't really believe that the dead can hear, there is always a certain whispered evasiveness in the behavior of all the survivors at funerals, as if the corpse might suddenly be roused from his eternal rest by the overly familiar sound of vulgar earthly haggling.

The undertakers, who are the natural beneficiaries of all these tactful goings on, are just as stony-faced and adamant now as the organized aristocracy of death always has been. They stoically collected their bitter tithes in ancient Egypt, where one third of the nation was in the embalming and burial business, and they still know how to make you cringe with embarrassment when you halfheartedly try to save a few shekels for the poor survivors who probably had the last anxious thoughts of the deceased when he was writhing in his final agony.

I was utterly disgusted with the whole proceeding, of course, and while I counted the house I kept carefully avoiding any special awareness of my poor shattered wife. Luckily, she hardly ever uses any make-up, so she didn't seem too terribly changed when she first entered the chapel and looked about her like a child that has awakened one morning upon a cold world which has forever been altered.

I noticed that some of my closest friends seemed particularly preoccupied, and I realized that they, poor dears, had suddenly come upon the unhappy thought that one of them, at least, ought to pronounce some suitable sentiments over my defenseless remains. One or two of them were already giving some pre-oratorical coughs, and I only wished I could have communicated with them and told them to please lay off. It occurred to me that the few remaining fragments of my wife's shattered composure were sure to be finally shivered by any impending self-conscious oratorical pomposities.

In fact, the whole brutally primitive and barbarian ritual was beginning to sadden me so much that I was strongly tempted to get out of it all and to get down to one of the deserted piers on the Hudson and to watch the rain come in layered sheets onto the khaki-colored waters of the wide, indifferent river.

But I hung on because I was curious and also because I'd always stayed on long after it was either useful or reasonable, even when I was still alive.

There's another thing that puzzled me—my awareness. How come? Here I was seemingly dissociated from my body, and yet I was fully conscious of everything that went on all around me. Maybe even a little more aware than usual. Only one thing was certain. My memory was no longer as good as it used to be. Indeed, as the afternoon wore on, I observed that it was actually getting weaker and weaker, and by the time the funeral was over I couldn't even remember the telephone number of my third wife's dopey brother. Of course, I hadn't spoken to him in about seventeen years; nevertheless, I was sure that only yesterday I had known both his address and his last phone number in Hollywood shortly after his marriage about twenty years ago.

That, indeed, is the worst about these things—that, with each man who dies, a whole world dies. When I am gone, who shall carry the memory of the multicolored sails as they dream themselves silently across the purple Adriatic, and who will recall the image of a child as it picks a silken star of edelweiss under the sun-soaked clouds of the high Tyrol? And even this is as nothing when I think that no one will any longer recall the sound of a camel coughing fitfully in the early dawn beside the Roman amphitheater by the seaside at Tunis. But, worst of all, what will become of my dearly cherished image of the pale-blue slip of ribbon that I saw peeking out of my loved one's hair on November 13 of last year? Who—who—

shall pay the world for this grievous loss and who—who—shall compensate the universe for this absolutely irreparable disaster?

Meanwhile the professional absurdities in the funeral parlor proceeded relentlessly. Near the doorway, as if undecided whether to enter, stood a little man I remembered having last seen in a night club over in Jersey sometime in 1939. His name was Frank Suhanotti and he used to run the dice table in the gaming room that was the real excuse for the existence of this sucker trap. What could he possibly want here? I had never been particularly friendly with him. Or had I? Maybe I had. This joint that he had been working in was run by some really big-time gangsters—with proper political protection, of course—and I'd gone there three or four times before I finally got around to speaking to this character. I'd won about $6,000 that night, and I suppose I must have been a little worried about being hijacked out of my dough before I even left the local grounds. At any rate, I asked him about it.

"I'm leery about carrying all this lettuce out of here," I said. "Maybe I could leave it in the safe until tomorrow. It's about two-thirty now, and you never know what you're liable to run into on the way to the George Washington Bridge."

"I'll get a couple of boys to take you across," he said. "You can give 'em something when you get home, if you feel like it."

"How much?" I said.

"Oh, I don't know. Give 'em a C-note if you feel like it."

"Fine," I said. "Where do I find 'em?"

"I'll phone downstairs," he said.

He did.

"You oughtn'a come here in the first place," he said. "I mean, a guy like you."

"You're a hell of a gambler," I said, "trying to keep the suckers outa here."

"I hope to get away from here myself some day," he said.

"I got certain obligations—but some day I'll get away, too."

"Married?" I said.

"Yeah. Two kids. The girl is at the Ursulines. She's fifteen —bright as a button. The boy gets out of college next year. Fordham."

"Well, good luck. I guess these are my guardian angels coming now, ain't they?"

"Yeah," he said. "Don't talk to 'em. Just shell out when you get home."

"The boys" looked like typical postgraduate hoodlums anomalously stuffed into tight tuxedos. But they clammed up solid throughout the ride to New York, and when I gave them a folded one-hundred-dollar bill in front of my doorway, they didn't even bother to look at it.

I went back quite a few times to this joint after that, but Frank seemed so obviously pained by my presence that I hardly exchanged another word with him. Also, after a couple of trips, I lost most of the money that I had won, and some of my own besides, which seemed to disgust him a great deal. So naturally we finally just ignored each other. I understood him perfectly well. Here was I, an educated man spending time in such a dive, when all his hopes for his children were centered on their education. I was just shaking the foundations of his whole imaginative life-structure. Education to him was a guarantee of getting somewhere in the world, somewhere noble and elevated and altogether unreachable by the likes of him. I was lousing up his whole philosophy—that's what I was doing.

I'd forgotten all about him during the following years and I wondered how or why he'd bothered to come here today. Probably read about it in the papers. I'd noticed that Catholics after their fifties have a tendency to read the obituary notices every morning, and that is where he had probably come across my name.

14

There were a lot of other strange people in that crowd, people whom I hadn't seen for quite a long time. Hatvanyi Tivadar, a Hungarian writer, whom I'd last spoken to some thirteen years ago, was there in the same reversible coat he'd had on when I'd last seen him. It is a strange thing about these reversible coats that the weather never seems to be quite suited to the side that the wearer has chosen to expose. With that crazy rain still going on outside, Hatvanyi was on this occasion wearing the waterproof side next to his skin. I recalled a visit with him one day in the upper West Seventies somewhere, where he festered in a ground-floor room in some dreadfully fungoid hotel that had certainly never seen better days. The morbid stink of that room stayed with me for years, and I don't think I ever saw Hatvanyi again after that one disastrous visit. Room smells have always had a potently depressing effect on me—especially furnished rooms, because I always felt that their sinister odors were definitely caused by the residual exhalations of boredom and despair that represented the cumulative emanation of the various derelicts who had led their anguished lives in these sordid surroundings. I recalled that on this visit of mine, Hatvanyi had read to me some pages from the manuscript of a novel he was working on at the time. It was a horrible, semiautobiographical piece of dreariness, full of old Hungarian local color, and after listening to him for about fifteen minutes I found that it would be impossible for me to keep my eyes open if I continued to pay any further attention to his words. Hatvanyi was a chunky, brindle-haired Central European with a baby-pink complexion and a manner that was always full of unmotivated expectancy. He seemed constantly on the *qui vive* for something spectacularly pleasant to happen, and it goes without saying that nothing ever really did.

At any rate, there we sat in that ghastly furnished room of his, almost penniless, the both of us—I soaked in mor-

15

phine and he drenched with hope-dope. We were a great little team, that's for sure, and the setting couldn't have been more appropriate.

I wonder if there will ever arise some great poet among us who will tackle and properly render the subject of the American furnished room.

What a theme! Just think about it—think of the furnishings of these places and try to envisage where all this junk could possibly have come from. It came from auction rooms, of course. I knew that well enough because I'd bought some of this garbage there myself from time to time. I think some of those auction rooms ought to be preserved intact for posterity, and believe me, when I say "intact," I mean with all the people that one generally finds there—the auctioneers, the furniture movers, the browsers, the clients—everybody.

Man, the collections I've seen in my life. I sometimes wondered whether this sort of shoddy, broken merchandise wasn't perhaps formed by the actual bodily exudations of the human refuse that invariably congregated in such places. That is really the only way to explain the origin of some of the incredible objects that were put on sale there week after week. It defies human imagination to believe that anyone ever deliberately designed any of these monstrosities, and yet I never saw anything put up for auction so utterly senseless and useless that somebody didn't think it worth the having.

This room of Hatvanyi's was full of little three-legged end tables that tumbled over the minute you came anywhere near them. This elderly, genderless creature had a huge bed that ate up half his room, and the coverlet on it would have been overly decorative even for a seraglio.

As his voice droned on and on and the hideous smells began to work their way more and more into my system, and as I kept staring at the peeling walls and the cracked ceiling and my eyes kept wandering across all that crippled furniture in that ignoble mausoleum of total failure, I suddenly found it quite difficult to keep myself from bawling out loud.

Well, after a while even that pathetic, self-absorbed noodle seemed to have noticed that I wasn't paying very strict attention to his reading, and since he had nothing else to offer me, not even a lemonade or a cookie, he finally got up and began to blunder vacantly around that fantastic room of his in search of some shred of hospitable diversion for me. At last he opened a closet in which the rest of his wardrobe had been decently hidden until that moment, and, rummaging around among some soiled shirts and torn, old-fashioned underwear, he finally brought out the most pathetic, blotched and scratched-up violin I'd ever seen in all my days. It really looked like a much-abused child's fiddle of some kind, and I noticed that the bow he had wedged under the strings had flung one messy strand of dirty gray hair across the body of the instrument, and this more than anything else gave that whole depressing tableau a positively obscene air of superannuated coquettishness.

"I never play it any more," he said. He started to plunk the strings of his musical ruin, and I could see that his pudgy fingers were quite embarrassed by this unusual exercise. At last he lifted the silly fiddle up against his chest as the great gypsy fiddlers of Hungary used to do and began to play.

He played very well.

I could hold it back no longer, and so I just started to bawl. Fortunately for me, he was so busy with his serenade to a preoccupied destiny that he didn't even notice it. I got up and went to the toilet, leaned up against the doorpost and wept for ten minutes without a stop. The music came to me through the closed door, and it was plain that he once must have been a very fine musician indeed. He had an enormous repertoire,

17

too; Mozart, Haydn, Liszt, snatches of all sorts of folk songs dribbled in on me, and I finally had to turn on both faucets just to drown him out. I found myself mechanically repeating a few lines of Rilke's poem "The Neighbor."

> *Fremde Geige, gehst du mir nach?* . . .
> *Spielen dich Hunderte? Spielt dich einer?*

> Strange violin, are you following me? . . .
> Do hundreds play you? Or does one?

It seemed to Rilke that wherever you landed, in some strange town, in some bitter, alien room, somebody somewhere nearby would be playing a violin. And that is why he wrote:

> *Fremde Geige, gehst du mir nach?*
> *In wieviel fernen Städten schon sprach*
> *deine einsame Nacht zu meiner?*
> *Spielen dich Hunderte? Spielt dich einer?*

> *Gibt es in allen grossen Städten*
> *solche, die sich ohne dich*
> *schon in den Flüssen verloren hätten?*
> *Und warum trifft es immer mich?*

> *Warum bin ich immer der Nachbar derer,*
> *die dich bange zwingen zu singen*
> *und zu sagen: Das Leben ist schwerer*
> *als die Schwere von allen Dingen?*

> Strange violin, are you following me?
> In how many distant cities already
> has your lonely night spoken to mine?
> Do hundreds play you? Or does one?

Are there in all great cities
such as without you would
already have lost themselves in the rivers?
And why does it always happen to me?

Why am I always neighbor to those
who fearfully force you to sing
and to say: Life is heavier
than the heaviness of all things?*

How altogether fitting that Hatvanyi had come to my funeral. I was only sorry that I had so completely forgotten him in the intervening years. If I had remembered, I might have asked Margie to tell him to bring his fiddle; and I think it would have added just the proper note to the occasion if she had requested him to play some of those tattered Old World songs on that dreadful, derelict violin of his. Meanwhile, there he sat, still pink-faced, the brindle hair just a shade grayer, although there was a certain unfamiliar touch of bewilderment in his moist blue eyes, occasioned perhaps by the one unavoidable fact he had encountered that day—my death.

Another one I hadn't seen in a long time was Doris Finger, who stood way up in front like a chief mourner. She wore black, but as a matter of fact she had always worn black, because it was her favorite color. Maybe she just went from one funeral to another. There are such people. This Doris person was artistic; that is to say, she used to sleep with artists and even support them if necessary. There are many women like that in New York. It is a kind of religion with them to worship artists. They all write poetry, and some of them even

19

paint. I'd never had anything to do with Doris at all. She just hung around for a while until I moved from her neighborhood and she could no longer find me. Well, today she had finally traced me to where I couldn't possibly escape her.

There were quite a few other people there in the same condition—people who had known me vaguely and throughout the years had finally gotten to hate my guts because my books had suddenly started to sell, and I'd become an undeniable success. They looked fairly cheerful now—almost as if they'd come to a particularly auspicious picnic. Most of these creatures had always been rather ill at ease in life, and never actually seemed to have quite recovered from their birth traumas.

Some years ago, after I'd been talking to a pretty shrewd and rather drunken psychiatrist who was bugs on the subject of birth shock, I even got around to planning a refuge of some kind for people who wanted to get back into the womb again. I intended this place for the rich, of course, since the chief business of psychiatry nowadays is to get the rich and successful reconciled to their lot. This resort that I had in mind was going to have rooms with soft, yielding walls, a little moist and perhaps even a little fetid, to simulate as closely as possible their places of origin. I even had a title for this intra-uterine retreat. I was going to call it Hotel Placenta.

Nothing came of this either.

Meanwhile, nearly two hundred people had collected in the mortuary when a big fat Jewish man with a scant Chinese mustache, called Otto Meidlin, suddenly got up and started to talk. He said, "Alex King didn't write a great autobiography; he lived one."

He said lots of other things too. He said I'd been a genius, that I'd been much misunderstood, and that a good many people who'd had the good fortune to know me intimately would never forget the glow of my personality; he also said that none of my work really did justice to my talents because my most valuable assets were untranslatable and had unhappily perished with me.

And a lot more along that line.

The truth of the matter was that Otto had once lent me twenty-five dollars, and he had never quite forgiven me for not paying it back. Nevertheless, he had tears in his eyes as he talked about me now, and it really did him a great deal of good to butter me up in this post-mortem summation. I don't think that anybody in that hideous, sterile room had the slightest idea who he was, and Doris Finger seemed the only one really interested in what he was saying. She was slowly wending her way in his direction because she hoped to talk to him at greater length about me and my problems later on in some quiet place, over a hot cup of coffee, of course.

I was depressed by what all this was going to cost poor Margie, because I knew that the undertakers were a relentless and fiendishly expensive lot. I remembered particularly that when I'd lived down in the Village some years before, my Italian neighbors would go into hock for the rest of their lives just because Poppa had to have a decent funeral. The poor man had never had a decent life, but his death had to be properly celebrated even if it ruined everybody for years to come.

The congregation was obviously getting restless, but Otto still held on with his jabbering. He was certainly getting his twenty-five dollars' worth out of me at last.

At this point I noticed one of the assistant undertakers beginning to whisper discreetly with my friend Herman Stoltz, who was sitting in the last row on the aisle, all by himself.

"Excuse me," said the undertaker. "Has there been any provision made for a proper receptacle for the ashes of the deceased? You see, we deliver them to the widow in just a simple cardboard container."

Herman looked at this character quizzically for a moment. "If you ask me," he said, "I think Alex will feel great in a cardboard box. Just remember to mark it 'Unperishable.' "

The funerary factotum wasn't the least bit taken aback. Not yet. "It is generally preferred by the family," he said, "to select a suitable airtight urn with discreet, decorative handles. We have about twenty-six styles to choose from— Classic, Renaissance, Modern—and I thought maybe somebody ought to discuss this with the widow."

Herman chuckled. "You know," he said, "there are sixteen sculptors sitting within spitting distance from me in this room right now who'd make Margie any kind of a pot she had a mind for. As a matter of fact, I've been doing quite a bit of modeling myself lately, and I think I've got just the thing she'd probably like. It was going to be a coal scuttle for my mother, but it shrank quite a bit in the firing in that homemade kiln of mine, and I'll bring it around to her later on. Glad you reminded me."

The undertaker looked stupefied, abandoned Herman, and as he moved off was in his turn accosted by Frank Suhanotti, my gambler acquaintance from Jersey.

"When do you think the services are going to begin?" he asked. "I gotta get to work in about half an hour and I wouldn't like to get up later on and disturb the religious services, see?"

"There aren't going to be any services," said the undertaker. "No services at all—by special request of the deceased."

Frank was puzzled and finally looked quite disturbed.

"You mean there ain't gonna be no minister or rabbi or nothin'?"

"No sermon, no prayers, no flowers, and no funeral," said the ghoul contemptuously.

"Well," said Frank, "I guess I'll just run along then. All I

22

can say is, he certainly carried on straight to the end. He lived like a nut and he died like a nut!"

When, a few minutes later, the gambler left the funeral parlor, he was instantly accosted by an obviously demented, hare-lipped little girl, who asked him to inscribe his name in her autograph album.

Which he promptly did.

CHAPTER TWO

THIS DAYDREAM about my funeral, in all its minute completeness, came to me early one morning while I was soaking myself in the bathtub. I often think about my death, several times each day as a matter of fact, but this was the first time I'd ever dwelt at any length on my final obsequies. Later on it came to me that I'd overlooked a good many other people who were quite likely to appear on such an occasion. Myra Crosley, for instance, was more than an even bet to turn up for a last look at my mortal remains. I hadn't thought about her in many years, either, but I had a strange feeling that parts of me were still in orbit on the outer fringes of her peculiar awareness. I had originally come to know Myra in an unusual and rather romantic manner.

I was living at that time over in the East Forties, in the Turtle Bay section of New York somewhere, and I recall that although it was the height of summer, I had somehow managed to acquire a rather shattering cold.

I had been suffering under the wretchedness of it for nearly ten days when one evening after I got home from work I felt so completely pooped I decided to call my doctor and have him come over for a look at me. The girl from his answering service told me that he'd gone away for the weekend, but she suggested that I consult another physician who was prepared to take over his patients during his absence.

For some reason, I decided against it and after I'd hung up the receiver I felt suddenly so feeble that I crawled onto my bed, clothes and all, and instantly fell into a deep stupor. I must have been lying there for quite a long while, too, because when I finally opened my eyes it was obviously pretty late at night. You can always tell what hour of the day it happens to be in the busier midtown sections of Manhattan by the mere sound of the traffic that happens to pass your door.

I judged it to be about one-thirty or two o'clock. My mouth was bitterly dry, my head seemed to be on fire, and I felt like a man who had reached an absolutely desperate extreme of physical and mental exhaustion. I happened to be between wives at the time and because such a circumstance was a rare occasion in my life, I began to feel very sorry for myself in my lonely and abandoned condition. Let me make this a little clearer. Ever since I was seventeen years old, and even long before that, I had, one way or another, never been without some female companionship. This is to say, there was someone around to listen to my jabbering and who, in an emergency, was prepared to hand me an icebag or a cup of hot tea. Now, then, although my little apartment was quite comfortable and beautifully furnished, and lacking in no advantage that a modern landlord with high rents could provide, I was suddenly steeped in the deepest doldrums of depression because once, for a wonder, I was living quite alone. My formerly tight little world was unhinged—fierce, deadly drafts were blowing at me from all directions, and not a single compassionate hand was stretched out to comfort or protect me.

It was a really dark moment in my life.

I hardly ever took time out for self-pity, but because this was a new sensation for me, I wallowed in it to the point of ultimate shamelessness. Also, I had, as it later turned out, about 104 degrees fever, and my carcass was racked by all the ghastly syndromes of a badly neglected case of influenza.

At this point, as I felt myself sinking into oblivion again, I reached down in sudden desperation, pulled off one of my shoes and flung it wildly in the direction of the nearest window.

And then I must have passed out again, because when I opened my eyes a tall, pretty young woman dressed in a very chic peignoir was leaning over me and putting a thermometer in my mouth.

When I made a movement to get up, she gently pushed my head back on the pillow and said, "Keep still till I take your temperature."

"Well," I thought, "this is surely a most agreeable figment of my fevered imagination, and, properly enough, she has a tiny mole on her neck, and, besides that, her touch is as cool as the fingers of an early-morning lilac bush. Has anyone ever had such an insane life as I? Here I am, dying of pneumonia or something worse, and suddenly this wonderfully composed hamadryad shows up at my crumpled bedside and puts a revivifying icicle into my burning mouth."

She took out the thermometer, looked at it critically, and said, "How long have you been lying here like this, anyway?"

"Since early this evening," I said.

"But you've been sick a lot longer than that, haven't you?"

"Yes," I said. "Could I please have a drink of water?"

She went into the kitchen and brought me a drink.

26

"You ought to have a doctor," she said. "Your temperature is way up, and somebody ought to stay here and take care of you. Is there anyone you want me to call?"

"We'll have to get a nurse," I said. "I'm all alone just now, and most of my friends are away for the summer. I'm sorry to trouble you like this."

"That's all right," she said. "I'll make you a pitcher of lemonade and get you some aspirins from over in my house, and in the morning if you aren't any better, I'll ring my doctor and get him to find you a nurse. I'll be right back."

"Just a minute," I said. "What's your name, miss?"

"My name is Myra," she said. "Myra Crosley. I'm your neighbor across the way. That is to say, I live in the next street, really, but our gardens adjoin. That is how your shoe nearly smacked me on the head while I was opening my window. I'll be right back."

In a little while she returned with the lemonade and the aspirins, and her beautiful and tranquil presence so definitely reactivated the vital juices in my harassed frame that I was even able to go to the bathroom and change into my pajamas. However, this splurge of energy did not last very long, and a few minutes after I hit the bed I dozed off again. I woke three or four times during the night, and each time I did she quietly got up from the couch across the room where she had bedded herself down and gave me a cool drink. I tried to thank her through my cracked and swollen lips, and once I even warned her about a possible infection to herself.

"Don't worry," she said. "I've been a lot around sick people, and I never caught anything yet. You just try to sleep and we'll get the doctor as soon as it is daylight."

I was still sleeping when the doctor eventually arrived, and he turned out to be an old friend of Myra's; and even in the state I was in I had no trouble noticing that he had more than just a casual interest in her. He was a young guy with a shock

27

of black hair, and he obviously loathed me on sight. Nevertheless, the healer in him took the upper hand in our first encounter, and although I'm sure he considered my ailment an intrusive nuisance in her life, he ministered to me quite effectively and proceeded about his business with an air of detached efficiency that I rather welcomed.

I discovered in a little while that Myra had a whole slew of such Launcelots in her entourage, and that most of them, including her lawyer, her dentist, and even her liquor dealer, had all at one time or another proposed marriage to her.

Meanwhile I was good and sick, and Myra, who by default seemed to have assumed responsibility for my case, decided not to hire a nurse for me after all.

"I can look after him this weekend," she said, "and if he isn't improved by Monday, I can always find somebody then."

The doctor and I tried to talk her out of it, but she finally had her way, and with mouth pursed in prissy disapproval, the Aesculapius finally left us.

Because this little event—I mean the emergence of Myra Crosley as a midnight Florence Nightingale in my life—could so easily be developed into a hideous serial for the *Saturday Evening Post*, I have purposely trimmed it of all extraneous details. I have told it as baldly and unceremoniously as I know how. But, as is plain to see, the romantic giblets were all present, nevertheless, and despite my strong desire to tell about this as matter-of-factly as I can, I'm unable to keep them out of sight any longer, because Myra was nothing if not a twenty-one-carat darling.

By the following Monday morning I was so much improved that I was able to sit out in the sun in my own little back yard, and when the next weekend rolled around, I even walked across to her little garden and paid my first visit *chez elle*.

After that, a good many unaccountable things happened, and although I have frequently thought about them in inter-

28

vening years, I must confess I never quite understood the curious psychobiochemical mystery that remained as an insoluble sediment at the bottom of our curious communion. It stands to reason that I got quite a crush on her. That was to be expected, and there was nothing insoluble about that. What was strange, almost from the very beginning though, was the fact that I was perfectly content to keep my relationship to her in a state of mercurial ambivalence; that I had no desire to establish any binding certainty between us, although it was perfectly clear to me that Myra had come to care a good deal about me, too.

Now, remember that I've always been a marrying type of man; I mean that I've never been happy with girl friends who were available whenever I just happened to have a hankering for them. In short, I was never the à la carte type, and although I've been occasionally involved with certain ladies whom I didn't finally marry, I can truthfully say that by and large my existence has always had a certain table d'hôte stability about it.

I liked Myra's way of life, as well as her person, very much. She had a fabulous apartment, and her garden, which at its inception must have been just a dingy back yard like my own, had, under her painstaking ministrations, become something more than merely decorative. She had a great deal of taste, and I say "taste" advisedly, because I have some rich friends who simply transplant whole tropical retreats onto their city rooftops, and these arboreal explosions only testify to their sound financial condition and nothing else. At the end of each summer these feverish landscapes have to be promptly thrown down the garbage chutes.

Not Myra's. She definitely had a way with plants, and the most collapsed and ailing vegetable derelict began to prosper unaccountably under the persuasive urgings of her cool, competent hands. At the end of each summer her little garden was carefully packed away under burlap, and at the first sign of spring everything began to bloom magically back into abundant life again.

Her home was equally well balanced. She had filled it with Early American antiques, but I had seen time and again how in other people's surroundings such a collection tended to engender a certain stultifying, museum atmosphere where all bodily or spiritual relaxation was out of the question.

She had a lot of style that was never oppressively evident. I suppose she was fashionable in the noblest sense of that almost senseless term. After we had become lovers, I had ample opportunity to study her at close range and at my leisure, and I can truthfully say, even after all these years, that I have never met anyone who moved in this uneasy world with a better sense of form and tempo.

In the beginning I used to think it was perhaps this ever-present feeling of instinctive decorum that precluded a final sense of intimacy between us, no matter how ultimately involved we became with one another. Later I discovered that this was not so, that my failure to achieve a total and uncritical submersion in the mainstream of Myra's life was due to some other factor, was probably due to the enormous difference in the spiritual and physical raw materials from which our characters had originally drawn their first conditioning, and that our emotional confrontation had occurred too late for an altogether successful welding.

This was also, of course, pure moonshine, since none of the other women I did get permanently involved with had ever had more than mere fragments of experience that could in any rational way be related to my own peculiar past existence.

I really didn't know what was wrong.

It is particularly puzzling since Myra was surely one of the most beautiful women I had ever known. She was about twenty-seven at the time I met her, and had been divorced nearly three years. She told me that she had been married to an aviation engineer whom she had originally met at college, and that their separation had had the usual depressing side effects but had, generally speaking, worked itself out without rancor.

"I didn't marry a stick-in-the-mud businessman," she said, "I married a stick-in-the-air aviator. He was never home for more than two or three days at a time, and I stood it as long as I could. I stood it for five years. We first met when we were practically kids, and we certainly should never have gotten married at all. The real reason I got mixed up with him, I suppose, was that all my friends at school had gotten engaged all around me, and since he was a good-looking boy with good prospects, I thought, Why not?"

"But surely you must have loved him," I said.

"It isn't hard to be in love at nineteen. Most of the girls I knew had gone to this coed school so that they'd find somebody to marry. I suppose that is the reason so many girls do jam into those colleges all over the country. It wasn't my reason, but I fell into the general pattern out of sheer nonresistance and also out of adolescent stupidity."

Myra was tall—about two inches taller than I, which, by the way, didn't bother me in the least, because I'm not one of those people who have to dominate their women by size. It certainly never seemed to worry her. She had a tawny complexion, dark hair, gray-green eyes, and carried herself like a high-priced mannequin. But actually she never could have been a fashionable model, because she had a sensuous figure and buoyantly developed mammary glands. As far as I've been able to observe, the seductive, pear-shaped buttocks of the Venus Callipygous never appear in *Vogue* and *Harper's Bazaar*. I just recently read in the magazine section of a local newspaper an article written by two of the best-known ladies in the world of television commercials in which these highly solvent cadavers cheerfully boasted about their physical limitations.

"We have no cleavage problem," they said, "and although we have the bodies of slender, adolescent boys, we manage to earn $200,000 a year posing for TV advertising."

All I can tell you is that these two pathetic creatures look like nothing so much as a couple of broomhandles with exploded bird's-nests on top—bleached bird's-nests, at that. As I looked at their sparse, angular dimensions, I couldn't help wondering what a lover could possibly do when he was alone with one of these hags. I suppose he could settle down to passionately fondling their money bags for lack of anything else to hold on to.

At any rate, these weren't my problems with Myra. She had originally come from Georgia, of all places, but had with infinite patience and taste managed to lose every last vestige of her native accent. There is no denying that she was still a Southerner. Some of her food preferences and, I think, some minor shades of her social predilections were unquestionably traceable to the state of her origin.

One of my friends who was also stuck on her, and who wondered why I didn't get really serious about her, said to me one day, "I think you'd marry Myra tomorrow if only she weren't white."

He was wrong of course.

I had a great deal of respect for the way she had integrated herself in the rhythm of her peculiar life. She was a beautiful woman living alone in a big, mischievous town like New York, and so it was inevitable that eventually she would become the much victimized target not only of proposals and of propositions, but even of certain amorous patterns of behavior which were frequently not too far removed from actual coercion and even blackmail. Amidst all these mostly male machinations,

Myra had somehow managed to maintain her admirable poise. Day after day she was exposed to the smirks and oglings of every accidental messenger boy who happened to stumble into her quiet life, and yet she functioned as tranquilly as if an invisible protective curtain had been draped around her.

It was quite a performance. I was very much impressed with it, and after a while I became deeply attached to her and the habit pattern of my life needed her very badly. We stuck it out together, that way, for the better part of two years, and then one day a magazine offered me a job which made it necessary for me to go to Central America. I took this job quite suddenly, packed my bags and went off on the trip without her. I won't pretend that it was easy. She had been unbelievably kind to me, and I was certainly very fond of her. During our relationship I had found many surprising facets in her character which profoundly affected and delighted me. She had an ardently passionate nature, she played an excellent game of chess, and she was deeply and intelligently devoted to all the arts I myself cherished most.

Later on, I often used to think of her with profound regret and wish I had paid greater heed to the whispering voices in my heart that had urged me to marry her. My life might have taken an entirely different turn. Who knows?

I saw her only once more after that critical separation which took me out of her life. Some fifteen years ago I ran into her again on the day before Christmas, in front of Macy's on Thirty-fourth Street. The big-city holiday madness was churning all around us when we suddenly looked into each other's eyes and instinctively reached out our hands in greeting. I touched her cold cheek with my lips and a great gladness came over me as I held her in my arms for a moment. But in less than thirty seconds it became clear to me that we had really nothing to say to each other, at least nothing that could be said in a holiday shopping crowd in the heart of New York.

33

Also I believe that neither one of us was actually too anxious to warm up the fragments of our memories in any of the nearby coffee shops; so, after exchanging a few standard banalities on the rackety street corner, we parted again, and this time for good.

When we finally shook hands she said, "Are you married?"

"Not at the moment," I said.

She looked surprised. "So what happens if you should suddenly get ill?"

"Oh," I said, "I suppose I'll just have to shift for myself as best I can."

"I see," she said. "Besides, if anything does go wrong, you can always throw a shoe through somebody's window, can't you?"

You see, a damned hep chick, too.

So what could have been wrong?

Could it be that she always did just the right thing at the right time? I suddenly remembered that in the old days she'd always had the right books, the right magazines, and even the right phonograph records on tap—Richard Tauber singing "Matinata," and Bunny Berigan blowing "I Can't Get Started," and all the other stuff that was current among the truly informed. I'm sure that nowadays she'd have songs by Dietrich Fischer Dieskau, *Carmina Burana* by Karl Orff, and very probably one of Gerry Mulligan's latest releases.

Could that have been what botched it between us?

I never knew.

I still don't.

I've just reread all that I've written so far about Myra and myself, and I find that, in my eagerness to be totally detached, I seem to have drained off the whole meaningful marrow of that story. I think I've been just a little too objective and have only succeeded in giving something of a lopsided account of

34

the various happenings between us. After all, two years is quite a long spell for a modern romance, and it stands to reason that our relationship must have suffered quite a bit of upsy-downsy-ness during that time. It did. There were occasions when I couldn't imagine my life without her, and yet it sometimes happened that I could barely get myself to cross the threshold of that bewitching house of hers.

For instance, I've never bothered to mention the fine old acacia tree that stood in the center of Myra's garden and the strange influence that this anomalous arboreal exile had on my whole emotional life. In fact, I think I can safely say that it was this tree more than anything else that set the tone for my peculiar misgivings about her, and in due time came to cast an ominous shadow across my euphoric heart. This tree had originally stood in someone else's back yard, quite a few blocks away from us, and Myra and I had just accidentally spied it through an open house door one Sunday afternoon.

"Look," I said, "an acacia tree. . . . What a strange thing to see in the middle of a stone quarry like New York."

"It is a beauty, isn't it?" she said. "I wonder how it got here."

"In the spring the blossoms have such a sweet odor," I said, "that as a child, visiting some friends in Hungary—where I saw this tree for the first time—I got so drunk with the smell of it I couldn't stop myself from eating a whole cluster of flowers."

"The same thing happened to me," she said. "I guess children are so impulsive and direct in their love, it must be a common thing for them to do things like that. I remember I used to do it with jasmine blossoms too."

And that was that.

But soon afterward I had to go out of town for three days, and when I came back to New York, the acacia tree was standing in Myra's garden and, what's more, some of its longest branches even reached over as far as my own back windows.

She had bought the tree, of course, and I remember quite clearly that, at the time, my mind consistently refused to picture any possible series of sequential events that could logically have led up to this transaction. I don't know why, but there seemed something ruthlessly piratical about the way that tree had been hijacked from its native loam and been transplanted, root and branch, into our compound, just for our special delectation and pleasure.

I've avoided saying it so far, but Myra was certainly very rich. What's more, she had always been rich, and although she had a stunning wardrobe and moved about amid unmistakably costly surroundings, I'd somehow managed for quite a while to ignore the basic implications of such a state of affairs.

So, she was rich!!! So what?!?

Well, it didn't really matter to me, since a rich wife is not necessarily an insurmountable handicap. Actually, it shouldn't have disturbed me any more than the fact that she was a couple of inches taller than I.

But, after a little while, it did disturb me; mostly because her family had *always* had money and so there were unquestionably whole areas of human experience for which Myra had no frame of reference whatever. It wasn't only that she'd never missed a meal in her life, it was simply that the anxieties and misgivings of her past had been trivialized by the overly facile application of money. Since she had been orphaned in early childhood, her problems had always been glibly dealt with by well-fed, well fee'd lawyers and administrative guardians who casually pretended that the world was populated by an aggregation of greedy mendicants who were more than anxious to be of service to their financial superiors.

I don't mean to imply that she was heartless or unimaginative. Not a bit of it. And, unlike other young women of her brand and ilk, she had no need to multiply her sensations in-

36

definitely just to feel alive. But the taint existed, just the same. She *was*, occasionally, rather alarmingly detached.

That was the real spook that shattered my complacence. You see, I'd always had the feeling (long before I'd ever known Myra) that it was much safer and saner for all concerned if the rich consorted exclusively with the rich. They had the same basic advantages and the same common ailments. They understood one another as kangaroos or giraffes understand one another. Their environmental conditions were not unique to *them* and they were able to communicate without the slightest fear of being misunderstood. The antennae along their alarm centers were tuned to the same critical wave lengths, and whatever frightened or reassured one of them would tend to terrify or assuage all the rest.

You mustn't think that I invented this setup for a deadly syllogism just out of an overabundance of wit or frustration. Oh, no. I'd come to my earnest conclusions by having frequently had occasion to hobnob with some of the well-heeled members of the human species, and I'd discovered quite early that despite their earth-bound status, they had, nevertheless, certain undeniable extraterrestrial attributes which definitely cut them off from a good measure of common human experience.

They couldn't help it. It just happens to them. Naturally, my diagnosis applies only partially to the newly rich. *They*, after all, can still remember the days of their great down-and-outness, and so they tend to overact and to overcompensate in all directions. I think they are really just like you and me, only a little more annoying.

I'm talking specifically about the ones who've *always* had it, and whose seat in heaven has been as surely reserved as their box at the opera.

And so, I think if there *is* any explanation as to why I did not get myself permanently mired in Myra's honeypot—it is a fair guess to say that it was much too golden for me, and that the rainbow which led to it might in the end not prove even as serviceable for my purposes as a rusty fire escape.

Come to think of it, there's another girl I never married because she was too rich for my plebeian taste. Her name was Hilda Varci, and her people owned the numberless Varcity Dress Shops all over the country.

The first time I came to see her, she lived in a penthouse atop the family mansion in the East Fifties, and her snug little eyrie was fitted out with the sexiest furniture I'd ever seen. I never knew that furniture could ever get itself into such a condition of seductive, almost orgiastic, frenzy. The curvaceously twisted legs of all those chairs and couches were encased in lacy frills and drawers of all sorts, and if you moved a few of these pieces together, it instantly looked like a Ziegfeld chorus line. I was young enough, and silly enough, to be gassed by all this writhing upholstery, and Hildy suited such an environment so perfectly that I accepted each day's goodness without a single Jewish afterthought.

Later on, I began to notice that my beloved never wore the same dress or hat for a second time—which made some kind of sense, too, since her people were in the business. What made *no* sense to me, after a while, was that she'd bundle up all these one-day-old clothes and hand them to her maid to get rid of.

I said to her, "Hildy, what does your maid do with all those discarded hats and dresses—sell them, or what?"

"I don't know," said Hilda. "I think she gives them to the milkman or the letter carrier, or to whoever happens to want them."

"In that case," I said, "I'd appreciate it if you'd let *me* take them, because I know at least a dozen young women in the Village who'd be damned grateful if they could get such nice clothes, and believe me, you'd be doing a real kindness to them."

"All right," she said. "I'll fill you up a couple of suitcases each week, and you can give them away to your friends if you like."

And that's what she did.

The hired help around the house didn't much care for this public-spirited move. I used to get pretty dirty looks from all of those with whom I had any personal contact, and subtle rumblings of mutiny came in rebellious waves, even from belowstairs, from the kitchen and pantry regions, and spent themselves ineffectually on the granite walls of my indifference. In a little while, a real cabal was formed against me by that group of leeches, and while I didn't actually find any ground glass in my meals, the service in my direction deteriorated perceptibly. What made it worse was that the kids to whom I passed on all this lush haberdashery would write fulsome letters of thanks to Hilda, and that fine girl would sometimes read these gushy thank-you notes aloud over the dinner table.

Meanwhile, all those freshly discarded clothes that I lugged downtown every week created an absolute fashion revolution along MacDougal street and the territories adjacent thereto, and at least half-a-dozen girls would be waiting for me every Monday night, when I usually arrived with a fresh haul.

It was great while it lasted.

And then, as is inevitable in sidereal human affairs, Hilda had a birthday coming up. You can imagine my problem. What can you possibly give a girl who throws away a complete wardrobe every twenty-four hours? You can do something spectacular, like get her pregnant, of course, but to tell you the truth, the thought never occurred to me. But I did think of something that seemed to augur a feasible solution to my dilemma—I remembered my friend Chris Postell, who was, in a manner of speaking, in the jewelry business.

This fellow Postell was a cripple and had for years been

immobile from the waist down. He hadn't always been in this jam, and I'd known him quite well long before he *was*. It had happened to him during a duck hunt. He'd been frozen into a marsh of some kind for nearly ten hours, and when they finally thawed him out, he'd permanently lost the use of his lower limbs.

Chris had always earned a very good living by making jewelry—very fine jewelry—by hand. He could take a piece of gold or platinum wire and spin such a filigree of wonders out of it that some of the fanciest Fifth Avenue shops used to bid eagerly for his services. It was a real stroke of fortune that I'd remembered him, because it was more than likely that he'd have something for me that might surprise even a not very surprisable girl like Hilda.

I recalled, while I was thinking about him, that I had probably been the last person he'd talked to in America before he'd gone off on a world cruise some five years ago. I'd gone down to the boat to see him off, and recalled remonstrating with him for going on such a daffy trip. I mean, he didn't have much money, really, and I had a feeling that he'd land somewhere on the other side of the world, in his wheel chair, and maybe get himself into an awful mess. So, although it was pretty late for caution, since they were going to pull up the gangplank any minute, I pleaded with him to give up the whole silly travel idea and to stick around, where some well-intentioned people might be able to give him some help if he needed it.

"What's the sense of your going away, in the condition you're in?" I said. "You're just looking for trouble, it seems to me."

"I have to go," he said. "I have to go, because I'm looking for someone—somewhere in the world—who'll say to me, 'Arise and Walk!'"

In short, there was no reasoning with him.

40

He was gone a little over two years—and he certainly seemed to have done pretty well for himself. When he came back, he rented a fine shop and, for the first time since his accident, he hired a trained nurse to care for him.

There was a good deal of gossip about him at the time of his return. Rumor had it that he'd successfully smuggled a load of precious stones—emeralds, sapphires and rubies—back into the States; that he'd hidden his swag in the extra-large hubcaps of his wheel chair.

It was certainly possible—but I didn't give it much thought.

During his absence abroad, Chris had spent most of his time in China, and he told me some fantastic stories about that country whenever I came by his house to pass an evening with him. He'd opened a small jewelry shop in Canton, and it seems he had no trouble finding some good customers among the wealthy foreigners there.

"But one day," Chris told me, "a couple of coolies stepped into my shop, and one of them put an American dollar bill on the counter. The other one, who'd come along to act as interpreter, tried to explain what their visit was all about."

It seems that these boys wanted Chris to make them a wire candlestick with two branches. They'd watched him through the window, and observed his dexterity with metal, and the owner of the dollar bill had decided to commission him for this job.

"I couldn't quite understand what they wanted," said Chris, "because when they made me a rough sketch of what they had in mind, I could see that they particularly didn't seem to want a *base* on this candelabrum of theirs. They wanted the vertical, center piece—the trunk, so to speak—to be made out of just a thicker piece of wire. And then it occurred to me that maybe they just wanted it unfinished on the bottom so they could hammer it in wherever they wanted it. Nail it into a plank or a table, or whatever. Well, at any rate, I made it for them out of good strong wire and, of course, I refused to take any pay for it. That dollar represented a week of brutally hard labor for that coolie—and I wanted no part of it. I just warned them to keep their mouths shut about the whole business, or I'd have been working overtime for all the underprivileged people in Canton. They came back a couple of days later, and they were very pleased with the job I'd done for them, and it seems I'd been absolutely right about that center wire, too, because they even asked me to sharpen it for them to a fine point."

(I am telling you this particular story at this particular time because, as you will discover in a moment, it has a peculiar relevance to the matter of my impending visit to Chris Postell's shop in search of a suitable birthday trinket for Hilda.)

"Well," continued Chris, "a couple of days later I had to go to the bank, and as I was wheeling myself along, I suddenly recognized my coolie customer, who was kneeling on a pad right near the main entrance. He was a beggar. And you know what he had done? He had shaved his head and had driven the center spike of my wire candlestick straight into the top of his skull. He had a couple of green candles burning in the two branches, and the hot wax was dripping right down on his bare scalp. I was so staggered, I just sat there and gaped at him for a full minute. I must say, he didn't really attract as much attention as you'd expect—but, then, you must remember, it was China, after all, and if you want to be a beggar in Canton, you sure have to trot out some unusual reasons for sympathy. Canton was certainly no bush-league town for beggars. They had the best—and, what's more, they displayed the most horrifying physical disfigurations that I've ever seen. A mere small-time cripple, like myself, would have starved to death among them.

42

"Later on," Chris said, "this beggar, who seemed to have lasted a lot longer than I'd expected, one day brought three pieces of unusually fine jade to my shop, and I bought them from him very cheaply. I think he knew he might have gotten a little more somewhere else, but I told him I wasn't a rich man, and so he left them to me, for my price, out of gratitude for the favor I had done him."

At any rate, I had seen these pieces of jade after Chris returned to the States, and he had once even playfully suggested that if I ever became engaged, he would let me have one of the stones for the very small price *he* had originally paid for it in Canton.

I wasn't really counting on that vague promise of his when when I went over to his shop a few days before Hilda's birthday, but the memory of it, and a sliver of pale hope, were certainly alive in me. Of course, there was always the high probability that he'd already sold the three stones long ago.

But he hadn't.

"Oh, I've still got them," he said, when I told him the nature of my errand. "We'll make a beautiful brooch out of the darkest of them and save the other two for a ring some day, later on."

When I called for my gift on the morning of the birthday, Chris and I had a real unveiling. The lovely jewel, in its dark gold setting, was resting against a cushion of night-blue velvet, and the whole was enclosed in a fabulously carved teakwood box.

"May this be worthy of her," said Chris, as we shook hands.

When I arrived at Hilda's home, I could hardly get into the living room for the mountain of presents that every relative and friend—and every farsighted clothing manufacturer in America—had managed to expedite to her door. It was not only stupendous—it was positively embarrassing.

43

She stood in the midst of all these treasures, dressed only in a bra and panties, so as to facilitate the trying on of endless bed jackets, blouses, skirts, ski pants, and other wearables that kept bursting out of seemingly inexhaustible volcanoes of tissue paper.

At last, when she had fallen, completely pooped, into the arms of one of her nymphomanic chairs, I stepped forward and presented my gift.

She loved it. She really did. She had no idea of the great, still beauty of the jewel, and she certainly had no adequate appreciation for the nature of the fabulous setting, but she did know that jade of that color and quality was very expensive—and while I clutched desperately at the lace drawers of her chair, she kissed me with considerable passion.

In a little while, after she had replenished her forces by a couple of old-fashioneds, she continued with the relentless rape of the cardboard boxes around her, and when, two hours later, we were finally ready to go out for dinner, she discovered that she had somehow, unaccountably, misplaced my gift.

"It isn't lost," she said. "It's in one of those smaller boxes. I'm sure I put it away especially, along with the tortoise-shell opera glasses. I'll tell Mother to go through all these packages very carefully."

My brooch was never found. Whether it got thrown out with the debris, or whether one of those servants who couldn't stand my guts anyway had deliberately absconded with it, I never learned.

Well, Hilda not only lost the brooch, she lost me, too. I couldn't take it.

I kept thinking of that beggar in Canton who, just to earn a few more pennies, had driven an illuminated spike through his skull—I thought of Chris Postell who, out of friendship for me, had woven a small miracle of gracious design around that ossified dragon's eye—and I felt that Hilda was surely a lost soul—and that I was most definitely unfit to rescue her.

The other two pieces of jade were auctioned off shortly after Chris's death, and I tried to stay in on the bidding as long as my resources (which is to say, my borrowing power) held out. When the price had gone up to eighteen hundred dollars, I took a long last look at them—and went home.

I wish I knew what has become of them.

CHAPTER THREE

As I keep thinking over the imaginary roster of people that are likely to come and pay their last respects to my mortal remains, I find that women outnumber the men by about five to one. And that's altogether logical, too, because my closest friendships on this earth have always been with women. That is to say, I never overrated them; I simply found them more congenial to be with, more trustworthy, and a lot less cheaply competitive than most of their male counterparts. I've had a few enduring friendships with men, too, but I must say that over the years the ladies of my acquaintance withstood the corroding influences of time much better than anybody else, and that includes homosexuals.

When I think back on the years of my early manhood in New York City, the years I lived mostly down in Greenwich Village, I recall with undimmed gratitude many of the young women who were my friendly and helpful neighbors during the period of my own early apprenticeship into life. Like most typical New Yorkers, these girls had been born elsewhere and had come to the big town for a diversity of reasons; but I soon discovered that, by and large, the chief propellent that had projected them out of their small-town environments was an unstillable appetite for some sort of larger experience of life than their native bailiwicks were able to provide.

I was enormously fascinated by these aspiring, hopeful dolls, and, because I was an immigrant myself, I had a great deal of sympathetic fellow feeling for all of them. After a while, I came to know five or six of them rather well, and from these genuinely harmless, disinterested intimacies, I came to certain conclusions which have, over the years, become practically codified in my mind.

I have, in my time, read a good many newspaper and magazine articles which expatiated at great length on the dangers that beset young girls in a big and heartless city like New York. Well—I've studied this subject at first hand, and I think my opinion should have particular weight and relevance since I myself, at one point of my life, surely represented one of these dangers.

Now, then, all of these kids that I got to know had ostensibly come to New York in search of fame and fortune, or at least a suitable husband who would graciously and imaginatively set about to harness this amorphous urgency of theirs and channel it toward some sort of solvent, domestic millenium.

Before I go any further, I find it necessary at this point to make an extremely important elucidative insertion. You see, when you really get to know the people involved and understand the different circumstances that make them tick, you are inevitably bound for the astonishing conclusion that the worst festering spots for incipient sexual immorality are invariably the small towns of America (and of the world, I suppose).

I've lived in quite a few of them, and believe me, I know a good deal about them, too. You can take my word for it that the members of the different ethnic groups in New York, at least the ones that I had come to know intimately in the past, had much clearer eyes for the possible temptations and pitfalls of youth than the average, overly permissive, middle-class American ever allowed himself to have. It is perfectly true that as these groups in their turn tended to become assimilated into the general milieu, their authority and power for guidance progressively diminished. Even so, the foreigners in large cities always maintained a certain national identity in their neighborhoods which automatically made any deviations or moral lapses from common practice a matter of communal, ethnic disapproval. I want you also to remember that kids in New York hardly ever have access to cars of their own, and so, in the very nature of things, it isn't as simple for them to escape strict parental supervision on such easy terms. Another thing, a big city offers the restless adolescent an enormous number of easily accessible diversions, and an alert young mind is not compulsively reduced to directing his most urgent investigative energies into biological researches of the opposite sex.

I can hear lots of you screaming from all the way back there—but, please, control your convulsions for just another moment, and listen to me.

When you look around the big cities that I have lived in, you'll hardly ever find kids of thirteen or fourteen, from respectable families, going steady together, or acting like young engaged couples, and that this happens all the time in the smaller towns of this country is just as well known to you as it is to me.

And I say this is wrong! And that the parents who smirk at this, and think that such a state of affairs is cute, are complete and incurable idiots!

Also, I think one of the biggest unpublicized reasons why so many youngsters get married so early nowadays is because a good many of the young girls have suddenly become the victims of galloping, unplanned parenthood.

I'm not just trying to be cheaply paradoxical at the small town's expense—I'm telling you on my solemn word of honor that I'm firmly convinced that adolescent morality in New York City is higher than nearly anywhere else in the country.

Please, don't bother to tell me about rampant gang warfare and wholesale rape in Central Park, because I'm just as well aware of all that as you are.

It stands to reason, doesn't it, that eight million people living together in the closest possible proximity are bound to breed certain tensions, and that there are also sure to be a good many unassimilable psychopathic individuals among them.

How many unstable personalities are loose in your own home town of only five hundred?

But we're not talking about psychopaths now—we're talking about average kids from average middle-class homes—and I tell you again that in a big city the children are not so easily seduced into chronically nuzzling each other, because the city just simply doesn't provide sufficient places or opportunities for this sort of frantic necking.

I think that the big breakdown in proper family supervision originated in the small towns and spread toward the big cities in a tide so irresistible that even the kids in those closely supervised communities were finally affected and contaminated by it.

Now then, let's get back to my story. As I told you before, those half-dozen young girls who were neighbors of mine in Greenwich Village and whom I got to know pretty well had, in every single instance, undergone some sort of climactic sexual experience back in their home towns.

They were, each of them, without question, properly

brought up, nice girls and could in no way be considered just a lot of indiscriminate sleepers-around. As far as I could discover, the immediate cause of their vital commitment had invariably been brought about as the result of sheer boredom coupled with a flagrant exposure to the only form of entertainment that was easily available to them in the stultified atmosphere of their native communities.

What I'm telling you is that these poor girls had brought to Greenwich Village an already damaged self-esteem and a terrible suspicion that life was sometimes likely to be played with marked cards. They had gravitated quite naturally into the tolerant bohemianism of the Village in the hope that they might accidentally stumble onto some form of indefinable idealism, some tolerant, rapturous involvement with existence that would erase from their damaged hearts the memory of their past mischances.

You can't imagine the goodness and the tiptoe expectancy among these dear creatures, and I can happily say that most of them found at least partial appeasement in that world of batik lamp shades and hand-painted cigarette boxes which eventually absorbed them.

The boy-friend problem was made comparatively simple for them by the fact that most of the available males who gravitated around them had originally sprung from small-town areas very much like their own, with this distinct advantage— that these boys had not yet had occasion to exhaust their burgeoning male curiosity along backwood lanes in the rumble seats of their family cars.

At least, not on these particular girls.

The few real native New Yorkers these young women happened to encounter represented only passing novelties against whom they continued to nurture their deeply ingrained, parochial suspicions.

After a few years nearly everybody got married and pro-

50

ceeded to add his and her share to the world's population explosion. For myself, I can proudly say that for five of their children I was eventually asked to stand up in the role of godfather.

So, you see, I have all through my life been on the most amiable terms with women, because I never made the common mistake of talking to them as man to man. I have always understood and valued their special, their peculiar, their unique qualities.

The young women I have told you about all turned out to be wonderfully devoted mothers and wives, because women are endowed with a miraculous gift which enables them to constantly renew their emotional virginity.

They are *so* different.

Newton *saw* an apple fall and discovered the Law of Gravity.

Eve *made* an apple fall and discovered the Gravity of Law.

One of the ladies I came to know pretty intimately during my earlier years was not exactly a neighbor of mine although she did live in the Village about eight blocks away from me. She, too, had come from a small town, but this village that had spewed her out was located somewhere in the Ukraine; and I don't mean Ukraine, Florida, either.

She was called Natasha. And that's exactly what she was. She was one of the earliest of those emancipated girls who threw away their corsets and had their hair bobbed around 1915, and I can only tell you that this chick was a really natural born oddball. Her flaming red hair stood away from her head as if she were constantly getting high-voltage electric shock treatments; in addition to this she wore long, tinkling earrings that hung down to her shoulder blades, and generally draped herself into hand-embroidered Russian smocks with high collars that buttoned up on one side. She smoked in the

51

street, never wore stockings or brassières, and she always managed to attract quite a bit of attention even in the pretty free-wheeling atmosphere of the Greenwich Village of those days. I'd seen her around town two or three times, and I was certainly very curious about her, but I never hoped so far as to expect that I would ever come to meet this amazing Amazon personally.

But, finally, I did.

It happened like this: A friend of mine, Bob Ament, had known for some while that I was looking to join an inexpensive art class of some kind, and one day he sent me a card telling me that there was a group called the Penguin Club that had a model in once a week, and that they charged only a dollar for each student.

Just my speed.

I went over to case the joint the following Wednesday (it was located on Fifteenth Street near Fifth Avenue, opposite the Rand School) and, sure enough, about ten people, all obviously muse-afflicted, were standing around a dingy loft making a lot of sloppy charcoal sketches from a live model.

The model was Natasha.

She had a great figure, one of the best; and I verified at once, with satisfaction, that the color of that astonishing hair of hers was real. (I know perfectly well that there could still have been room for some sort of hanky-panky, and that the whole works might still have been a fake—but I just want you to believe me that nobody, and I mean *nobody*, not even Natasha, would have done such things forty-five years ago. Nowadays everybody's sister does it, of course, but human ingenuity was in a far less advanced state in those pre-automation times.)

So I got myself a little rickety easel, and I too proceeded to cover myself with charcoal dust. There was no official teacher in this group, but some of the older members sort of vaguely took charge from time to time—handed out papers, collected the money, and so on. Also, after each five minutes of posing, when Natasha was taking a little breather, some of those old-timers would indicate to her what sort of pose they wanted her to assume next. After a few minutes, that is to say, after I finally got interested in my drawing, the hour passed quickly enough, and I must say I felt that I'd gotten quite a lot of benefit out of that first session. I went every Wednesday after that, and somewhere along about the fourth or fifth time I was there I started to talk to one of my neighbors, a man called Ben Benn, who is still living, I think, and who later turned out to be a very fine painter.

"How come," I said to him, "that this Natasha dame never turns completely around? I've come here over a month already and I have never yet gotten any more than the profile of one of her buttocks."

Ben Benn smiled at me and put down his piece of charcoal. "Now you are a full member, at last," he said. "You're really initiated." He kissed me on each cheek (like a French general who is promoting a buck private to become latrine-corporal) and finally patted me paternally on the top of my head. "Arise, Sir Penguin!" he said.

To cover my confusion, I began to laugh along with him, although I hadn't the vaguest idea what he was talking about. Later on, by drips and driblets, I did find out a couple of things, but these too led only to a more protracted series of hangups for me.

It seems that Natasha had been modeling for the Penguin Club for the better part of two years, and everyone was quite pleased with her. I found out that originally, when she had first applied for the job, she had made one cast-iron stipulation —she would never show the full face of her backside to the club, no matter what happened, and no matter *who* asked.

"How come you guys all agreed to this?" I asked.

"Only one of us agreed," said Ben, "but nobody can remember who it was. At any rate, her fees are less than any other model's in town, and since we have no money, we're glad to keep her on her own terms. Besides, you're still a very young man, and I'm sure you can't have too much trouble imagining her behind. I'm certain it is worthy of her."

And that's the way it stood all through that winter.

Then, sometime around March, I noticed that Natasha was obviously trying to fight off a cold, and since there was a huge, unused brass samovar gathering dust in one corner, I went out during one of the rest periods and bought a package of tea, some lemons and a small jar of honey, with the intention of brewing our Lady Godiva a little warm drink of some kind.

And that's just what I did. The samovar actually worked, and when the next intermission came along, I poured some of this balm into a little glass and proceeded toward the model stand to serve it up to her.

As I came closer, I noticed that Natasha was resting quietly with her eyes shut, so she didn't notice my Samaritan approach at all. And then I ran into a little difficulty. The other men had placed their easels so near to the modeling stand that I couldn't possibly reach her from the front. I stood there irresolutely with that hot glass in my hand for a moment, and then I turned aside and walked all around the raised dais. In short, I suddenly had my first view of Natasha's complete rear end.

Unauthorized and uncensored!

And then I knew why she had made that seemingly willful and fantastic stipulation.

Natasha had a tail!

She had a real tail—with hair on it!

I spilled most of that tea all over myself, and I can only assure you that this disaster proved a most welcome diversion in my miserably mixed-up condition.

I can't quite make up my mind what Natasha could possibly

have thought when she suddenly opened her eyes, turned her head—and saw me floundering around in back of her. All I can tell you is that without a moment's hesitation she hauled off and gave me such a sock in the jaw that I finally had to drop the damned hot glass of tea altogether. The next thing that happened—I was scurrying across the room trying to find some rags to clean up the mess I had made, and that's how I somehow managed to dodge, at least partially, the full and direct onslaught of her rage.

And she *was* angry.

Finally, after I'd mopped all around her stand for much longer than was actually necessary, she suddenly put her naked foot on my back and said, "Get up, you idiot! What were you trying to do to me, anyway?"

"I tried to get you some hot tea with honey and lemon," I said. "I'd noticed you had a cold coming on, so I thought it might warm you up."

She was mollified at once. "You silly, goodhearted boy," she said. "Come here!"

I stepped up close to her, and she kissed me on my forehead. "Clumsy Galahad," she said. "Don't ever do me any favors without warning me first. Now go back to your easel!"

There was a round of spontaneous applause from the class.

And I suppose that that might have been the end of that story (or that tale, as too many of my witty contemporaries would say), excepting that I was a very high-strung, over-emotional youngster (I was less than sixteen at the time), and I felt very strongly that I had somehow, inadvertently, but nevertheless irrevocably, compromised an innocent girl who was just trying to earn an honest living. A brave and emancipated girl to boot, who was courageously breaking lances all over the place, trying to liberate enslaved and taboo-ridden womanhood.

I cannot account completely for all the nonsense that roared through my confused mind at the time but, at any rate, I felt that since I was now the intimate sharer of her dark secret I ought certainly to make some sort of stupendous amends to her wounded pride. Marry her, if necessary.

First I went to call on a doctor friend to find out whether such spinal malformations, or whatever the hell she had, were at all common among people.

"Oh, we come across them every once in a while," he said. "It isn't really a 'vestigial tail,' as you call it; it's just an elongation of the coccyx."

"Whatever *you* choose to call it," I said, "I tell you she has a real tail. What's more, she has some red hair on the end of it."

"I think," said the medic, "she probably has some pathological condition of the coccyx, but I'm quite sure that the hair that you claim to have spied is just a figment of your own overly active imagination."

So what could I do with this lummox? Like most doctors I've known, he preferred not to believe the evidence of my own eyes.

Let me tell you, I went home feeling pretty depressed and guilty about the whole thing.

At last, a couple of days later, I equipped myself with an enormous, dollar-and-a-half floral bomb and went up to Natasha's apartment. Meanwhile, her cold had obviously taken full possession of her, because I could smell all sorts of antiseptic, curative odors all the way out into the hallway. When I stepped into her living room, sure enough, she had her feet soaking in a tub of water and the place was as hot as the steam room in a Turkish bath.

"Look who's come to see me!" she screamed. "Galahad himself! Don't knock anything down, please! Sit over there, near the window, where you can't do any harm. And flowers, too! Oh, you are really too much! Put them in the sink right behind the curtain; I'll take care of them myself later! And now, sit down, and let me look at you!"

If I had come on a less purposeful errand, all this screeching and ordering about would certainly have shattered me completely, but I was there on a sacred, personal mission, and I didn't forget it even for a moment.

"I'm sorry you're ill," I said, "but I'm only staying for a moment. You see, I've come to tell you what I've decided about the two of us."

"Decided about *us?*" she said. "What in the world is there to be decided? I've forgotten the whole thing, and if you're smart you'll forget all about it, too! Now don't look so somber, and help yourself to one of those tangerines."

Little did she know *me.*

"I've decided," I said, "that since I've accidentally gotten to know your secret—and there is nothing that I can think of to undo it—I'm prepared—if you are willing—to *marry* you."

She looked at me quietly for about ten full seconds, and then that wonderfully voluptuous body of hers was shaken by such a tornado of laughter that, after watching her dumfounded for a spell, I myself began to laugh so hard that I nearly fell off my chair. We carried on like two hysterical hyenas in that way until we were both too exhausted to do more than just wipe our eyes while we gasped for breath.

"God!" she said. "That was good! That'll knock out that cold of mine better than anything I've taken so far. Oh, you are priceless! You are absolutely *priceless*. I haven't laughed this hard since I was a child in Russia. I thought they didn't make those kind of laughs any more; not in this country, anyway."

"Funny," I said. "You know, until you started laughing, I thought I had a great little idea there."

"Well," she said, "it just shows how young you really are.

Believe me, if I had married everybody who knows about my tail I'd have more husbands than a queen bee. Don't let it worry you, my boy. I just didn't want those dopes at the Penguin Club to know about it."

I was completely stupefied by the harmless way it had all turned out.

"Tell me," I said, "what makes you care so particularly about all those elderly codgers at the Penguin Club? What do *you* care what they know about you?"

"Don't you see," she said, "they're artists. They'll start painting likenesses of me as if I were a witch or something worse, even. Long after I'm dead my tail will be haunting the studios and the art galleries of the world. Just suppose I have some children some day, or even grandchildren—well—I certainly don't want them to blame me for not having left a more rational posterior for posterity. That's all I really care about. And now, take a tangerine and don't spit the pits all over the floor."

I must say I was greatly impressed by the astuteness of her reasoning. I also realized that she must have given the subject a good deal of minute thought and pretty subtle analysis, because "a more rational posterior for posterity" wasn't something that had just popped accidentally into her mind in the last seven seconds. She had obviously been brooding about the whole matter for quite a while, and I considered her attitude a thoroughly mature and self-respecting one.

"You are quite right, Natasha," I said. "The state of your behind is certainly your own private affair, and I don't think that any notoriety that accrues to it through the dissemination of a lot of scurrilous graffiti is necessarily in the public interest. So, to hell with the Penguin Club."

"You are not such a stupid boy, after all," she said. "And now, if you'll sit down here quietly beside me, I'll peel that tangerine for you."

CHAPTER FOUR

IF SHE HAPPENS to be anywhere around New York
City on the day when I finally go up in smog, *Stettatorna
Sybilla Maya* is pretty sure to be one of the people who will
drop by and add a much-needed decorative note to the proceedings.

I consider her a really rare bird, whom I first came to know
through Marty Hellmuth, around 1947, I think. He brought
her around to my house on West Fifty-sixth Street one afternoon, and I recall that he introduced her to me as the widow
of an old friend of his. Her name was Sybilla Mayhew, he said;
although, oddly enough, Marty often referred to her as Sybilla
Corwin—which led me to suppose that he'd probably known
her for some time before she'd married this Mayhew character.

At any rate, whatever her name, she was a real looker. I

later figured out she must have been around thirty-eight when I first met her, but she certainly seemed at least ten years younger. She had very dark curly hair, deep black eyes, a complexion almost translucent in its pallor, and was what the French so perceptively call *une fausse maigre*. (Which, very freely translated, means "a thin one who actually has a lot of substance in the right places.") Also, in some indefinable way, she seemed overly intense, as if she were operating on the very outer fringes of her nervous system. I think she had a tendency to make men fidgety. Women who seem sexually easily accessible, and who are nevertheless quite intelligent, do often engender this feeling in people.

Incidentally, if you happen to be something of a misogynist, I think it is high time for me to warn you that this book is mostly about women; not a justification or an indictment of them, but rather a well-intentioned bestiary full of illuminating case histories which through the years have come to my special knowledge.

Now that you have been properly alerted, I will proceed with my little yarn about Sybilla. The first big surprise about her was the fact that she was a graduate anthropologist with a truly distinguished scholastic record. You would never have suspected, on first meeting her, that she had spent almost twenty years of her life tramping all over Central and South America, doing strenuous field work of all sorts. You certainly would never have guessed any of this by her appearance, which was quite definitely corny in its dated seductiveness. She dressed by preference in tight-fitting black satin frocks that seemed pretty anachronistic, even in the far-out bohemian circles in which she preferred to navigate at that time.

I suppose I got to know her pretty well over the next couple of years, but the really conclusive story of her past finally came through when Marty Hellmuth, the guy who'd originally introduced her to me, got awfully plastered at my house and spilled her strange little saga all over me one evening.

He arrived at my place about a quarter of eleven, and because he knew that I hardly ever had any liquor around the joint, he very thoughtfully had brought his own bottle of booze along. I think he got drunk very purposefully, too, because he was certainly very eager to unload his freight of anguish onto somebody else, and he was probably worried that he'd be too timid to go through with it if he remained stone-sober.

This fellow Hellmuth was an anthropologist too, and I already did know that he'd attended the same university as Sybilla. Although they hadn't been exactly classmates, they'd known and dated each other pretty regularly nearly up to the time when she suddenly got married to the head of a science department.

From the rumors I'd heard, I'd always assumed that the older man had copped him out, but, after all, he was dead now, and, as far as I could see, there was nothing standing in the way of Marty's legally attaching himself to his old inamorata.

The minute he started talking I realized that this was exactly what he'd come up to see me for, to give the blow-by-blow low-down on the situation. So, after he'd downed about a third of his bottle, I guess he considered himself sufficiently primed to dish up the untidy results of his internal dredging operation.

"You never heard about this Professor Mayhew, did you?" he asked me.

"I didn't," I said, "but then, as you know, I'm not overly familiar in anthropological circles."

"He wasn't just an anthropologist," said Marty. "He was a sort of Jack-of-all-trades in all the various related sciences. He's been written up quite a bit in a lot of the daily newspapers, and there have been long pieces about him in most of the news magazines too. A couple of times he nearly got the Nobel Prize for something or other he'd discovered. He had at least a dozen different degrees from various universities. He was an expert in zoology, archaeology, folklore, languages— whatever he put his mind to. He was a whiz—no question about that. At any rate, when, after forty years of plugging away like a mole, he finally lifted his nose out of all those grimy books, he suddenly looked up—and there stood Sybilla!"

"He must have been a lot older than she," I said.

"About twenty-three years older, to be exact—but he'd never been married before, and so it hit him like a depth bomb."

"I see," I said. "And she was flattered, as is only natural, and she threw you over. Is that it?"

"I can see you've read the synopsis," he said. "But what you don't know—and what you can't guess—is how hard that bomb hit me too."

"Well," I said, "she's free now; she's still very young—"

"That's what's so horrible about the whole thing," he said; "that there seems to be no reason for me to go on griping. The trouble is that nobody suspects that Sybilla is haunted."

"Aren't we all?" I said. "Isn't everybody everywhere haunted by the people he's loved and lost—haunted by the scenes he's known—the appetites he once had that have forever vanished. . . . Take a good look around you, son, and you'll notice that everybody you talk to is a perambulating ruin through whose cracks and crevices the bats of memory are constantly fluttering."

"You don't understand what I'm talking about," he said, taking another shot. "You can't really understand it until you know all the facts."

"Go on," I said; "you just point out to me what makes *her* facts any different from other people's."

"Well, I'll just start in with one fact," he said. "It seems that Mayhew planned to spend the rest of his life teaching, and so he bought a fine house right near the university, and he furnished it just the way Sybilla wanted it. And then they gave a housewarming, and when the party was over he announced to the assembled company that he was going off on a two-year field trip to the highlands of Ecuador."

"Alone?"

"No. Sybilla was going with him."

"So what? He'd changed his mind. That's not so unusual."

"I'll tell you why he did it. He threw up his job and his new home because at that housewarming party of theirs he'd, for the first time, seen Sybilla dancing with other men. He was so insanely jealous of her that he nearly committed murder a couple of times that night. I know all about it, because first of all I was there; and second, because I've since then read all his private diaries. I'm telling you that guy was a dangerous psychopath."

"Oh, I suppose that could all be just as you tell it," I said, "but what's that got to do with her now?"

"I'll get to that in just a little while," he said. "Anyway, he took her off on this two-year field trip, and, believe me, those field trips are no laugh, even for a man. I've been on a couple of them, and I can tell you all about it. You know Sybilla. Does she look like a mountain climber to you?"

"Doesn't seem to have done her any harm," I said. "She looks great."

"She got malaria right off the bat, of course, and Mayhew had to nurse her and take care of her wherever the hell he went, because he always hired only the most primitive native help. No white man—no doctor—no nobody was ever allowed to come near her—even once—during those two years."

"But they did come back."

"Yeah, they came back. I must admit, after reading those

diaries of his, he really made an honest try to be human and decent. He'd promised her to take up the old job that he'd thrown over before they'd left, and to give her a chance to have some sort of normal life in civilized surroundings. But he couldn't make it. I tell you, I read those pages in which he wrote about that return of theirs, and even *I* almost felt sorry for the crazy bastard. He just couldn't take it. I'm not talking about her just dancing with anybody . . . if he'd see her talking to a grocery clerk or a garage mechanic, he'd nearly go off his rocker. One night he got up, sneaked out of the house, and threw a gun he owned into the river because he could no longer trust himself to be in a house that had a loaded pistol in it."

"It does make you feel sorry," I said. "What did he pull next?"

"Another safari into the wilderness, of course; of enormous scientific and even aesthetic significance, that trip of his turned out to be. He found thirteen stone statues, weighing a couple of tons apiece, sunk way down into the jungle muck. He not only raised the lot, but got his picture printed in all the newspapers and magazines all over the world. I really don't know why I'm torturing you with this stupid story, but let me tell you that Mayhew had been pretty well known in academic circles before he ever married Sybilla, but after he started keeping her away from possible rivals he performed such astonishing feats of discovery that even the taxi drivers and the elevator men in any town in this country could have identified his name and his face without the slightest trouble. He became absolutely notorious in a nice way. His mania was driving him to entirely new heights of scientific distinction, and honors just showered down on his poor demented head like confetti. He'd come back every three or four years, collect his prizes and his academic scrolls, and—off he'd tear again like the raving lunatic that he was. Not many people can properly tell what hardships the two of them suffered during those years. I'm perhaps one of the very few who is really in a position to give you a firsthand account of that too, since I ran into them one winter in Bolivia, where I'd gone off on an Edison Foundation grant. I was marooned high up on a mountain, freezing my can off, when I first got word about them. They were camped still higher up in some place where an ancient city had once stood in pre-Columbian times. At any rate, an Indian came to my tent just before sunset and he carried a piece of paper—from Sybilla. She asked me if I could spare them some quinine. They'd heard about me, too—that is to say, she didn't know I was a friend of theirs; they'd only been told that another white man was somewhere in the neighborhood. I didn't wait. I started out right away. I can't tell you what a hellish climb I had; I can only tell you that for some crazy reason I started to cry, stumbling along in that icy darkness. I cried out of pity for Sybilla, I suppose—poor Sybilla, who was condemned to this inhuman existence by the frenzy of a jealous madman. It was still dark when I finally reached them. He was down with a siege of malaria, and after she'd taken care of him she sat down with me at the fire and started to talk like somebody who is on the verge of hysterics or a nervous breakdown. She wasn't asking me any questions, you understand; she just jabbered on like an overwound automaton, until I got the absolute willies. So, just to divert her, I unpacked a little portable phonograph I had along —I put on a Mozart record, I think; anyway, the poor girl instantly quieted down. I handed her a couple of magazines I'd been carrying in my knapsack, and I just can't describe to you how she fingered those pages, or how she looked at some of the women's fashions and their hairdos that were pictured in some of those ads.

65

" 'They're wearing their hair shorter again,' she said, 'and their make-up is like actresses used to wear just a few years ago.'

"She was absolutely lost in those pages, and when the record was finished I put another one on of a popular song that had been all the rage just when I'd left the States.

"She jumped up in those crazy, dirty clothes she was wearing and said, 'Let's dance, Marty. You must teach me the latest dances!'

"I was so sorry for the poor kid, I actually got off the ground, and we started to totter around like a couple of drunkards on that uneven, stony ground where they'd pitched their camp. And, suddenly, Mayhew was right on top of us, with an enormous ax in his hand. 'Get out!' he yelled. 'Get out before I split open that skull of yours!' He lifted the ax over his head, but she threw herself at him and screamed, 'Please, Fred—it's only Marty Hellmuth—he just brought us some quinine—it's Marty Hellmuth, one of your old students —don't you remember him?' He pushed her aside and went for me with murder in his heart, and, believe me, if I hadn't jumped right out into that black night, he'd have decapitated me without the slightest hesitation. My Indians grabbed up my gear and ran off too, and it took me the better part of two days to round them all up again. I'd like to hear *their* account of that night's happenings. Wouldn't you?"

"When did he finally die, and where?" I said.

"He died three years ago on Chimborazo, and before he finally took off he made another discovery, not a major one this time, but about something that had been puzzling scientists for quite a while. He completely identified a bird that seemed to have everybody guessing since the time of Cortez."

"A new species?"

"No. Not really. Everybody knew the bird existed, but no one had ever seen its eggs, its fledglings, or its nesting place.

It was a real mystery. He solved it. He found that the bird nested in caves right alongside of all the bats that generally infest these places. Because it is born and lives for a while in darkness, the young bird is pure white, and only later on, when it leaves the cave, it turns dark brown and pale gray. He named it *Stettatorna Sybilla Maya*. After Sybilla."

"What's Maya stand for?"

"Maya was going to be the name of their daughter, if they ever had one."

"But," I said, "you still haven't told me what's standing between you *now*."

"Her past," said Marty. "When she first came back, after she'd buried him, I naturally came around again, and she certainly was very nice to me. But, pretty soon, I noticed that there was something wrong with her. She started to wear the strangest clothes, like a dizzy flapper of some kind, and all sorts of Pola Negri outfits like the vamps in the silent movies used to wear."

"Well," I said, "she's been out of touch with things for a couple of decades, and it might just take her a little while to get the hang of things again."

"It goes a hell of a lot deeper than that," said Marty. "No—she's *haunted*. Definitely *haunted*."

"That's where I came in," I said.

"And, I'm afraid, that's where I go out," he said. "You see, she was robbed of her whole young womanhood—her post-adolescence, as a matter of fact—by that jealous maniac, and the minute she got back to civilization she tried to compensate for it to the exclusion of everything else. She ran from one party to another; we did nothing but go to dances and night clubs—month after month—until I myself thought I was going to lose my mind. What is really crucial, though, is that she started to sleep around with all sorts of guys—people you'd think she'd never give a second look to. Believe me, I care an awful lot for her, and I was patient and forgiving with her to the point of imbecility. We'd have hideous scenes—scenes that would leave us both almost dead with exhaustion. It was hopeless. She's haunted by that past she has never lived —the normal social past of other young women—that other young women can look back on or ignore if they choose. You say we're all haunted by our memories. She's haunted by the ghost of a past that never had its proper fulfillment. Don't you see—she's a howling tragedy, and I'm just a spooky accessory to all the bitter facts of her bitched-up life. Do you know what she did the last time we really had a bad bustup? She left town. Because I was terribly worried about her, I followed her. She went to Washington, and I had no trouble at all keeping her in sight. I must admit I was ashamed of spying on her, but I couldn't help being afraid that she might come to some harm, so I excused the whole shabby business on that score. She checked into the Willard, and do you know what she did the next morning even before eating breakfast? She went to the Smithsonian, and, what's more, from the sure way she walked through those halls, I could see that she'd been there many, many times before. I followed her at a distance, and finally I saw her stopping in front of a small glass case. I tell you, I was so curious I threw all caution overboard and tiptoed right up until I was standing right in back of her. I was practically breathing down her neck. In that glass case she was looking at, in the right-hand corner—the one nearest to her—perched on a little leafless twig—there stood a stuffed white bird with beady black eyes. The identification tab said: *"Stettatorna Sybilla Maya."*

Sybilla's little legend reminded me of the much higher death rate among men in this country, and it made me aware

68

again that the one thing we consistently fail to teach our wives is how to be widows. I spend a great deal of time worrying about it, because American women don't seem to have the slightest aptitude for this quite common state.

It didn't use to be that way. Widows used to take over where their husbands left off, and they carried on as a matter of course with the management of their families—with the various business obligations and certainly with the friendships that both of them had developed throughout the years. My grandfather had been a wholesale lumber dealer, and when he died my grandmother continued to look after the home and the children, as she always had done, and, besides this, she proceeded to run a pretty complicated business, sensibly and lucratively, until the end of her life.

I think what has changed most of all is that a good many women nowadays are treated by their menfolk like a lot of mentally retarded infants. I also notice that too many wives talk about their husbands as if they were just a lot of well-intentioned, blundering boys. Look around you and see if I am wrong.

A ponderously overweight husband is often whimsically chided for raiding the midnight refrigerator, and the revolting, possibly deadly, ring of lard around his midriff is cutely referred to as a "tummy."

Wives, on the other hand, are coquettishly proud of the fact that they can't even do the simplest problems in arithmetic and that they are never, under any circumstances, able to balance their bank accounts.

All this deliberate diminution in proper age-responsibility, all this elaborate pretense that we're just a lot of little boys and girls together, becomes a howling disaster when the husband dies. The reason it is worse for women to be left is because they are suddenly compelled to make some sort of grown-up decisions. (The husbands have been making them for years, behind their backs, to keep the bloom of their stupidity at its most virginal freshness.)

Alas, a good many wives are tortured by a belated sense of guilt, feeling that they have perhaps overstrained the earning capacities of their cherished life partners. (By expecting too many mink coats, emerald earrings, and other essential household necessities.)

Now, then, out of this feeling of guilt, coupled with their general, chronic ineptitude, there is born the most farcical of all modern tragedies: The American Widow!

You can see her everywhere, helplessly looking around for another sweet little boy who will go on playing house with her; well, sadly enough, in nine out of ten cases she discovers that the world is full of smart operators who are all just looking to do her out of her nest egg.

In short, her lifelong symbol has completely lost its magical potency. Her symbol has been a tiny pair of lace-trimmed drawers drying in the morning sunlight; and this pennant, which has been worshipfully looked up to by her Launcelot as if it were the Holy Grail, suddenly elicits nothing more than a lot of lurid wolf-calls from the assembly of half-attentive males.

It *is* an awful comedown.

So, if you want to do your wife a real favor, one that will outlast your life—teach her a little rudimentary arithmetic, tell her something about how you earn your living, and stop pretending that she's just the little girl next door, and that you are her favorite itsy-bitsy woolly lamb who is going to last forever.

CHAPTER FIVE

Some people have observed that I rarely speak about nature. This is true. The chief cause for this creative lapse in my endeavors is that nature has always had the greatest power to evoke my most painful spasms of unstillable nostalgia.

So I concentrate on men, or women, as they sauntered or stormed through my past, and although this too can certainly be very upsetting to one's emotional equilibrium, I have, through long experience, acquired a nice technique to cope with this uneasiness on less exhausting terms.

I recall that quite a long time ago I became aware that I frequently wore a public smile like an acrobat who has just fallen from the high trapeze into the dust of the arena. This desperately false grimace which, for all I know, reassured nobody, was brought on by my constantly increasing knowledge of the human heart and by my feeling that I would never leave a testament sufficiently painstaking or convincing to benefit anyone, excepting, perhaps, other acrobats who had miraculously survived equally hazardous falls.

Nowadays, I sometimes think of myself as tiptoeing among my memories like a highly selective gardener who is constantly tempted to serve up a lot of noxious fertilizers along with his blooming corsages, merely to achieve a proper balance between cause and effect, and to shock into critical awareness those barely attentive consumers whose tastes are insatiably geared to witty and whimsical nosegays.

No matter—let us proceed.

In envisaging the various people whom I myself would like to be remembered by, at least on some crucial occasions, I often think of Barbara Davis. She goes back to the time when, many years ago, there used to be a couple of additional tabloid newspapers in New York and, if such a thing is conceivable, their ethical and intellectual standards were even lower than anything along their lines that exists today. Barbara had a writing job on one of them. She was a sort of sob sister, I suppose; she would, as an example, interview the widow of a man who had been killed in some barroom brawl—and then she would follow this up with a piece about the murderer's girl friend, who was pregnant up to her ears and who was going to stand by him loyally until the bitter end.

You get the drift.

At any rate, the editor of this ghastly sheet she worked for was a man called Reuben Fosko, and this guy was born for nothing else but just his revolting job. He was a real lulu. He was the sort of managing editor whose celluloid ectoplasm has appeared in endless movies, but, believe me, in this case the real article surpassed the most sordid imaginings of the most irresponsible fictional imagination, and anyone who worked for him for any length of time was eventually doomed to lose all guide lines on what constituted even halfway decent human behavior.

I knew Barbara through her father, who had been a newspaperman in Chicago during the early part of this century and who, later on, after Barbara's mother died, retired to the country and bought himself some kind of a grass-roots weekly. This sheet of his proved so original in its editorial point of view that many of the more hep columnists on the big metropolitan dailies would frequently quote long excerpts from its pages.

That's how it happened that some magazine editor commissioned me to do a piece about Hal Davis, and I went out to Oklahoma to interview him. Barbara was turning sixteen then, when I first met her, and she certainly gave promise, even in those unbecoming duds she was wearing, that some day she was going to turn out quite a dish. She kept house for the old man, and also helped him with the paper—subscriptions, correspondence, and so on. Sometimes she also wrote pieces for him—woman's angle stuff—of all kinds.

During the three days that I hung around their small town to collect material for my article, I heard some pretty wild stories about Barbara—but I dismissed most of this guff as just a lot of envious small-town gossip. I couldn't quite overlook all of it, because some of her own actions were only too obviously out of line and not very easy to explain. She introduced me to some of her personal buddies, and I must confess that even by my very liberal standards these close pals of hers were nothing more than just a couple of smalltime hoodlums.

So I'd known from way back that Barbara had a special taste for a peculiar breed of tomcat, and when she finally got to New York it didn't strike me as particularly out of keeping with her character when, after a while, she became Reuben Fosko's official girl friend. She must have been about twenty-five or twenty-six by that time, and rumor had it that before she'd come on East, she'd had a pretty speckled career for a couple of years with some rather repulsive types around Chicago.

The weirdest thing about Barbara was her appearance, which was so soapsudsy-pure it was positively virginal. It was mostly her special coloring, of course. She had long ash-blond hair, baby-fair skin and pale-blue eyes, and when she went out with Fosko to eat or to a night club somewhere, even the most blasé headwaiters couldn't help showing a little astonishment at the disparity in their appearances. Fosko was one of those short, overly hirsute, ill-dressed types, and no matter how closely he shaved, he had a bluish-gray tinge of sharkskin along his jaw. She was generally dressed in flowered chiffons and, walking in front of him, looked like a diaphanous woodland creature about to be raped by a garbage-dump satyr.

Anyway, this relationship of theirs went on without any memorable disturbances for about two and a half years.

And then, one day, news came across the wires that the Prince of Wales, the one who later married Mrs. Wally Simpson, was about to pay his first visit to this hemisphere. It is just about impossible to describe what an almost cataclysmic effect this piece of information had on various sectors of American life. Try to imagine it: the Prince of Wales, the most eligible young bachelor in the whole world, was coming to this country on his first visit and was not only going to attend a certain prescribed number of official receptions but was reputed to be looking forward to a lot of private festivities, at which he would have occasion to hobnob with American society and to dance with—and to exchange perhaps very meaningful courtesies with—some of the fairest flowers in our Republic.

You get the picture?

It goes without saying that practically everybody was agog.

Milliners, dressmakers, florists and all the procurers, *shamesses* and hangers-on of the moneyed riffraff that passes for society in our midst had a wild surmise that some kind of an unbelievably big break was about to come their way. And, then, there were also the thousands of peripheral phonies and con men who all looked expectantly toward the horizon for the first sign of the royal bore royalis.

It was a gay time as I remember it.

I was working on the *Sunday World*, and my editor had told me to make a weekly picture and word reportage of how the common man—the man literally in the street—was taking this important visit.

Let me anticipate and tell you right now how he did take to it. Well, generally speaking, he hardly bothered to take the pipe out of his mouth, even to answer me. After all, you can't really blame him. The people I accosted were, mostly, working stiffs with lots of kids at home and plenty of worries on their minds—and here, suddenly, they were supposed to throw flip-flops just because a young man in his early twenties—a boy, really—who'd never done a day's work in his life, was going to be entertained by a lot of rich people whose very lives were alsolutely unimaginable to them. It might as well have happened on a different planet for all they cared. I remember one afternoon I interrogated a motorman who'd just gotten through with his route on the East Belt line.

"Let him come," he said. "I understand he's fallen off every horse in the royal stable, so maybe they can find him a real tame one up in Central Park—the ones the kids ride on Sundays—that he can finally manage to master. I've had a terrible day today. I stepped into a puddle of water just before I got on my trolley, and I've had my feet wet for hours and hours. I'd better get home and get me a hot drink of some kind before I come down with the flu."

75

As you can see—a totally blighted man, a man who had no imagination at all, and no feelings for the larger affairs of the day.

I'm sure his daughter might have felt differently about it. That's how women are—they are involved in everything that goes on, no matter how far away they may themselves be from the center of interest. I met and talked to dozens of working girls who planned to get permanents and manicures to celebrate the Prince's arrival here, and a couple of them even said they'd take the day off to watch him from the curb on Fifth Avenue as the royal parade went by.

Naturally this stinky paper that Fosko edited devoted endless pages to the impending visit, and I knew for a certainty that Barbara Davis was sure to be enrolled to do a special feature of some sort. I never could have anticipated *how* special.

It worked out something like this: Six weeks before the Prince was expected on this side of the water, Fosko called Barbara into his office and said, "Can you ride a horse?"

"A little," she said. "I mean, I've done some riding back in the sticks, and I suppose I'm as good as anybody else that hasn't been especially trained for the horse shows."

"I want you to take lessons, beginning today," said Fosko. "I want you to go up to Abercrombie's and get yourself a snappy-looking riding outfit and tell them to send the bill to me."

"What's up?" she said.

"I'm gonna send you to Canada, Barbara, up to this town where the Prince is first going to stay after he arrives here. I'm going to plant you in the hotel where he's supposed to stop, and I want you to register under another name—right now—get it?"

"Not yet," she said.

"I'm going to get you a respectable chaperone. I just talked

76

to a couple of prospects this afternoon, because I want somebody real solid, some ex-society woman who's down on her
luck, maybe, and I want you to behave yourself impeccably—
for a change—you hear me?"

"And then?"

"And then, with your looks, the Prince, or maybe one of
his henchmen, will spot you, and if you play your cards right,
you'll be in a position to get me the kind of story that all the
other newspapers in this country would give their rotten
pancreas for."

"I see," she said. "And your idea is that he'll fall for me, is
that it?"

"I don't care what *he* does. I just want him to talk to you
like he's sure never going to talk to anybody else, because he'll
be watched like crazy by everybody after he gets into *this*
country. But up in Canada, where they'll respect his privacy
a lot more—I mean the papers and the cops and all the rest of
them—it'll be our only chance to get at him—don't you see?
He just mustn't suspect that you're connected with a paper,
so we'll set up the chaperone and all the rest of it; and the idea
will be that you're waiting for your folks who live on the
West Coast, and that they'll join you in a couple of weeks,
and that you're all planning to go to Europe together."

"And why do I have to take riding lessons?"

"You'll have to go riding every day—for exercise—long
before he's even expected, so that all the reports about you
are of the highest order. I'll get you a top-notch wardrobe in
the best shops—better still, we'll let your chaperone go and
pick it for you, so that everything will be in the best of taste—
no feather boas, and no leopardskin coats with boots to match.
Now go downstairs and draw three hundred dollars for the
first expenses."

That's how it began.

Later on he lectured her at great length about her conduct.

"Don't keep tugging at your clothes all the time—you hear? Your girdle and your bra straps is what I mean. When a real lady has once left her boudoir she's finished with herself—she doesn't constantly go on touching her face or curling the hair on the back of her neck, and she certainly doesn't constantly feel her flanks or her rear end to see if they're still all there. There's lots of stuff you'll have to learn, but I guess this beldame that I'm hiring to act as your chaperone will tip you off to all that. I particularly want you to watch yourself about not getting involved with any of the riffraff up in Canada. Remember, by the time the Prince arrives, I want that whole town to have accepted you as the model of a well-brought-up young woman. If you'll follow my instructions and we pull this thing off together, you'll be swimming in dough from then on. If you want to, I'll even marry you!'"

He'd never made such a stupendous offer to anyone before in all his life.

Barbara did everything he had asked her to, and did it without quibbling or afterthoughts. She bought good clothes, she took riding lessons, she changed her name, and finally she went off to Canada, accompanied by an unexceptionable chaperone. This elderly dowager was a real ex-society woman. Her name was Mrs. Liddell Hodgson, and her blood was so blue that you could have tapped her for fountain-pen fluid.

And then came the days of anxious waiting, for Reuben Fosko. Although he trusted Barbara, he had, nevertheless, installed a couple of precautionary stooges up in the town where she was staying, because he wanted to be instantly alerted if she should suddenly revert to type and start consorting with some of the less desirable elements of the town. But his fears were completely unfounded. Barbara proved to be a real trouper. She rose early each morning—ate her chaperoned breakfast—went riding until eleven—had her chaperoned luncheon—visited the public library or some other innocuous place of local diversion—ate her chaperoned dinner, at which she partook of half a glass of wine—and went early to her chaste bed. This, with very slightly varying alterations, was the daily program of her life.

Finally, one day, the Prince of Wales arrived.

It instantly altered the modus vivendi of the whole town, but it certainly made not the slightest difference to Barbara. She sat at the same table of the hotel dining room three times a day and barely lifted her eyes from the plates that were served up before her. A few whispered words with Mrs. Liddell Hodgson—an occasional responsive smile by way of reply to some remark by that reserved lady—and that was about the sum total of her outward social activity.

And then it happened in the course of developing events that the Prince of Wales and some members of his close entourage took dinner one evening in that same hotel dining room. They also took luncheon there the next day, and it was during this meal that an equerry from the royal suite came up to Barbara's table, saluted, and introduced himself. His name was Captain Barrett Wynant, and he asked on the Prince's behalf whether the two ladies would take tea with His Royal Highness in his chambers that afternoon.

That evening Barbara talked to Fosko in a prearranged code on the telephone. She told him that the apple blossoms were falling like a spring snowdrift, and Fosko nearly fainted with ecstasy when she also informed him that she had been invited to go horseback riding with the Prince on the following morning, alone.

Fosko's sense of triumph at that moment can be easily imagined. His scheme had worked. The kid was in—the story of the decade was about to break. Well, the story of the week anyway. But a week is a long time in the catch-as-catch-can life of a newspaperman.

That afternoon he took a couple of his cronies on the paper

in on his secret, and the three of them decided to hold the presses that night for even as long as an hour after the usual press time, on the bare possibility that Barbara might be ready with her little bomb.

And that's what they did. They held the presses for nearly an hour and a half—but nothing came through.

Nothing came through the next night, either, and by that time Fosko was in such a dither that he almost phoned Barbara, although he knew that such an unscheduled step might queer the whole setup.

On the fourth day, when still nothing happened—he finally put through a call to the chaperone.

"What's going on with Barbara?" he asked.

Mrs. Liddell Hodgson seemed to have a load of hot cornmeal mush in her mouth, and he had a lot of trouble making her out.

"Come on, you old bitch!" he screamed. "Talk up or I'll come around and strangle you with those false pearls of yours. What in hell has happened to Barbara?"

Mrs. Liddell Hodgson whimpered for a moment. "I haven't seen her in twenty-four hours—"

"You haven't seen her in twenty-four hours?!? What do you think I sent you along for, you silly old bag? You get her to the phone this minute!!! You hear???"

"I'm sorry, she isn't here now. She's with the Prince. She's been with him all day—all day long, I'm telling you—" And then the poor old woman broke into hysterical sobs.

"Of all the crazy, unreliable bastards in this world, I've got to end up with the worst. Listen to me, you nitwit; you tell Barbara to call me here no later than eleven o'clock tonight—or I'll be up there to talk to her myself—you hear that??? I'm coming up to Canada myself!!!"

Then he banged down the receiver.

He waited until midnight, and then he boarded a flyer and set out for Montreal.

The rest of the story was told to me by one of his secretaries after he'd returned. It seems that Fosko got to the hotel and found the chaperone in the sitting room of their suite, getting quietly plastered. He took the half-empty bottle out of her hand and smacked her on the side of the head with it—so the good lady just gently slid out of her chair and, after straightening out her disarranged skirts, stretched out lengthwise on the floor and passed out.

With murder in his bloodshot eyes, Fosko stamped into the bedroom.

Barbara was lying in bed reading the morning papers. An unfinished cup of chocolate was standing beside her on the night table. Fosko stepped forward and sent the cup flying across the room until it shattered to bits against one of the radiators.

"Are you out of your mind?" he screamed. "Get the hell out of that bed and start writing that story of yours—before I bring that goddamned chandelier down on your head!!!"

Barbara looked at him very humbly, but Fosko, who was an old campaigner among recalcitrant females, suddenly realized with a sinking heart that she was not the least bit afraid of him.

"I'm not going to write any story for you," she said softly, "and, what's more, I'm not going back to New York. You'll just have to make other plans."

"You're not going back to New York? What *are* you gonna do—stay *here?*"

"I'm arranging something for myself," she said, "and you'll find out about it in due time."

"What are you gonna do—become his mistress or something?"

"Let's leave *him* out of this," she said.

81

"Leave him out of this? You crazy tramp—do you know what this story is costing me so far? It's costing me seven thousand five hundred dollars. You *met* him—didn't you? He *talked* to you—didn't he? Just as we *planned*. You've been *alone* with him—weren't you? Well, by God, you'll spill that story onto a typewriter or you'll never work another day again as long as you live!!! You poor sap, do you think he takes you seriously?"

"I don't know what he thinks," she said. "Whatever it is, it doesn't make the slightest difference, since I have no intention of ever seeing him again."

Barbara reached for her dressing gown and got out of bed. "There *is* no story," she said. "All I can tell you is that whatever happened between the Prince and myself—*is sacred!*"

And that was *it*.

Fosko came back to New York and went on a drunken binge that lasted for a month. When I met Barbara about a year later, she told me she was doing some kind of social work and was living over in the Sixties in one of those all-women hotels.

Now Barbara had never been my kind of doll at all, but when I finally shook hands with her on that windy corner near the park, I was suddenly flooded by a great wave of uncritical affection for her.

After all, she *had* brilliantly demonstrated my old thesis about women—the one I told you about a little while ago— that they have a wonderful capacity for self-renewal—what I called a truly magical gift for recovering their spiritual virginity.

CHAPTER SIX

A LITTLE WHILE AGO my wife said to me, "Last night I read most of what you've written so far, and I'm surprised you overlooked two people who are quite devoted to you—Amadio Peperdi and Mr. Kilian."

She is quite right.

Peter Kilian walked into my life some twenty-three years ago, when I was living out in the country and trying to write a play. Six plays, in fact. At any rate, I was living in an enormous mansion that a friend of mine had loaned me while he had to go abroad on some urgent business of his own. One afternoon there was a knock on the door, and when I stepped out on the wind-blown porch of this fraudulently lush edifice, I was confronted by a little gray-haired character who seemed to have come straight out of a novel by Charles Dickens.

"Mr. King live here?" he asked.

You must remember that for quite a few years before this

weather-beaten gnome had landed on my doorstep, I had been dodging squads of sheriffs, miscellaneous process servers and assorted bill collectors with an agility which the hunted wildlife of the world tried vainly to emulate. So, naturally, although my visitor looked harmless enough, I had no intention of offering up my true identity without further painstaking investigation.

"Which King do you want?" I asked.

"I'm looking for *Alexander* King," he said. "I'd like just a word with him, if you don't mind."

For one unguarded moment a cunning look came into his moist blue eyes and for just the shadow of a second a certain ominous twitching in his shaggy brows gave potent warning to my ever-alert, precautionary antennae.

"Well," I said, "my name is *Gabriel* King, and you're looking for my cousin *Alexander*, who isn't around just now."

"Ah," he said, "that's too bad, because I've really taken quite a bit of trouble to find this place. It isn't listed anywhere, and I had a heck of a time locating it."

I can't tell you why—but I had suddenly developed a kind of liking for the old goat, and although it would certainly have been to my advantage to get rid of him, I simply couldn't get myself to turn him cold-bloodedly away. You know how it is with people—there are occasionally incalculable bonds of sympathy that spring up between them, mysterious radiations that encompass two human hearts—so that from the first moment they meet they cannot ever again feel indifferent to one another.

"Come in," I said, "and I'll rustle you up a cup of coffee."

"Thank you," he said. "I take that very kindly of you. It's a pretty raw day, and I *could* stand a cup of something hot."

He proceeded to wipe his clean shoes very elaborately on our phony seafaring door mat and followed me into the house. He was wearing a sort of oversized Scotch-plaid Mackinaw that had at least a dozen pockets on it, and when he removed his poison-green cap with thick ear flaps that could be tied under the chin, his bristly gray hair stood out wildly in all directions. He looked like an elderly schnauzer that had died on me some years before, and it may very well be that this resemblance was really the secret keynote to the harmonious *rapprochement* between us.

"Perhaps something a little stronger than coffee would be more to your taste," I said.

"It might, at that," he conceded. "I've been out since six-thirty this morning, because I wanted to catch the seven o'clock ferry at Nyack."

I took him into my workroom (which he instantly called a "study"), and proceeded to pour him a shot of Scotch.

He held the glass up to the light and said, "You're a most generous man—Mr. King. May you never lack the wherewithal to serve it, nor a grateful friend to appreciate it." Then he poured it down in one eye-watering swoosh.

"Want a chaser?" I asked.

"Naw," he said. "There is nothing like natural saliva."

"Sit down," I said.

"I will, for a moment, if you don't mind," he said. He took out a dark, measly little pipe and proceeded to stuff it, getting crumbs of tobacco all over his coat. With methodical care he slowly collected all this debris, and when he finally lighted up, he filled the room with acrid clouds of what subsequently turned out to be some of his own home-raised weed. "Grow everything I can myself," he said, smiling comfortably. " 'Be sufficient unto yourself,' is my motto. Tell you the truth, this man Alexander King, this cousin of yours, would be a lot better off if he had that as his slogan."

"Is that so?" I said. "What do you know about him, anyway?"

"I know that he owes the telephone company twenty-three

hundred dollars, and I came around today especially to talk to him about it."

"Oh, yes," I said. "I've heard about that phone bill of his—and I must say he isn't altogether to blame."

"Ah?"

"He had a crazy house guest up at his place in the country two summers ago, and this cookie was in love with a geisha girl in Kobe, Japan, and I think he called her up at her native teahouse a couple of dozen times between Friday and Monday."

"That's certainly unfortunate," Kilian admitted, "but it is the ironbound duty of a responsible householder to look after his property and the welfare of his chattels. That's the code of Abraham."

"So you're a bill collector for the phone company," I said. "I would never have guessed it."

"No, you wouldn't," he said. "There's lots and lots who wouldn't; that's why I get the worst accounts. I get the terminal cases, after everyone else has given up. And, if I do say so myself, I've had some remarkable results."

"I bet you have. Are many phone bills as high as all that? How come they let them run so long?"

"Unusual circumstances often prevail—as in your cousin's case, for instance. Now then, just a week ago yesterday, something happened that pleased me mightily. Yes sir, it was a real pleasure for me to see happen what happened on that day."

"Care to tell about it?" I said.

He took out an enormous old railroad engineer's watch that had a tick in it you could hear plainly all over the room, looked at it with knotted brows for a moment and said, "I've got thirty-seven minutes to get back to the station and catch my train, so I'll have to make it brief.

"You see, Mr. King, some collection cases are so difficult that, after a while, you can't help forgetting all about the money that's involved, and you just sort of get interested in the chase itself. It brings out the Nimrod in you."

"The primitive hunting instinct," I said.

"Exactly! Well, then, I'd had this case that I'd been tracing for almost three years, and a couple of times it had come so close to solution that I finally decided to forget all about it. It was too heartbreaking to be right on top of a pay-off when suddenly the subject took your wind and was lost in the underbrush without leaving a spoor behind him. This party's name, by the way, was Millard Tompkins. Ever hear of him?"

"No," I said. "Can't say that I have. This guy Tompkins was very discouraging, was he?"

"The worst," he said. "And it was in this spirit that I was going home late one Friday afternoon, and, as I may have mentioned before, I generally take the ferry up at Nyack—that's where I make my home. I've been a widower for twenty years, and I'm very punctual in my habits—so I generally catch the same ferry each evening. Now, then, I don't know if you're familiar with this ferry, Mr. King; if you aren't, you ought to take a look at her sometime, for she's a real beauty. She's an old Mississippi side-wheeler—trim and lacy and white, like a bride—and if you stand on deck and look alongside that little beauty, you've got a feeling that people who travel in airplanes have already missed most of the fun in life at the very start. At any rate, I'd always had a nodding acquaintance with the captain of this vessel, and when I went up on deck from where I could see him, he smiled to me and suddenly gave a loud blast on the horn. I couldn't have been more surprised. It was a most unorthodox procedure, and before I could recover from the shock of it, he blew another blast even louder and longer than before. And then he opened the door to his little glass-enclosed cabin and waved to me to come closer. 'He's drunk for sure,' I thought to myself, 'and I just hope we make it to the other side all in one piece.'

" 'Come on up here,' he shouted to me. 'Come up and take the wheel if you like.'

"So I climbed up the iron stairs, and when I came abreast of him I could plainly smell that my suspicions about him were only too just. 'You're feeling very gay, for a weekday,' I said. 'What's the cause of all the joy, anyway?'

" 'It's my last ride on this ferry,' he said. 'I'm retiring from active service tomorrow. Go ahead and take yourself a shot. It's on the house!'

"I stepped up and poured myself a little one. 'You don't look old enough to retire,' I said, by way of truth rather than flattery.

" 'I ain't,' he said. 'I ain't supposed to quit for another five years. But I've had some good luck—some mighty good luck, lately—and there's no use carrying my rheumatism up and down this river if I don't really have to, is there?'

" 'There is not,' I said. 'And is it permitted to ask what the nature of this luck of yours happens to be, so we might keep an eye out for it ourselves, in case it ever passes in our direction?'

" 'You may ask, indeed,' he said, 'and I'll tell you what it is. You see, some eight years ago that daughter of mine married a no-good Hollywood character who, for the next six years, wasn't able to earn a penny for himself, much less for *her*. Then, two years ago, he suddenly got a job to go off to Africa and make some kind of a film with natives and wild animals and everything—and—now listen carefully—this film is making such a mint of money that my daughter and my son-in-law insist that I give up the river and come and live with them in California. Now, I'm asking you—*is* there a Santa Claus?' He turned away from me and gave another fierce toot on the horn; then he slapped me on the back and said, 'You'll come up to the house with me the minute we land, and I'll introduce you to the lot of them. Besides, you'll get to meet my son-in-law, who's a real celebrity now—and you'll have a chance to boast that you know him personally. You may have heard of him already. His name is Millard Tompkins.'

" 'I *have* heard of him,' I said. 'And you tell me he's rich now?'

" 'He's rolling in the stuff,' said the captain. 'And not a bit proud, either. You'll have a treat shaking hands with him. Finish your drink—we're ready to land.' "

"It was this guy you'd been looking for for three years," I said. "How did he take it?"

"Like Trader Horn—philosophically."

Later, after Kilian had gone, and only the smell of his home-grown shag still permeated the premises—I wondered whether he knew that he'd been talking to Alexander King that afternoon. I really couldn't make up my mind. He was such a *cozy* old codger.

But when, during my first television program, two years ago, I happened to look casually out over the audience, I noticed him sitting on the aisle down in the very first row. He waved to me reassuringly, like an old friend, and after the show he came back to my dressing room and said, "You served me the best whisky I'd drunk in maybe ten years—and real hospitality is an institution so *rare* and so *sacred* that I wouldn't have profaned it for the world. After all—there's more to life than just money, isn't there—although I'm mighty glad you're finally making lots of it. By the way, I think there's a little account of yours that is still outstanding—isn't there? . . . And *some* accounts—as you perfectly well know—are never outdated—are they, Mr. King? They are never outdated, even if they happened twenty-five years ago, because, as you and I know, they are inscribed—*indelibly*—on the heart!"

The second male stowaway in a book ostensibly devoted to women is Amadio Peperdi, a peculiar hoodlum whom I originally met when I was living down in Minetta Alley. This was also quite a long time ago.

Amadio owned a poolroom right near me, on Sixth Avenue. It had only one table, which nobody ever played on, because the whole grimy, one-room emporium was just a blind for all sorts of bootlegging operations. All this took place during those trying years when I used to wear pink ties exclusively, and so you can imagine the whistling and caterwauling that used to take place every time I had occasion to pass that disgusting poolroom. All the young understudy gangsters, such as would nowadays be called juvenile delinquents, started to scream and yodel themselves into apoplexy every time they got a gander at my tie. They weren't juvenile delinquents, because there was nothing juvenile about them; most of them looked prematurely aged and wizened, and the clothes they wore were sharp and slick in the most depressing sense of those two deadly words. There wasn't a leather jacket among them, and nobody displayed any effeminately luxuriant locks. Snap-brim hats were *de rigueur*, and if any one of them had played any musical instrument—like a guitar, for instance—they would automatically have disqualified themselves from the fellowship of truly tough men.

And they were plenty tough. You *had* to be in the booze racket, because you weren't only up against the city cops and the Federal men; you were also constantly at war with other gangsters who were just as ruthlessly brutal as you and your friends.

Amadio, who was the leader of this outfit around the corner from me, was a sort of Napoleonic type of leader—that is to say, he couldn't have been more than five feet two inches tall. He was also handsome in a strange, carved-up kind of way—dark-haired, dark-skinned, with a rather disarmingly sweet smile. He had beautifully kept teeth and could have been cast without difficulty in some movie epic about Sicilian bandits. I found out that he *had* a smile a lot later, because, for quite a while there, whenever I saw him and gave him a friendly nod, he merely stared at me out of those cold, obsidian slits of his and offered me a mask of complete, deadpan nonrecognition.

Me and my kind just didn't exist for him.

And that's how it went on for the better part of two years. And then, one afternoon just before dark, he was standing in front of his dump all by himself, and when I passed and offered him my usual abortive little smile, he suddenly showed his teeth and said, "Come on over here!"

I nearly fell over, of course, but I at once approached him, sideways, like a schooner that has suddenly changed its tack.

"You an oddist, ainchoo?" he said.

"Yes," I admitted.

"Wanna see somet'in' real byoodiful?"

"Sure," I said. "Any time."

Without another word, he turned around and stepped into his mildewed poolroom, with me practically stepping right on his two-inch rubber heels. I'd never been inside this cavern before, and I certainly hadn't missed anything. The table was so huge it hardly left any room for players; the cloth was in terrible shape, and about half the cue sticks had been sawed off for purposes only too easy to be imagined. From the wire racks on top, where you were supposed to keep score, there dangled two pairs of shorts and a sweat shirt. They had been recently washed and still dripped water down onto the pool table. At the back of this room there stood an enormous, old-fashioned steel safe on which an American eagle had been stenciled between the words "Goldberg" and "Kaminsky."

I couldn't for the life of me imagine what this sinister nut was planning to show me. He manipulated the lock on the safe and, after opening the ponderous doors, he took a key out of his waistcoat pocket and opened a smaller compartment that was now exposed, way in the rear of this treasure trap.

While he was judiciously sifting among some of his papers, I noticed that a ring of perspiration had started to form inside my shirt collar. Finally, he pulled an ordinary, penny envelope out of the safe, turned around—and gave me a long and ominous stare. It was clearly a stare of last-minute appraisal, and I had a strong feeling that I had better not do any smiling just then. So I stared noncommittally back at him. And that's how we stood for a goodish spell, like a couple of strange buffaloes who have suddenly come face to face on a prairie somewhere.

"You like pigeons?" he asked me.

Luckily, I had known for some time that most of the Italian gangsters in my neighborhood were great pigeon fanciers. In fact, I'd often watched as some of these strange monsters "aired" their flocks just before sundown, up on the roofs of the corrupt buildings they infested. This airing was done by swinging enormously long bamboo poles around the various dovecotes and nesting places of the birds, whereupon these mystically agitated creatures, strangely affected by such maneuvers, would swoop and swirl by the hundreds over all those tenement dwellings. It was also by means of such stratagems that the various pigeon *aficionados* would attract stray birds from other flocks; and I'd been told by some of my better-informed neighbors that after some of these successful abductions, it frequently happened that bloody gun battles ensued among our local caravan leaders.

So, when Amadio asked me whether I liked pigeons, this awareness of the prevailing conditions around me stood me in very good service. I was nearly on the verge of saying, "What do you mean, do I *like* pigeons? I was *raised* among pigeons. I'm a pigeon *myself!*"

"When I was a kid I used to raise some, out in the country," I said.

"Country pigeons!" he said contemptuously. "Dey're mean and dey're full of lice. Dere ain't a bedder pigeon alive den de pigeons below Fourteen Street. I seen 'em all an' dey all stink except de pigeons 'round here."

He slowly opened the envelope and took out a pale-gray feather with tiny white bubble markings near the tip. "Looka dis," he said, and I noticed that his voice was all choked up with suppressed feeling.

I took the feather from his hand and placed it in my palm for a moment.

"That's a real beauty!" I said. "I never saw a prettier feather in my life!"

"You can say dat again," he said. "Dat's Rover's right side, tail splash. Dere never wuz no bedder lookin' boid dan Rover. Never!"

I realized that he was terribly drunk, and that I had very good reason to be scared. After all, this prehistoric man was baring his innermost heart to me—while he was plastered—but what would be his attitude after he sobered up? The possibilities for mischief seemed so unlimited that the little feather in my hand suddenly started to tremble.

"Rover wuz de best in de goddamned neighborhood," he said, "an' evvybody knew it, too. Dat's why dey knocked him off, de sons o' bitches—knocked him off while me back was toined. Well, I got even wid dem. I fixed Whitey Harris fer dat. Whitey didn' live out de winter. Fell off de roof. Well, it didn' bring Rover back; dat's fer sure."

He took the feather out of my hand and unashamedly wiped his eyes on his coat sleeve. "You're an oddist," he said.

"You kin appreciate dem colors. . . . Dat's why I showed 'em to you."

He turned from me and put the envelope back into the safe. After he'd locked the door he said, "You wanna beer or sump'n?"

"I got ulcers," I said. "I can't drink nothin'—not even Cokes."

"Dis beer'll never hoit ya," he said. "Dey give it to kids."

"No, thanks," I said. "I'd better be running along now."

And I beat it. I was in a jam, that's for sure, and I just wondered whether it might be a good idea to move away from that neighborhood altogether. I thought about it for a few days, but you know how it is—after each eruption of Vesuvius, the surviving peasants move right back into the shadow of imminent disaster and start replanting their vines. I settled for avoiding the poolroom as much as possible and pretending that perhaps he'd just forgotten the whole thing.

But about ten days later I absent-mindedly found myself in front of Amadio's door, and before I realized it I was right on top of about half-a-dozen young punks who generally hung out there. And then a strange thing happened. As I landed, plop, among them, they made way for me almost deferentially, and, although I was wearing a pink tie, nobody squealed or whistled *at* me—or *after* me, when I had passed them. I couldn't believe my senses. Pure magic!

From that day on, nobody ever bothered me again. I passed Amadio's fearlessly at least a couple of times a day, and I never heard a peep out of anybody. I had come through.

The following year I moved uptown and forgot all about the pigeon lovers. It must have been nearly seven years later that they suddenly came to my attention again. I was working on a newspaper and had just come home from a miserable day in the swamps of New Jersey and was running myself a hot bath while looking through my mail, when there was an unexpected knock on my door. I opened up, and two very unpleasant characters were standing out in my hallway. Out of the corner of my eye I could see that one of them, who looked like a cockroach, instantly placed his size thirteen shoe over my doorsill.

"What is it?" I asked.

"De boss wantsa see ya."

I thought to myself, I've certainly fallen asleep somewhere in a Jersey trolley car, and I'm dreaming a piece out of a bum old movie; that's what it is. The only thing wrong with that consoling thought was the smell that emanated from those two creatures. They had obviously doused themselves in some kind of horrible male toilet water that was advertised all over the place—the kind that is strictly masculine—that is to say, it was distilled out of dog sweat and pheasant feathers. At any rate, before I could get any further information out of them, they had stepped into my living room and had left me standing out on my door mat.

So I joined them. "You guys are making a mistake," I said. "Whoever 'the boss' is, he certainly don't want to see *me*. I'm a newspaperman, and I keep my nose clean."

"Give 'im de ledder," said the shorter and more frightening one, the one who looked like a dung beetle.

The cockroach took a piece of paper out of his pocket and handed it to me.

It was a note from a priest whom I knew. Father James, his name was, and he officiated in one of the most relentlessly bitter slum sections in all of New York. He had done me some small kindnesses throughout the years, but I had never been really very close to him. By kindnesses, I mean he'd saved me lots of trouble and fruitless running around, when I was trying to check on a story, by tipping me off if I was chasing down the wrong alley. He knew the city's darkest side as no cop or postman could ever have known it, and it was certainly very

95

useful for me to have such a thoroughly informed man amicably disposed toward me.

His note said: "I thought about this for quite a while, and I have decided you might be of some help in a matter which concerns someone we both know. I hope you will feel like doing something about it. My best wishes to you."

"O.K.," I said. "I'll have to get dressed. Who we going to see? Father James says I know him."

"It's Amadio," said the dung beetle.

"Oh, him!" I said. "I ain't laid eyes on him in seven years. How's he doing?"

"You'll see."

They had a car downstairs, and we rode through the wet, sleeting night in absolute silence. When we passed the neighborhood where Amadio's poolroom had once operated, I noticed they showed no signs of slowing down but were actually steering further east, toward the Bowery.

"Where's he hang out now?" I asked.

"In Brooklyn. Right on de odder side o' de bridge. Ten minutes, dat's all."

Silence again.

When we hit the other side of the bridge, they had me completely at their mercy, since I've never in my life been able to figure Brooklyn.

At last, we finally landed—landed at a warehouse of some sort—and we had been expected, too, because the minute we pulled up, a huge double door opened automatically, and we drove right in.

I found Amadio lying on a bed in a frantically overheated room, deeply preoccupied with cleaning his nails.

As I told you in the beginning, like a bum movie.

After we were alone, we shook hands, and it was clear to me at once that he was drunk again. Well, I hadn't done so badly the last time I'd seen him plastered, so I took heart and sat down opposite him.

"De boys say anythin'?" he asked.

"No. They showed me a note from Father James, that's all."

"Yeah, he tole me where ya lived. How ya been?"

"Working hard, but not too bad."

"I ain't been feelin' right," he said. "I ain't been feelin' right for nigh on two years."

He sat up on the bed.

"It all started wid Carola. You remember Carola? . . . Oh, I guess she wuz just a small kid when you wuz around last. Anyway, she's Nick Lerata's sister. You remember Nick?"

"Yes," I said. "He once helped me to build some bookcases —pretty cockeyed bookcases, too—but I remember him."

" 'At's the one," he said. "Well, his sister Carola toined out a very byoodiful goil. I went out wid her a couple of times—a couple of years ago—Coney Island and stuff—an' I guess I wuz startin' to get stuck on her pretty bad. I didn' know what to do. She was just a kid—a decent kid—an' I wuz fordy-four —so I jus' didn' know what to do. But den, suddenly, evvy-thing got suddenly outa hand."

Amadio reached for the bottle and took a great swig.

"We got caught in a bad pour, out near Jericho Turnpike, one Saddy, a cloudbust or somet'in', an' we stopped off at this tavern a friend of mine runs. Well, dis guy give us a room to dry off in, an' before ya know it we wuz in bed togedder. An' den a funny t'ing happen to me—it never happen to me before in all my life—I went like crazy—I just couldn' stop kissin' her. I kissed her all over—every place—all over—like I wuz drunk or somet'in'—but I wuzn't drunk—I never drunk nothin' when I used to take her out. I kept on kissin' her—I just couldn' stop myself."

He reached forward and put an iron grip around my wrist.

97

If I had inadvertently smiled at that moment—then, surely, that moment would have been the end of my biography. Luckily, I was in no mood for smiling. I was deeply moved. I was moved because before me there sat an unregenerate, Stone Age man who was completely shattered by something he couldn't understand.

He had fallen in love.

Love, in his circles, was for softies and sissies—but *real* men, men like *himself*, never admitted that they needed *anybody*. Of course, they slept with dames from time to time, and spent money on them—but the feeling which had suddenly over-whelmed him while he was lying beside this lovely young trusting creature was something so altogether out of relevance to the rest of his existence that it just threw him for a loop.

I put my hand on top of his and said, "It can happen to anybody, Amadio."

He released his hold on my wrist. "Yeah, dat's what de priest said. He said what husbands and wives do between themselves ain't nobody's business. You see, I married Carola. I had to. I couldn't let a dame walk around wid odder guys that had somet'in' like dat on me—could I? I made her do the same t'ing to me, right away—and she seemed glad to do it, too—but I figger de priest just budder evvybody up—dat's his business, ain't it? He don't want nobody to feel dey's too far outa line. But it kept on buggin' me. Any time I hoid anybody say anyt'in' dat sounded like a doity crack—dat sounded like he meant *me*—I'd knock 'em cold, on the spot. Couple o' times I nearly killed a couple o' guys. Some guy would say, maybe —go on, you doity muff diver! Not sayin' it to me, ya under-stan'—jis sayin' it—I'd be right on top of him, and maybe put a knife between his ribs. It happened again, yesterday, right in Father James' parish. Den he tole me to talk to you. He said you were an educaded man—a guy dat had been around—and dat you would know about it."

He looked at me like a dog that is waiting to be beaten but is hoping for an unexpected reprieve. My poor, tough friend was utterly baffled and cowed—by love.

"I got a book at home," I said, "and this book was given to me by a doctor friend. It is called *The Moods of Love*, and it was written by a man called Harold Carter, a doctor too. In this book this guy Carter writes a few pages about love-making between married people, and he describes in detail just what you've gotten through telling me. He's all for it. He's all for everything that makes people show that they care for each other, or whatever makes them happy. You've been telling me an old story, Amadio, and I hardly know anybody who would have been surprised to hear it."

He jumped up, put two fingers in his mouth and gave an ear-piercing whistle. The cockroach and the dung beetle were instantly in evidence.

"Dis guy's got a book up in his house I want you to get right away," said Amadio. He turned toward me. "Give dem de keys to your place an' tell 'em where dey can find it."

Fortunately I knew. "It's the first book, on the left side, on the third shelf from the bottom," I said. "It's got a dark-red binding and gold lettering. It's called *The Moods of Love*, by Dr. Harold Carter."

"Write it all down fer dem," said Amadio. "An' now make it snappy, boys—get uptown and get back fast—I got a lot on my mind—so scoot!"

After the beetle and the cockroach had left us, he lay down on the bed again, and in a few moments he was asleep.

I looked at him, stretched out quietly, and wondered for the ten-thousandth time about the great mystery of the human heart. This slum child had probably never seen unashamed love or unself-conscious affection between men and women. He was a man as some fierce creature in a jungle is a man, and never throughout the years had he ever doubted the well-prescribed route of his own willful virility. He knew, of course, that there were other weaker men who allowed themselves to be carried away by their feelings for some women —men who made foolish sacrifices for their bedmates and who, in extreme cases, even permitted this affection to color every aspect of their lives.

He and his fellows had nothing but contempt for such weakness.

He also knew that there were some decadent side pockets in sexual behavior, and, by his standards, people who were trapped in such deviations were actually beneath all contempt.

And this had been his code until that soul-shattering night when the naked body of the beautiful girl beside him had torn him out of the clutches of a lifelong sexual cliché and had suddenly turned him into a *Lover*.

It was too much for his poor stultified imagination—so much too much that he was compelled to seek some sort of answer to his shameful problem from the priest; and when that answer had proven too glib or too facilely consoling, he had finally brought his deeply troubled heart to a total stranger—to me.

I don't know how long I speculated about all these matters in that revolting, overheated room, but at last I could hear the returning emissaries stumbling up the stairs again.

They had the book.

After we were alone, Amadio said, "Sit down next to me on de bed—an' read it to me. Read it real slow."

I found the place quickly enough, and I read to him the case history of the woman who had come to the author because she was troubled by profound misgivings about her connubial life. She and her husband were in the habit of abandoning themselves pretty freely during their sexual involvements, and since they were highly respected members of their community (her husband was even a deacon of the local church), she was deeply disturbed in her conscience about what seemed to her their excessive nocturnal indulgences. The doctor instantly put all her fears to rest and assured her that she had no cause whatever for any uneasiness, that their sexual behavior was perfectly natural and normal and was only the inevitable out-come of their passionate affection for each other—and so on.

Amadio took the book out of my hand and slowly repeated what I had just read to him.

And then he gave a laugh—such a laugh as had probably not issued from his mouth since he had been a small child. He laughed three times like that—then he tore the page out of the book and, after folding the paper very carefully, put it into his inside coat pocket.

I thought to myself, That page will land right alongside that old pigeon feather that he showed me seven years ago. It will be another one of the few symbolic artifacts of his desperately troubled life.

"You done me a great favor," he said, taking my hand. "You done *yourself* a favor too—'cause I ain't never gonna ferget what you done for me. If you need anyt'in'—ever—jis let me know. Anodder t'ing—" He pulled a fifty-dollar bill out of his pocket. "Here—go buy yerself anodder book."

"No," I said, "I've read it all, a long time ago, and I ain't ever gonna read it again anyway."

"You might some day need anodder copy—fer anodder emoigency, like tonight. Here—take it—it's damn cheap at the price!"

"All right," I said. "I'm glad I was able to be of use."

"You sure wuz. Imagine dis guy—a *deacon* in a *choich!* A *deacon*—can you beat it? *Man*, you sure don't know what people do when de window shades is down—do ya?"

"No," I said, "you most certainly *don't*."

CHAPTER SEVEN

SOMEBODY who is surely not coming to see me off at my final departure is Nina Marafiotti, the opera singer. I'm rather sorry about that, too, because I think that my wife, who has never met her, would have grown very fond of her.

Perhaps I had better explain my lifelong, rather curious, relationships to sundry opera performers and ballet girls. Let me tell you, right at the outset, that I have always found most of these creatures absolutely insufferable and, at the same time, utterly fascinating. It might be a good idea if I clarified the special conditions which tend to produce these peculiar monsters.

You see, an opera singer or a ballerina generally functions under such nerve-shattering conditions that almost no other human enterprise or occupation can hope to match the extravagance of its unpredictable dangers.

102

An actress, or even an acrobat on the high wire, once she has mastered her special routine, performs her task well, or ill, before the eyes of people who have never, or hardly ever, seen her work before. The opera singer, on the other hand, presents herself to the public in a character that the public is not only thoroughly familiar with but has had occasion, over the years, to compare with the greatest performances of that role which have ever been given.

And that's not the whole of it. If the singer already happens to have a great reputation, then she is permanently in competition with her own last outstanding appearance in that same part. Consider, also, how many things may go wrong with a *singing* voice—or an overburdened *toe*—and you may learn to be more sympathetic with the outsize eccentricities of some of our most famous opera divas and prima ballerinas.

If you live around such people for any length of time, and are therefore in a good position to judge the multiple hazards which beset their chronically jeopardous lives, you will end up by understanding and forgiving a good many of their irritating foibles.

I was once connubially involved with a young ballerina for nearly six years, and it became second nature for me to always carry an extra pair of toe shoes in my pocket—just in case. In winter, fortified by an overcoat with a lot of extra pockets, I sometimes carried as many as five or six pairs about my person. It was an amorous hazard with occupational overtones.

So, the next time you read in the papers that some well-known opera star has thrown a seemingly inexplicable fit, just try to remember that the poor harassed creature functions in the world like an exposed nerve. She can be shattered by the footfall of a cat, and a molting canary in the next apartment may suddenly cause her to break out with hives or even create an allergy in her throat, which instantly means a canceled engagement.

103

Now, then, if the average actress, by the mere nature of her exhibitionistic calling, is very likely to turn into an unbearably vain and frivolous ass—how much greater are the possibilities that a singer, whose every breath may spell the end of her career, is going to wind up as a paranoid blight to everybody who has anything to do with her.

I could go on like this indefinitely, but I hope I have made reasonably plausible the special anxieties which are bound to beset anyone who chooses such a disastrously unstable career.

I have been an avid opera fan since my earliest childhood and attended the Viennese Hofoper for the first time when I was six. As a young man in New York, I have stood many hours patiently in line, along with many other music lovers, for the chance of hearing Caruso, Tetrazzini, or Chaliapin in one of their great roles.

I remember the first time I took Margie to the Metropolitan, to hear *La Perichole*, I bought her a bouquet of winter violets, and later, in the theater, I told her that one of the great joys, for me, at least, was the fabulous, many-tiered gold curtains that rose and fell like a magician's cloak at the beginning and end of each scene. It all made a great impression on my young wife, and afterward she timidly showed me a poem she had written to commemorate that occasion. Here it is:

CURTAIN CALL

Coldly preserved by the florist's frost,
The violets you gave me were without scent.
Only their carved blue blossoms and dark heart green leaves
Echoed the bloom whose fern-filtered perfume
Stains a spring shade with velvet promise of summer's warmth.
This nosegay, made to grace a lady's glove, was sterile as fashion.
But when at last the gold satin curtain gave way to its weight
And in spiraling brocade ripples cascaded silently to the stage,

Precipitating a purr of approval, ruffled by applause,
Rustled programs, and rising taffeta muffled in furs,
Then, my violets, as if aware the play was over
And reality restored, suffused the air with the truth
Of their sensuous vital essence, their unique essential presence,
And in dying, they began, again, to live.

Now, let me tell you about Nina Marafiotti. I'd met her a long time ago, on my third revisit to Vienna, during an opera festival which the Austrian government was sponsoring to encourage *tourisme*. I was introduced to her by an acquaintance of mine who, during those years, was doing some sort of European field service for the Metropolitan Opera Company in New York. This scout, whose name was Spencer Greenberg, believed that Nina Marafiotti was the greatest voice at large in the world at that time, and he nearly ruptured himself daily trying to get her to sign a contract with him for the Met. This rupturing bit is not just a figure of speech on my part, because Nina, when I came to know her, weighed two hundred and thirty-six pounds, and, if you constantly danced attendance on her, as *he* did, you always took a calculated chance of being mashed to death by any accidental misstep of hers. She wasn't very tall—she was just an enormous eater, and during those easygoing years it didn't really matter so much if a singer happened to be ludicrously shapeless. It was the voice that counted.

The svelte ones came in *with* and *after* Maria Jeritza, and I, for one, can assure you that the slinky brigade never managed to achieve what the pork sausages accomplished with laughable ease.

However, the reason Nina wouldn't tumble for Mr. Greenberg's blandishments and refused to sign his contract was that she was in mortal dread of the sea. She had never been on it, but she remembered with horror a short voyage on the Danube of her childhood, and the mere memory of it turned her absolutely livid.

That's why Greenberg introduced her to me in the first place. He offered me a sizable bonus if I could persuade that lady that her fears of the sea were childish and that she owed it to the world of Art and Culture to bring her great talents to the rest of the Western Hemisphere.

We took Nina to a restaurant, and I can only assure you that I have never in my life known anyone who could put away more food at one single session. I will not overtax your credulity by enumerating the number of dishes that that fine woman ate during that memorable luncheon. I will only tell you that the other three of us who were present at that stupendous meal ate less in our totality than she did all by herself.

And she showed it too. She was not only extremely fat—but hundreds of tiny, bewildered blood vessels in her cheeks and arms had already become discolored and broken down with the sheer volume and richness of the vital fluids they had to carry. In fact, if you sat anywhere close to her, she looked quite a lot like a braised cauliflower.

"It doesn't show from the front," Greenberg assured me. "In make-up and costume she gets by without any trouble at all. And when she *sings*—" He rolled his eyes like a man under deep enchantment, and I could see he was absolutely heartbroken that he was unable to sign her up for the States.

"You *must* help me," he said. "You've got a way with women—and you're absolutely my last hope. I've been hanging around her all summer, and I'm really at the end of my resources."

"I'll do what I can," I said. "In fact, I have a very good idea. See what you think of it."

"What is it?" he said. "Are you planning to become her lover?"

"I don't think any *one* man could safely undertake such a venture," I said. "I think she has to be wooed by a committee, at least, and that would take time. No, my suggestion would be that you get her signed up to sing in London for one season."

"*London?!?*" he said. "What in heaven's name would be the sense of that?"

"That she will have to make a short sea voyage to get there," I said. "Don't you understand—if she survives the Channel without mishap, you're in!"

He became thoughtful. "The Channel is sometimes worse than the Atlantic."

"But a lot smaller, and a lot more calculable," I said. "You can write the Meteorological Bureau, you can consult the Geodetic Survey—and I think it will be a lot easier to talk her into an overnight trip than into a six-day voyage to New York. Try it, why don't you?"

"It's *your* idea," he said. "Why don't *you* try it?"

I did. I made a real campaign of it, and by September she and I had become such good friends that, after a particularly successful six-bottle afternoon tea out in Grinzing, she finally agreed to go to England.

She wouldn't sign for a full season, but she agreed to go and give it a try.

Triumph!!! Tarantara!!! Tarantara!!!

I still had a lot of misgivings, of course, chiefly because of her gargantuan appetite. If she ate her usual quota of grub, it certainly wouldn't take very much to make her seasick. An agitated glass of water on the captain's table might do it. Well, since I'd already gotten so deeply involved I agreed to go along with her to the embarkation. It wasn't much of a hardship for me, since she had a great fund of anecdote and I'd really become very fond of her.

She was going to cross from Calais to Dover—at least, the atmospheric and seismological conditions seemed to favor such a route, and I had also arranged for her to make a night passage.

"She'll climb into bed the minute she gets aboard," I said to myself. "I'll give her a couple of sleeping pills—and she'll wake up in England."

Such was the plan.

Naturally, it wasn't quite that simple, because the minute she caught sight of the boat she turned olive green. To get her used to the whole idea very gradually, I sat down with her at a terrace café, right near the harbor, and started talking to her very animatedly about her impending triumphs. Unfortunately, the waiter showed her a bill of fare and she inevitably started to eat. The worst of it was, I didn't dare warn her about it, and so she put away a load of vittles that was materially going to alter the freight distribution on that Channel steamer.

At last, her shoulders covered with layers of protective shawls, her head draped in endless veils to keep out the poisonous night air, I took her aboard and installed her in the stateroom. Since all servants take on and perpetuate the worst idiosyncrasies of their employers, her old Italian maid had flatly backed out of the trip, just the night before. However, by an act of simple bribery, I had arranged for one of the ship's stewardesses to function as her personal maid throughout the trip, and so Nina was appeased.

Arrived in her cabin, she took six sleeping pills and, covering herself with all her crazy rags and flounces, got instantly into bed.

When I went ashore in the oncoming dusk and looked back at the harbor, I saw the boat silhouetted clearly against a pure and windless Hokusai firmament.

All was well.

Since there was, for some reason, no decent train back to

Paris until the following morning, I ate a quiet supper at a local hotel and went to bed quite early.

I suppose I ought to have a drum roll or something, at this point, to show the relentless passage of time, but I'm afraid that the events which finally ensued are not likely to be drowned out by mere drums, or even timpani.

I heard all about it later on.

It seems that Nina got deathly ill only a few moments after I'd left her, and, considering the meal she'd put away, it's a miracle she didn't capsize the boat altogether. She kept on ringing wildly for the stewardess, and when she didn't get any answer, she just lay down on the tiny bathroom floor—covered with all those unmanageable drapes of hers—and proceeded to heave and yoik all night long like old man Vesuvius in his most regurgitative mood.

It was a night she would never forget. It was certainly a night she would never let *me* forget.

When daylight at last came shimmering through the porthole, she crawled back on the bed and made another attempt to rouse the stewardess.

This time her call was answered.

My hired help rushed into the cabin and approached the soggy mountain of absolute misery, which was spending its last pitiful energies in spasmodic retchings.

"Please—please—" Nina finally managed to whimper; "please take me ashore. No one knows what I have been through this night. No one—not even my patron saint—will ever know. Oh, my God! How am I *ever* going to get back to France again?"

"But, signora," said the stewardess, "you *are* in France. We are still in the harbor of Calais. Didn't anyone tell you—? The sailing was canceled last night, and the signora should really have stayed at a hotel!"

CHAPTER EIGHT

ONE PERSON who probably won't come, but who'll have kind thoughts and even a silent prayer for me, will be Eileen Hobart. She lives in Miami, Florida, and I had a little note from her only just before Christmas. Eileen doesn't go quite as far back in my life as most of the other people I have cited so far, and I came to know her sometime in the early fifties through a retired cotton broker called William Westmark.

Westmark is the first businessman to win a place in my recollections, and I can truthfully say I have hardly ever written about anyone whom I have esteemed more. I originally came to know Bill because I once owned a boat, and, like most boat owners, I spent nearly all my time fussing with it in drydock. A boat is, at the very least, constantly in need of calking and of painting, and it was up on Dyckman Street, in the McGraw boatyards, that I first exchanged pseudonautical grunts with him. I liked him right away because he was one of the very few boat owners I'd ever met who felt a little silly about his hobby. To me this betokened such a fund of philosophical detachment that I realized at once I had struck an honest-to-God original.

After we'd both finally gotten rid of our albatrosses, our friendship continued, and I don't think a single month passed during the following years but that we met at least once or twice for dinner, and over the course of time talked ourselves into pretty close emotional proximity.

Bill Westmark was a reasonably well-read man, though certainly without any intellectual pretensions. Like most other rich men, he'd sent his sons and daughters to good, or at least expensive, schools all over the country, and this traditional piece of parental strategy had, naturally, come as an effective barrier between himself and his offspring. It amused the old man endlessly to see his children squirming over the fact that their father had remained a completely unpretentious man who never made a secret of his simple, proletarian origins.

"I needle them in a harmless way," he once told me. "My wife gets along fine with them, of course, because you know how it is with women—they're naturally born to any position they happen to find themselves in."

In short, I've briefly outlined for you the kind of setup that would most elegantly lend itself for exploitation in a boring magazine or television serial; a situation comedy that doesn't even have to be written—it actually happened, in all its most hideously obvious ramifications.

Well, then, out of this terribly banal and unpromising material I still propose to garner for your attention a truly astonishing tidbit, since, luckily for all concerned Bill Westmark was a man with an exceptionally imaginative mind, and such a character, as far as I know, can never be encountered in the slicks or on any currently exposed TV tapes.

I'm glad I brought up the subject of businessmen, because it is perfectly true that all through my life I'd had almost nothing to do with any of them. The reasons are obvious. It has always been natural for me to come into contact with painters and sculptors and writers of all sorts, since I have always been very much concerned with what passionately concerns *them*. Even the actors I know—and some of them are certainly real dopes, and may not have the vaguest idea of the meaning of the words they are mouthing—are at least in a position to give lip service to things of profound spiritual significance.

Business is something else altogether. I'm sure it can be fascinating stuff, but let me confess it—it just never properly *sent* me. And the men who are involved in it—what about them? To tell you the truth, I can't even *imagine* most of them.

Nevertheless, for the next few pages, I'm going to tell you about a retired businessman—a great big square, whom quite a few people just referred to as W.W.

Let me first list his deficiencies.

He didn't care for E. E. Cummings—for T. S. Eliot or Henry James. Pound and Proust both puzzled and bored him, and he was totally indifferent to most of the paintings which have stirred my own deepest emotions since I have been a child. Once when I played him a new recording of *Daphnis and Chloe* he nearly fell asleep.

In a haphazard sort of way, that's the *minus* record, more or less.

Now let me tell you about the *plus*.

He had what the French would so aptly phrase "the refinement of the heart."

112

Now I'll give you the proof.

Bill had a friend, a retired building contractor called Philip Kramer, and these two lads had fallen into the habit of going down to Florida every couple of years; but since they both hated recreational mobs, it was their custom to take these trips exclusively during the off season. They had known each other for quite a long time and were in many respects a good deal alike. Phil was a little more serious perhaps, and sometimes inclined to brood about his missed opportunities, but as a general thing they held nearly the same world views and could sit and smoke at each other for many hours with great content and satisfaction.

When I say Phil brooded about his missed opportunities, I don't mean financial or social ones. He had worked very hard, amassed a great fortune, raised a fine family, and had known "remorse and power," but somewhere along the line, he felt, a great many of the graces of life which he'd encountered on the way had been neglected by him in the relentless drive for his basic goals.

Charles Darwin in his old age felt exactly the same.

At any rate, these two characters had again gone off on one of their unseasonal visits to Florida—and a little later Bill Westmark called me on the phone and asked me to take dinner with him at his home.

"The family is away," he said. "I know you don't really mind them—but you don't exactly relish them, either—so why don't you come over, and I'll have some choice beef for you, just the way you like it—thoroughly burnt inside and out and absolutely revolting and inedible."

All through the dinner, which was excellent, and entirely to my taste, I noticed that Bill seemed preoccupied. It was difficult for so artless a man to keep any secrets for any length of time, and the minute the coffee was served he quickly unwrapped his little nugget for my special delectation.

"You know that Phil and I were just down in Miami," he said, "and a curious thing happened to us down there."

"You gambled," I said.

"No, I'm not much of a gambler," he said, "and Phil, I think, has even certain moral scruples against it. No—we had a sort of adventure. That's not right, either—we had no adventure at all—we *did* something—that is to say—*Phil* did something that is completely out of line with the rest of his character, and I even aided and abetted him in it. I'm telling you all this in the strictest confidence, of course, and I'm *only* telling it to you because I'm going to ask your advice about it later on. You know, Phil has for years been suffering from mild insomnia, but, being the sort of man he is, he always refused to take any sleeping pills. So, the first night, after we'd turned in and he again found himself quite sleepless, he thought that maybe a glass of milk or something might be helpful in getting him to sleep. Because this is the dead season down there, he didn't want to bother room service, so he got dressed and went out to look for an all-night diner, or some place where he could get a small snack of some sort. He walked about three blocks from the hotel and found a crazy little place, what *you* would call a cookie-nookie, where they made only pancakes with maple syrup. A new place that was all shiny and obviously not doing too well. Phil went in and ordered a portion of pancakes and a glass of milk. He was the only customer. Now then, the waitress that waited on him was a young girl, about seventeen or eighteen at the most, and she was a particularly polite and sweet young person. I don't think I've ever told you, but Phil is diabetic, and so he has to watch his sugar intake. At any rate, he talked to this girl a little about his problem, and she made him some thin orange slices to put on top of his pancakes, and, what with one thing and another, he must have spent about an hour in that

114

place. When he got home, he fell asleep almost instantly. Of course, I didn't know anything about any of this. The way I found out was that a couple of nights later, *I* was sleepless and went downstairs to rustle up some magazines. There was nothing in the hotel, everybody had closed up early, and when I walked down a few blocks to look for a newsstand, imagine my surprise to see Phil sitting in this pancake place and laughing and joking with a young waitress. Her name, by the way, is Eileen Hobart."

"Well, well," I said. "The old faun has finally come out of the woods. More power to him—better late than never."

I could see that my frivolous interjection had greatly disturbed Bill, and he looked at me appraisingly for a moment, as if he were undecided about the advisability of going on with his story. He sat down beside me on the much-too-upholstered couch, put his hand on my shoulder and said, "I'm sure you're only joking. You know Philip—and you must realize that he is a man full of innate rectitude. There is not a shred of hypocrisy in him, and one big reason why I'm talking to you about this at all is because I took it for granted you'd feel the same way about him."

"I'm sorry," I said, "but, after all, what would be the great wrong if he *did* get a crush on this girl? He isn't planning to shack up with her or to elope with her—is he?"

Bill Westmark looked reassured. "That's more like how I expected you to feel about it—but it really isn't even as simple as that. In fact, it's a great deal more complicated. You see, the reason he didn't mention it, even to me, the first couple of times he'd gone out at night to have those pancakes and milk is because I don't think he himself quite knew what it was he felt about that young girl. Phil is sixty-five years old, and I have a pretty good idea what *you* would consider proper at sixty-five—but Phil has led a life of such absolute conventionality that he wouldn't jeopardize his fine record no matter how great the temptation might be. Besides, what I'm telling you is that there *is* no temptation. He doesn't want a thing from that young woman that she hasn't already very graciously given him. A kindly respect and a sweet smile. You see, Phil has three sons and never had a daughter. I'm sure every father would like to have at least one daughter. Even my two daughters are much closer to me than my sons. Also, he is ill. Also, who knows what lost face in his past she reminds him of. All I can tell you is we went to visit that waffle shop every night for the rest of the week, and, when we left, that young woman had tears in her eyes when she said goodbye to us."

"And now what?" I said.

"And now nothing," said Bill. "We're not planning to go to Miami for two years, and for all I know the both of us will be dead by then."

"So what is it you wanted to ask my advice about?" I said.

"Well, I've had a kind of a strange idea rumbling around my head," said Bill, "and I just wondered what you'd think about it. Our club is tendering a luncheon to Phil a couple of months from now. He's given a big chunk of money for some charity that is a special pet of theirs. At any rate, they're giving him this luncheon. It's strictly stag, and the only women present will be the usual club waitresses who take care of the tables during lunch hours. Now then—I had the crazy idea to fly this Eileen Hobart up here for just two or three days, maybe, and have her wait on Phil's table during that meal. I can easily arrange it. I want it to be a surprise, of course, and I want you to be there when she steps from behind his chair and he first recognizes her. There's another thing—the *main* thing, really; I was wondering whether your young wife would be kind enough to make herself responsible for Eileen for the few days she stays in New York City. For obvious reasons, I can't talk to my family about it; but if it seems an excessive burden to you, then, please, just let's forget the whole thing. Anyway, I haven't yet asked you what you think of the whole idea—anyway. *Should* I do it?"

"Of course you should," I said. "I think Phil is a very, very lucky man indeed to have found one friend such as you."

And I meant it with all my heart.

Just think about it for a moment. Here was this totally uncomplicated human being—with nothing in his past to prepare him for it—and yet, when the occasion came, he was as perceptive as the most sophisticated worldling could have been, even down to the most minute niceties involved in this pretty delicate situation. Not only did he attempt to fairly understand and to loyally sympathize with the strange dilemma that was troubling his friend's heart, but he was equally concerned with the good repute of the young woman in question, and had especially asked me for the protective chaperonage of my wife in her behalf. I think that's the real reason he'd talked to me about it all in the first place.

It was done just as he had planned. When Eileen arrived in New York, she stayed at our house, and I shall ever be indebted to Bill Westmark for the happiness of knowing her. She proved a rare, pure blossom out of the contaminated swamps of Florida who, by some miracle I have never been able to fathom, had somehow managed to keep herself absolutely clean-minded and intact, despite all the sordid temptations which certainly must have surrounded her on all sides. It was a great pleasure to have her around, and when, after three days, she finally had to leave us, both my wife and I had a sense of real loss at her departure. She was a complete anachronism, of course, and so she had come to New York without the slightest tinge of calculated self-interest to stain

117

her visit. She entered at once, and quite unself-consciously, into the spirit of the little surprise that Bill had planned for his friend, and I never heard her say anything about the trouble or the expense that such a gesture must have entailed.

"You know," she said to us, "I lost my father when I was only seven, and I can't tell you how much Mr. Kramer's interest meant to me. He talked mostly about how beautiful the world was—if only young people took time out to see it. He said he'd always worked very hard when he was young, and that a lot of fine things had passed him by. Anyway, I'm so happy to be up here at this banquet that they're giving him —I'm sure they couldn't give it to a finer person."

At the luncheon, when she stepped up to Phil's side and saw his expression turn from sheepish surprise to sudden, unutterable happiness, her sweet eyes brimmed over with joyful tears.

It had all worked out just great.

On the third day of her visit Phil took her to a jeweler, *not* Tiffany's, and bought her a little keepsake. It was a very thin gold chain that supported a fleur-de-lis pendant with a diamond chip in its calyx.

Only my wife accompanied her to the airport.

A year later, I myself saw her in Florida, wearing Phil's little trinket; also she wore a modest engagement ring that Art Roback had given her. Art owns a filling station down there, and I understand he's been sweet on Eileen for quite a while.

Someone who had been to Miami a few months after the marriage came back and told me that Eileen wasn't wearing the necklace any more. Oh, well, I thought, probably the new husband didn't like it.

So, a few months ago, after Philip Kramer died (Bill, I'm sorry to say, was buried the preceding winter), I wrote a letter to Art Roback, and this letter contained, in essence, almost everything that I have written in these last few pages.

Art never answered me, but, as I mentioned before, I had a note from Eileen around the middle of December.

She said:

Dear Mr. King,

We are doing fine, Art and I. I have even learned to keep his books for him, and I guess an old friend like you might as well know that we are expecting a baby around the end of March. Art was so busy he didn't have time to answer your letter, besides he is not really very good at letter writing. He sends you his best and hopes you will come down to see us soon. I want you to know that the day after your letter arrived Art took my little gold chain out of the box where I have kept it and hung it back around my neck. I am wearing it ever since.

Our very best wishes to you, Mr. King, and may God keep you well, for all our sakes.

Give a kiss to Margie for me.

Eileen

I'm going to mention just one other person who wouldn't be able to make it to my funeral, and that person, I'm quite grieved to tell you, is Robert Capa.

I met him in 1938 or '39 when both of us were working on *Life* magazine—he, as an itinerant photographer, and I, as a sort of general idea man. Capa was a bushy-browed, stockily swarthy Central European, one of those ingratiating characters who speak every language with a strong Hungarian accent. His native Hungarian pronunciation was, in its turn, heavily colored by all the other languages he had never quite managed to master, and the result was a truly international type whose simplest thought processes required the services of at least three tongues. He had an enormous polyglot vocabulary, which he used with careless facility on waiters, taxi drivers, editors

119

and women of all ages and stations, and in an emergency he was prepared to solve all locutional dilemmas with loud and hearty laughter.

Since I myself was born in Central Europe, and am also multiple-language-tainted, I had some wonderful times with Capa, both in New York and all the other places where fate happened to bring us together. I just hope that some day someone who knows more about him than I do will sit down and write his fabulous biography. I, for one, would certainly rejoice to read it.

In short, I do not intend here to synopsize his career for you; nothing could be further from my mind. I'm only going to tell you the one anecdote about his life which he told me the very last time we met face to face.

We had taken a long and leisurely dinner together in one of those phony East Side bistros which Capa seemed to fancy, because, I think, he liked to be reminded of how futile it was to reproduce the real thing he loved, on this side of the Atlantic. The ostensive purpose of our meeting was to discuss for the x-teenth time an idea for a photo-reportage which we had been planning together for about three years. Not for *Life*—nor for any other existing magazine—but rather for ourselves—perhaps for the day when some dizzy Argentine or Greek millionaire was going to give us enough money to start a magazine of our own.

The idea was to show, by means of words and pictures, what an American divorcee does and thinks in the course of a week. This notion had been haunting us for quite a while, and some of the dolls in that condition, whom we both knew, seemed willing enough to go through the necessary motions for us. We didn't mean to fake it. There was no necessity for that. We'd just have to fix it so that nobody would sue us if the stuff ever got published.

We wanted to start off this little essay with the bridal

photograph at the marriage—the music, the rice, the confetti, and all the rest of the nuptial and postnuptial nonsense—including even some pictures of the honeymoon. Next—a couple of scenes from the amiable domestic life—and if there were any children, by all means bring them into the scene, too. All this material was to be mere introduction, of course, worth only one or two pages at the most, since our chief interest and concern lay with the divorced wife. Capa and I knew about a half dozen of them around town, and their peculiar condition and mode of life had always fascinated us.

You may not think this such a promising idea, but that just shows that you know very little about it. These women are a real problem in certain circles, and the divorcee whose age range is between twenty-eight and forty-eight is, as far as I can see, in most cases, just a perambulating disaster.* Her misery is, of course, infinitely aggravated if her ex-husband happens to be a celebrity. It is bound to be a lot worse for such a dame, because for quite a while she will still have entree to a lot of homes where her distinguished spouse was really the one whom the hostesses generally had in mind when they used to invite *both* of them.

I'm glad to concede that there are certain exceptions to this generalization, but they concern a comparatively small number of women—the few who get married over and over again and who figure in the daily press not so much as human beings but as chronic brides. I've checked into the matter carefully, and there aren't enough of these loose in the country to damage my thesis to the extent of a feather's weight.

Take Beula Blakey, for instance, a lady of infinite leisure, who, I'm quite certain, will sacrifice a whole afternoon and even part of an evening to commiserate with my widow, when

* I'm referring particularly to women who get $10,000 or more alimony per year.

121

that sad time comes along. Beula began to live the *life* at sixteen—some thirty years ago—and, by means of certain magical propensities no one can account for, landed in bed with a few men who figure frequently in the gossip columns of the daily papers. She was not particularly beautiful, and she certainly wasn't witty, and I finally decided that her accomplishments were predicated just on the simple fact of her easy accessibility. One thing is certain—she was, even in her early youth, as completely asexual as an uncooked veal cutlet. I'm equally convinced that she never had any particular enjoyment out of her sexual activities, and I would wager my soul's salvation that she was terrible to sleep with. None of this is really a handicap to a young woman on the make in our civilization, in which men shy away from all amorous preparatory build-ups that can't be achieved by the simple process of getting quietly drunk together.

She did have that advantage—she was a good and steady drinker from the very start.

I really don't know how the transition finally crystallized and how Beula became, at the age of thirty, the sort of official whore without portfolio for most of the well-known men who happened to gravitate into the orbit of show business.

I didn't see her for a couple of years after that, and when I first became aware of her again, she was happily married to a very nice guy with lots of money. She told me all about it quite breathlessly, while I was waiting for someone else to join me at the Plaza for luncheon. I had always had a rather special, I might say even an exclusive, position in Beula's life, since I had never had an affair with her. It was purely accidental, of course, and almost entirely due to the fact that she was always on the most excellent terms with my various wives.

Well, now, at last, she was a bride, and I must say she certainly blossomed out under it. Her husband was a famous something-or-other in the movie business, and the sea-tossed caravel of her life seemed finally to have reached a safe harbor.

Two years later she was divorced.

Don't bother pointing out to me that Beula's background was far from typical and bears little resemblance to the lives of other divorcees, since I'm only too ready to grant this to you in advance. The reason I brought her up at all is that Beula had had infinitely more experience in getting along by herself than most of the other dames who had, one way or another, shed their husbands via the divorce courts.

My point is that Beula, who had managed comparatively well through all the years *before* her marriage, suddenly, right after her divorce, became absolutely pathetic.

Now, widows aren't a bit like that. It is only the members of the alimony brigade that make even parakeets in their cages pretend to be asleep when these babies come around to unload some of their distillate of stultification.

I have occasion to meet these creatures from time to time, at the homes of some of my friends, and after I'd talked to a few of them I realized that the poor twerps had become the prisoners of their own shortsighted self-interest. They no longer dared to get seriously involved with unmarried men, for this might eventually lead to a discontinuance of their steady alimony checks.

Drink and sleeping pills had become their souls' exclusive anodynes, and the boredom they themselves suffered, and engendered, hovered around their multiple-dyed heads as palpably as the sunset clouds around the Matterhorn.

In my photo-reportage about them I planned, among other things, to show their day-by-day activities—their compulsive primpings at their overloaded dressing tables—their agonies and torments in exorbitant beauty parlors—their falsely enthusiastic meetings with their equally purposeless counterparts in various depressing cocktail lounges around town, and so on, and so on—the whole gruesome bit.

You may wonder why their lives should be any different from that of all the other kept women who have no special hobbies or aptitudes with which to beguile their time. And yet there *is* a big difference between the kept tootsie and the dame who has been the legal bedmate of a man of reputation and who might, at any moment, have become the mother of his children.

That's another depressing point. If one of these gals has a son or a daughter, or both, hovering about somewhere in the background, then her condition is not only pathetic—it is absolutely pitiful. Not many men like to mix themselves up with ready-made families, and so, while she may still look pretty seductive, she has gained something that nearly totally annihilates her romantic chances— *She is somebody's mother.* And that is *never* a laugh.

Curiously enough, it is quite different with widows. Indeed, I've come to think that widows are more actively in demand than almost any other type of female. The widow has unassailable status and very frequently is possessed of very easily assailable bank assets; besides, she doesn't live on a monthly dole that ceases the minute she decides to marry again.

The widow faces one great hazard, as I've already told you in an earlier chapter. She is far too desirable not to become the immediate target for all the rampant scoundrels and leeches who happen to have gotten wind of her demurely solvent sorrow.

The divorcee is like a side dish that nobody remembers having ordered. She sits at other people's festivals, coifed and curled and dyed within an inch of her life, smiling bravely, and hoping against hope that nobody will inquire about her teen-age daughter, or make tactless remarks about her ex-husband—who has happily remarried.

At any rate, what does such a social supernumerary *do* all

week long? That's what I wanted to put on record; and Bob Capa seemed like the ideal man to do this job with me.

The last time I saw him, we talked about a lot of other things, too—particularly about the tough times he'd had after he'd left Budapest and, as a mere youngster, had landed in Germany, and later on in France.

I shall not try to reproduce his accent—that would be quite hopeless—I just want you to remember as I write about him that Robert was a man whom most people took to almost instantly. It seems that he did pretty well in Paris for a while; he had a lot of friends, particularly around the Ritz bar, where he met most of the famous and comparatively well-to-do American expatriates. But after a time, almost imperceptibly, it seems these guileless spenders drifted south as the seasons changed, and, suddenly, one fine day Capa found himself quite alone with the bartender. His various jobs had also petered out, and finally he was reduced to pawning all of his hard-gotten photo equipment. For a photographer to hock his camera represents a sort of suicide, I suppose, and when poor Capa was down to his last fifty francs he decided to hitchhike to the Mediterranean resort towns, where he certainly would have a much better chance of encountering a helpful hand.

"So I started out early one morning," he said to me, "and I stayed near a gas station on the edge of town, where cars would stop to refill their tanks. Before I go any further, I just want to tell you that the French as a people just aren't yet orientated for hitchhikers. Not yet. Maybe in the next millennium, but certainly not in *our* lifetime. Anyway—I had no luck, so I finally tried to catch a ride further out of town, and so I walked a couple of miles and kept signaling to every car that passed. A driver would sometimes slow down and ask me what I wanted—and when I told him that I wanted to ride along with him, in his car, he looked at me as if I'd lost my mind. You have to take into consideration the frugal, sober French character if you want to understand how silly the whole idea seemed to him. Here he was, sitting in an automobile that *he* had paid for, out of his hard-earned money, and—suddenly—out of nowhere a total stranger approaches him and want to sit on *his* upholstery—maybe use *his* ash tray—and help wear out *his* floor-board carpet. It sounds completely insane to him. When one of them asked me what I offered to do in return for all this—I said to him, '*Monsieur*, I am prepared to offer my profoundest gratitude.' He nearly slapped me. I think that the whole social mystique on which hitchhiking is predicated is completely antithetical to the French national spirit. You cannot tell *me* anything about it, either, because I've lived among these dribbling winebibbers and snuffling cheese fanciers for years. They grow the most sun-drunken grapes, they have endured the most stupendous history, they have invented the best cafés in the world, and their bread is surely the loaf which God in his great goodness originally handed to Adam. But they sit amidst all these glories with greasy account books in their fingers and parcel out their immortal souls like so many shriveled raisins."

"I thought you loved the French," I said.

"I love to sit on the Boulevard St. Germain," said Capa, "and I love to see the little saucers accumulate in front of me while my friends pass by and give me warm greetings; I love to go to the flea market on Sunday morning and eat *pommes frites* along with young lettuces for which I have prepared the dressing; I love the smell and the sounds of my little hotel on the Quai Voltaire and, most of all, I love to watch the children in the bird market and in the flower market; and I love all the people of France who can't afford to buy an automobile. The others are mostly a dead weight around the neck of the *Grande République*—and all I can tell you is that I had to *walk* most of the way to that damned Côte d'Azur of theirs. You know,

126

as I was walking along on a poplar-lined highroad one afternoon, I felt so bitterly frustrated that when somebody finally came along and offered me a lift *going in the wrong direction* —the one I had just *come* from—I accepted the ride, because I simply wanted to be *driven somewhere!*

"Well, at last, after much agony, I finally arrived at the sea. I looked at the Mediterranean for the first time. I happened to land there just about noon, and so there wasn't another living soul anywhere in sight. Even *I* knew about the midday siesta— and I realized that I had that whole freshly laundered shore all to myself. I was desperately hungry—and all I owned in the whole world I was wearing on my body. I had a beret, a striped basque shirt, my shorts, a pair of beautifully tailored English slacks, and, on my feet, a pair of very badly worn espadrilles. I also had some sunglasses which one of the bartenders at the Ritz had given to me as a farewell present. I knew that nobody was likely to stir out for quite a while—so I went down to the beach, right near where a raft was anchored offshore, and, since I had nothing else to do, I decided to take a swim. In my famished condition that swim was the last thing I needed—but how could I resist dunking myself in the sea that had known the triremes of Carthage and of Rome? What was it Xenophon's battle-scarred and weary troops shouted when, after their long and killing overland trek, they again saw the ocean? They shouted, 'Talatta!!! Talatta!!!' And, since I am a man of a lot of useless but diversified information, I too screamed 'Talatta!!!' as I flung myself into the cool embrace of those beautiful waters. First, of course, I had distributed my little wardrobe along a picket fence that some thoughtful soul had planted along the ocean front. Wearing my white shorts in lieu of bathing trunks, I swam out to that blistering raft and lay there for heaven only knows how long. My stomach kept rumbling so loud that I would have fallen asleep several times if my internal noises hadn't constantly wakened me. Also, I was afraid of getting too sunburned. So after a good long while I dropped into the water and swam back to shore again.

"Now, listen carefully, because what I am telling you now is the whole reason why I told you this whole crazy story in the first place. When I got back to the picket fence where I had hung up my clothing, I saw that right alongside of them somebody had hung a brand-new Leica camera. It was one of the latest models too, worth about three hundred and eighty-five dollars. I blinked a couple of times, because I was sure I had suffered a sunstroke—or something even worse, maybe—but when I touched that beautiful little machine with my hands, I finally had to admit to myself that it was *real*. And then a terrible thing happened. Remember what happened to Saul of Tarsus on the road to Damascus? He heard a voice—and that voice changed the course of his whole life. Well, standing there on that hot sand, *I* suddenly heard a voice too—it was the voice of an honorable Jewish Hungarian seamstress who was my mother—and the voice said, '*You must never take anything that doesn't belong to you!!!*' It was absurd, of course; I was a professional photographer who didn't own a camera—*that* was the desperate truth of the matter. And then, when Destiny, through one of her servants, had miraculously placed a fine camera within arm's reach of me—*I was hearing voices and hesitating!* Insane, isn't it?

"It gets even wilder. I simply *couldn't* take that camera. I mean, I could not take it—just like *that*. But I made a deal with myself: I would swim back to the raft and count up to a thousand slowly, and when I came back to shore again, and that Leica was still hanging there beside my clothes—I would consider it a sign from on high and requisition it without any further fear or misgivings. And that's what I did. I swam back to the raft, lay down flat on my back, and counted up to *fifteen hundred*—slowly. At last I dropped into the water and made it back to shore again. I purposely kept my eyes to the ground until the very last minute, and when I was so near that with lowered eyes I could see the bottom of the fence—I suddenly looked up. The camera was gone—and—whoever had taken it had also stolen my pair of English slacks.

"I stood for a few minutes staring at that empty place on that fence, and I had a sudden shocking realization that Destiny had gotten tired of me at last. You know, I used to think that nothing is emptier than the place where money has *once been*. I mean an empty pocketbook in which you used to keep it, or even a secret drawer in which loose bills used to lie scattered. I mean that after the money is gone from such places where you were in the habit of seeing it—there is suddenly such an emptiness that it seems positively palpable. The emptiness is so shockingly acute that it achieves a definite identity. Well, let me tell you, Alex, that that spot on that picket fence, where my pants had once been, was emptier than any place I had ever seen before in my whole life. I was too shattered to do anything for quite a while. I didn't even swear—though that probably seems hard to believe. I just stood there and stared, unbelieving, at that space, like a cow at a newly painted barn door. I started, mechanically, to put on my things—my espadrilles, my beret, my T shirt—and, with my shorts still wet on my behind, I tottered along the shore in a complete daze.

"After a while I landed near a stone staircase that seemed to lead up to the villas that I had seen nestling in the foliage above me. I had no plans to go anywhere, so I plumped myself down on the bottom steps—and my exhaustion must have been so complete that I fell asleep instantly. I was awakened by someone who was coming down those stairs, and when I turned around and looked up, there, above me, stood a huge man wrapped in a white terry-cloth bathrobe. It was Ernest Hemingway. Of course he recognized me. 'What are you doing

129

here?' he asked. 'I thought you had a job in Paris.' I was so glad to see him I started to cry. He came alongside of me and looked at me very puzzled and, I think, a little irritated. And so I blurted out the whole list of my stupid misadventures to him. When I came to the part where I'd lost my pants, he suddenly became very grave. 'You are really unbelievable,' he said. 'You are obviously totally unfit to cope with life. I can't imagine what's going to become of you. Really, you are too much!' Then he turned around and walked back up the stairs again and left me sitting there in my misery. I stared after him for a while and, I suppose out of weakness and probably out of general despair, too, I must have fallen back asleep again. I must have slept quite a while, too, because when I woke up this time it had become a little cooler and the beach was full of people. As I looked down I noticed that there was a fine pair of slacks lying at my feet. For a moment I was too stupefied to react at all, but finally I got up and put them on. They were a little too large for me, but they were absolutely elegant. And you know what else? In one of the pockets I found a thousand-franc note, which was worth forty American dollars in those days. So, as I'm telling you, and proving to you, Hemingway is not only a great writer—he is also a great *host!*"

Nina Marafiotti was certainly quite foolish to be so distrustful only of the sea—because, just a few years ago, poor Robert Capa died in China by accidentally stepping on a land mine. May the earth rest lightly on his wonderfully ebullient heart.

On that last afternoon we had together, *I* told Bob a little story too, one that had been told to me by his Hungarian compatriot, the playwright Ferenc Molnár. Molnár, whom I came to know quite well after he'd settled in the United States, was in some mysterious way particularly drawn toward the activities of radio. He was utterly fascinated by this medium and wanted very much to do some writing for it. I tried to convince him that radio was achieving a doubtful maturity only in very small areas, music mostly, and even this was only true rather locally, just around New York City. He had no intention of writing any romantic, fictional material for the airwaves; what he had in mind was that somewhere, along all those loquacious wave lengths, there might be room for an elder statesman of the theater like himself to talk to the public about some of the lesser known aspects of show business. Naturally, nothing ever came of this notion, but in the meantime, since I was going to act as his translator, I had some really instructive and amusing meetings with the old man.

He was particularly interested in demonstrating to the world at large how rigidly confined was the operating area of the professional playwright. Even intelligent theatergoers, he maintained, were quite unaware of the tight framework which circumscribes the activities of the man who writes for the stage.

"It is a desperately exigent craft," he said to me, "and it is full of limiting and baffling compulsions. Take, for instance, the matter of stage directions. You have three or four words at the most to indicate your wishes to the actors and the director who finally get to work on your script. It is sometimes enough to break a sensitive man's heart. I happen to have an especially good example to demonstrate this to you.

"During the First World War I was stationed on the Russian front as a war correspondent. By that time, the war had gone on for three and a half years, and so there started to be a good deal of fraternization among the Russian population and our troops. It was only natural that this should have happened. If an occupying force was settled in the same village for a year or more, let us say, it was only reasonable, human nature being what it is, that some of our soldiers should have set up some sort of livable, and even amiable, rapport with the local peasantry. In the course of time they were bound to do each other all sorts of small kindnesses, and, as a matter of fact, I believe that this was indeed the human nexus which became an important factor in breaking down the morale of the Austro-Hungarian forces in that sector of the battle front. At any rate, to prevent any more of such comradely relations between these officially specified enemies, our general headquarters suddenly issued an order that anyone caught fraternizing with the Russian population was to be instantly courtmartialed—and summarily executed.

"A few days after this order had been published, I stepped out of my lodging shortly after sunup and I met a young lieutenant of my acquaintance, who told me that a courtmartial was about to be held on the outskirts of the village that very morning. I asked my friend whether it was possible for me to witness this event, and he at once offered to escort me to the scene of action. In a little while we arrived at this locale, and because the trial had already begun, we halted a little distance off, on a slight elevation, from which we had an excellent view of both the set and the proceedings. Although we were too far off to hear what was being said, we had no difficulty in following the procedure, since everything in this highly concentrated little tragedy was only too obviously plain.

"The court was held in front of a thatched peasant hut which was generally used as a staff rallying point. Four long tables covered with white cloths served as the judicial rostrum, and half-a-dozen high army officers were sitting behind these tables in the capacity of judges. Facing them, with his hands tied behind his back, stood a common private of our own army, and he remained so completely immobile throughout the whole action that it was hard to believe he was a living man. The lieutenant by my side, who was thoroughly familiar with the case, quickly informed me of the substance of the charges which had brought the soldier before this court. It seems that he had, some time before, been billeted in the home of a Russian peasant and had, after a while, gotten involved with the eldest daughter of the household. This was a common enough occurrence all along this quiet sector of the front; it was just unfortunate that this particular man was going to be made an example of to demonstrate the sudden upsurge of revitalized army discipline.

"As I was standing there in the morning sunlight, deeply disturbed by what was happening such a short distance away from me, my eyes strayed for a moment and I noticed a young peasant girl standing off on one side, just a little ahead of us, and it was clear that she too was concentratedly watching the unfoldment of the grisly military drama before us. I saw that only her tightly clasped hands, which she held behind her back all through the trial, were quite pale beneath her sunburn. She wore the usual holiday regalia of the girls of that part of the world—short skirts standing wide away from her legs because of the many petticoats she had on underneath, a tightly laced flowered bodice, and a short-sleeved linen blouse. Her wheat-colored hair was wound in a thick braid around her head and her feet were bare. It took no particular prescience on my part to realize that *she* was probably the girl in question. She was the *femme fatale* in this tragedy. She had come uninvited to the scene, although it would certainly have been more prudent of her to stay away. I watched her riveted there in agonized stillness, and it came to me that at that moment she and her lover had only one thing left in common beside their terror, and that was their stonelike immobility.

"Suddenly the six judges rose simultaneously, drew their swords out of their scabbards, and laid the naked blades upon the tables before them. My friend the lieutenant said, 'They are about to pronounce judgment. They have drawn their swords to show that they will judge the man without bias.'

I strained to hear some words that were being uttered by one of the officers, but it did not really matter that I could not hear anything he said—it was only too obvious, in the changed posture of the accused, that he had been summarily found guilty. For the first time since he had been inducted into the army, his body slumped into civilian grief as he stood limp in the presence of his superiors. Two men, proudly sure that they were going to survive him, led him quietly but sternly away. The officers sheathed their swords—and the trial was over. The lieutenant at my side shook hands with me and left. I stood alone in the warm morning sunlight on my little hillock. I had just seen a man condemned to death. The peasant girl still stood in the same spot where I had last observed her, and only after all the army personnel had gone she unclasped her hands, gave an automatic swing to her short, wide skirts, and she also slowly proceeded to walk away. She was headed toward a birch grove that grew not far from the village and, without even thinking about it, I found myself slowly following her.

"As I stepped along in her footsteps on that dusty road, my mind was profoundly stirred by numberless disturbing and sometimes even conflicting images. I thought to myself, she is very beautiful, as all things that have triumphantly survived are beautiful. The fine yellow down on her strong, sunburnt arms is going to enchant other men some day. Her rich, luscious body is full of the ripe juices of affirmation. . . . And yet she walks like some creature who is trying to hide the fact that it has just suffered a fatal blow; like an animal that seeks the denseness of trees before it stops to examine its wounds. Also, she is like mother earth, which is fecund even during the greatest upheavals. She may be bearing his child and is, even now, gathering her forces for the life that is slumbering inside her. She is, also, like all womanhood that has followed the armies of the world and borne children among caissons and between cart wheels of supply wagons. She will suffer and prevail—to suffer and prevail again—as the mothers of the world have been doing since the days when the vapors of the universe solidified and combined to make a home for that most astonishing of all creatures—Man.

"I thought of all this and much more as I followed that girl along that country road—and it suddenly came to me that if I were writing about her in one of my plays, and I had to dispose of this walk of hers in a stage direction, I would be reduced to indicating her action by the words—*Peasant girl exits*."

CHAPTER NINE

HOW COULD YOU HAVE KNOWN so many and come to live contentedly with only one?

It was easy as pie!

At my age, of course, one has to face certain problems. I'm sure you would never guess what some of them are. You see, I have a rival. His picture appears as the frontispiece to this book and, believe me, this likeness of his has caused me considerable uneasiness. It is a photograph of me taken when I was twenty-three years old, and a friend of mine who has held on to it through all these years sent it on to us last April. It proved a perilous gift—a token that I find a pretty constant stumbling block to smug content.

Sometimes, when she thinks herself unobserved, I find my wife studying this nethermost layer in the palimpsest of my life, as if she were searching in it for some illuminating clue to my present identity. It may also be that, in her youthful inexperience, she regrets that she never knew me in my prime.

As somebody who looked at this picture the other day said to her: "You're damned lucky you *didn't!*"

Come to think of it, most Americans are ashamed of being poor, of growing old, and of being deeply in love. Many of them even try to hide that they are gravely ill. You can plainly see how untypical I really am, since I constantly violate every one of these curious national taboos. Also, as I've so frequently said before, in America nobody ever dies any more. They are elevated, they are surplused, they pass on— but nobody ever just dies. Nowadays it is considered very morbid for anyone to dwell on the fact of death, but I can't help talking about it—since I've been *thinking* about it for more than half a century. It accounts for a good deal of my behavior during that time, too, because if I had believed that I'd ever get another chance, somewhere else, I would not have been so greedy or so eager to crowd my existence with every possible sort of available sensation. This so-called morbidity has also made me patient and good-humored in times of serious adversity since, even at the very bottom of the barrel, I somehow always managed to find miraculous consolations that made my human awareness a glorious treasure. To tell you the truth, I never had any trouble finding love, no matter on what level of well-being I happened to be functioning. Indeed, I found the greatest love of my whole life when I was poor—when I was sick—and when I was addicted to drugs.

There is another thing that bothers me, and I wouldn't be surprised if I have already told you about it, because it is almost constantly on my mind. You see, I'm afraid of leaving too large an estate, because it is bound to attract the worst kind of people around my widow. Every South American

137

gigolo, every café-society moocher, and every idle, cocktail-party free loader will crowd around my darling the moment my ashes have been blown away by the wind. If, on the other hand, I leave just a *little* money—just enough for her to manage decently and without immediate harassment—the chances of her meeting some fairly honorable people are infinitely improved. All this worries me quite a bit, although I know only too well that life will go on very successfully without me. I would just like to think it will continue along with a special measure of grace and kindness for one whom I have loved so much.

I honestly believe that anyone who lives his years without frequent thoughts of his own death—and I don't mean just in terms of insurance policies either—is, somehow, robbing himself of an important dimension in appraising the great wonders that the world is constantly lavishing all about us. In short, I believe that a feeling for tragedy gives one not only a properly apprehensive heart—it also makes for a perceptive and a grateful one.

Of course, I realize that I am just talking into the wind and that my preoccupied contemporaries will go right on pretending that they are destined to live forever. They *will* go so far as to buy policies that guarantee the mortgages on their houses, or that will pay for the education of their children, after they are gone—but they will, all the same, most circumspectly ignore any implications involving their constant and perhaps imminent perishability. "It's going to happen thirty years from now—or maybe ten years," they think, "but even ten years is quite a long time—isn't it?"

So is *one* day.

There is a very good reason, they will tell you, not to think about death—it may rob you of the vital forces required for going on with life. I heard about that one, too. I admit it takes a little more moxie to go on functioning with the constant thought of death in your mind, and yet the best people, the ones I loved and esteemed most—have always managed to do it. *I* managed to do it—and yet I'm not at all a depressing person to have around.

Just a little while ago I had a letter from my friend the Baroness Blixen, who, under the name Isak Dinesen, has written some of the noblest stories of our age. She wrote to me from her home in Denmark, and, among other things, she says, "I seem unable to gain any weight. I still am down to sixty pounds. With me it is a constant race against death, but I have just finished writing the last few lines on my new book."

Now then, if this great woman should die before this book of mine is printed, let me say that I have always had many reasons for loving her—but most of all I held her dear because, even during the gravest periods of her long illness, she never ceased to marvel at the world—and to bow her fine head gratefully, and even joyously, in thanks for each day that Destiny vouchsafed to her.

That's *my* idea of being grown up.

But enough of death—let us get back to the more frivolous matter of my funeral.

Do you know who, I think, is pretty sure to put in an appearance at that grotesque function? It is a girl I met in the winter of 1946 when I lived over on West Fifty-sixth Street. I have a friend who is some sort of a tenor. I say "some sort" because I've never yet heard him sing, but he *talks* like a tenor; that is to say, he's got a pebble loose in his esophagus somewhere that gives a weird treble to everything he says. His voice is very high-pitched, and I've seen provincial cart horses around Sixth Avenue cavort wildly about and even rear up on their hind legs if he suddenly started blasting off a little too near them.

Well then, this man, whose name is William Tiomkin, came

up to my house one day and started trumpeting at me with that crazy voice of his.

"There's a girl," he said, "a true idealist, who has no place to stay."

"That's how it generally is with true idealists," I said.

"I want you to listen to this," he said, "because it concerns a richly furnished human heart. This girl is going to Israel next Monday as a pioneer. She has spent four months in a camp over in New Jersey, and the group she lived with disbanded yesterday. She has to stay in New York for the next four days and she hasn't any money, or whatever little she has she doesn't want to spend on hotel rooms; so I thought, since you have a great big empty apartment here, with two separate exits—it would be a *mitzvah*—and besides it wouldn't kill you—if you let her stay here for the next four days."

"You absolutely nauseate me," I said. "Whenever you're in a jam, and you don't know where to plant one of your vagrant tomatoes, you come to me."

"You ought to be ashamed of yourself, to talk like that about a young pioneer," he said. "She and her kind are the hope of the world!"

"And where is this hope of the world staying right now?" I said.

"She's downstairs in the hallway," he said, "waiting upon your decision."

You can see I was trapped. Trapped by a dopey tenor, of all people.

"All right," I said, "let's take a look at her."

Two minutes later, his protégée stood smiling in my doorway. A tootsie. An obvious and blatant tootsie. She was dressed in a khaki Girl Scout uniform, with bare dimpled knees and a knapsack on her back—but the posture she struck was something you generally see on the covers of *Vogue* or *Harper's Bazaar*. I couldn't have been more miffed.

"What's your name?" I said.

"My name is Bubbles Gallagher," she said.

"Gallagher, eh? Well, that's a pretty well-known Palestinian family. Haven't I seen you somewhere before?" I said. "Didn't you used to hang out at the Rumble Club, over on West Sixty-third Street?"

"No," she said. "I've never been up nawth before. You pro'bly saw my pitcher in the papers las' year. I was Miss Daytona Beach."

"And you're going to Israel, are you?"

"Dass right, I'm leaving Monday mo'nin' fum Hoboken."

"You certainly look like a very promising little *chalutzi* to me," I said. "God help all the poor Jews in Jerusalem! O.K., Bubbles, you can stay in one of the rear bedrooms. Here's the key to the front door, and when you leave on Monday, just drop it in the mailbox."

She gave me a mock curtsy and marched off to the other end of the house.

"It's the room on the left," I screamed after her, "and your bathroom is directly across the hall." Then I turned to my lymphatic tenor friend and said, "How come this crazy dame is going to Israel?"

"She was in love with a boy who planned to go there to till the land. He was even learning how to use a tractor and all the rest of it. So they came up here from Florida and joined this training group over in Jersey. I don't know exactly what happened, but her boy friend changed his mind after a while and went back south to work in his father's dry-cleaning business. Bubbles refused to go along with him. She had become a dedicated pioneer and is going off to become an asset to Zion."

"Well," I said, "America's loss will be Israel's gain. It couldn't happen to a nicer country."

Bubbles stayed in the apartment for the next two days, and

141

I must say she was no trouble at all. I never even saw her. On the third day, when I got home around six o'clock, the whole block was cordoned off by cops—because a fire had broken out in my building. Fortunately, the blaze hadn't happened on my floor, and one of the firemen assured me that there would be no damage to my apartment. Fine. Excepting, of course, that I would certainly not be able to sleep at home that night. And then I suddenly thought about Bubbles and what was to become of her. Father of mercy! I couldn't shoulder the burdens of the whole world alone, could I? What a mess! Just at that moment I noticed my janitor giving carefully considered news tidbits to some drunken reporter, so I fought my way to his side and grabbed him commandingly by his sweater, which, by the way, had once belonged to me.

"There's a young niece of mine stopping in my apartment," I said to him. "I'm terribly worried about her, and if you see her around anywhere, please give her this telephone number!" I wrote down the phone number of my tenor friend and handed it to him.

"She was home when de fire staaded," said the janitor. "I seen her runnin' out o' de buildin' wid a haversack on her back. Is dat de one?"

"It is," I said. "I'll check into the Great Western on Fifty-eighth Street—and you call me there if anything happens that I should know about."

After that I had dinner in a place nearby and went over to the hotel. I'd stayed there before, and I told the manager all about what had happened. "I don't need anything fancy," I said, "just something to crawl into and something to lie down on. I'll call my younger son and tell him to bring over a suitcase with some stuff later on. I can't go back home until the hallways are dried out. They sloshed the whole building from top to bottom, as they always do."

The manager, whose name was Jim Doty, was as sympathetic as most managers who run a numbers game on the side generally are.

"You'll be treated royally," he said. "You'll have a fine room—and if your son wants to stay over too, he's welcome. There'll be an extra bed in it."

I called my son and told him the circumstances. "I'm going to the theater," I said. "If you'd like to join me for a snack later on, meet me at Lindy's. I'll be there right after the show."

"Very good," he said. "What do you want me to take to the hotel—pajamas, slippers—anything else?"

"Buy me some tooth paste and a toothbrush," I said, "and if you can spare a bathrobe, it would be nice too, because you can never tell how those damned hotels will be heated."

And that's the way we left it.

After the theater, Merv and I had something to eat, and at about twelve-fifteen we hit the reception desk at the Great Western. I wasn't a bit tired, so I asked the night clerk for a deck of cards. I thought maybe we'd play a few rounds of honeymoon bridge before I went to sleep.

I unlocked the door to my room, and the moment I turned on the light my son gave a soft but very meaningful whistle. He stepped quickly back out into the hall again and said, "Why didn't you tip me off? I didn't mean to intrude."

He kept on flailing his arms about until I was convinced that the poor boy had lost his mind. He finally started to point hysterically into the room, and when, more by instinct than for any clear reason in my mind, I turned around—there—sprawled on the spare bed—sunk into a profound sleep—lay a *dame!* Bubbles! ! !

I have hardly ever in my life been more stupefied.

"I don't know who this is!" I said. "Or rather—I know only too damned well who it is. It's a kookie doll who is going to Israel on Monday to be a pioneer. She was staying over in my apartment—oh, what the hell is the use? Who in hell is ever going to believe it?"

"*I* believe it," said my son. "Don't forget, I've known you for quite a while."

"I guess you have," I said. "Can you imagine the crazy nerve of this creature? That dopey janitor of mine must have told her I'm staying here—so she just marched over and stowed herself away on me."

"I'll tell you something else," my son said. "By the looks of her she isn't a day over eighteen—which means she is strictly jail bait. If you sleep here with her you may land yourself in a hell of a lot of trouble."

"You're right," I said. "Well, we might as well sit down and play some cards, if you like."

So we pulled out a bridge table and dealt out a few hands, and when, after a while, we both started to sag a little, we just crawled into the other bed. We slept pretty good, at that. Once, around four o'clock in the morning, by the dim light that came in from the street, I saw Bubbles get up out of bed and go to the bathroom. That is to say, she didn't really *go*—she *hobbled*. She hobbled like somebody who is crippled in some strange way—and I suddenly felt very sorry for the poor kid. I hadn't noticed anything wrong with her before, and I can tell you it hit me pretty hard. Well, I figured, let her stay on till Monday. It's just one more day anyway. The hell with it!

Next morning when my son and I got up, Bubbles was gone, and so was her knapsack.

"I guess she saw us and got frightened and decided to clear out," I said. "Well, Godspeed to the poor invalid."

"Invalid?"

"Yes," I said. "She limps—or hobbles—or something. I saw her last night, and she could barely make it across the room."

"That doesn't make any sense," my son said. "They're not importing cripples into Israel; at least, not yet. Besides, if she's been training out in Jersey, they would certainly have eliminated her right at the start . . ."

"You're probably right," I said. "Maybe she just got hurt yesterday. Maybe in the fire, or something. Whatever it is—I'm glad she's gone."

I didn't get back to the hotel until very late, and when I put on the light, there—as sure as malaria—was Bubbles, sleeping again.

I was too tired and too befuddled to make a fuss in the middle of the night, so I just put on my pajamas and went to bed. I slept very far into the morning, and when I finally woke up I found a note pinned to my pillow. It said:

> Thanks for the generous hospitality. I am leaving today and I will always remember your kindness. I really mean it!
>
> *Shalom!*
> BUBBLES

She was gone, at last. Later that afternoon, my son came by to pick up the bag, and when he opened the closet door he pulled out a wire hanger with a long nightgown dangling from it. "What's this?" he said.

"Bubbles, that poor sap, probably forgot it," I said.

"It sure is long," my son said. "Look what it has, here on the bottom . . . !" He bent down and lifted up the hem of the oversized nightgown. "It's got a zipper all across the bottom of it and a little padlock attached to one end. How about *that?*"

We looked at that insane garment until both of us suddenly burst out shrieking with laughter.

"Wait a minute," my son said. "There's some writing embroidered right near the padlock."

145

Sure enough, there was. It was a large four-leaf clover, and inside it stood this legend:

DEAR BUBBLES,
　　Life is a trial. May you always be found innocent.

LOVE,
MOM

"That's why she hobbled, night before last!" I said. "She was inside that nightgown with the zipper closed. Now that I come to think of it—I did notice her wearing a little key on a string around her neck. I thought it was for her knapsack. I just hope this isn't the only nightgown she owns; well, she's sure to be a credit to Israel, whatever the hell happens to her."

Much later, I learned that she *was.* Someone who returned from the Holy Land brought me greetings from her. "She drives the truck from Dan to Beersheba, I think," this person told me. "All I can tell you is, she's the most popular bus driver in the whole country."

Three years after bivouacking with me at the Great Western she came back to the States again. She was married to an Israeli boy, and they were here on some business or other that would keep them in the United States for quite a while. She told me she was unbelievably happy.

"There's nothing like building a new country!" she said.

So, you see, you can't tell what makes a good pioneer, until you give it a try.

As long as I'm writing about dizzy dames, I might as well tell you about Googie Cleland too. She is one I was pretty badly stuck on, for various reasons. I came to know her in the most roundabout way imaginable, and the mere prospect of telling about it makes me smile.

When I was quite young, I knew a cellist from one of the big symphony orchestras. Since he was a first-generation Armenian who, in the pursuit of music, had never quite managed to master sufficient English, he often consulted me on his varied correspondence.

One day he came to see me about a particularly ticklish piece of business—he wanted me to write a sort of love letter for him. I don't think I've mentioned to you that his name was Aslan Hagoopian, and I think he must have been about ten years older than I. This lady he was writing to, he told me, was unhappily married (Big Surprise!), and although she was originally a native New Yorker, she now lived somewhere in Virginia. It certainly amused me enormously to play Cyrano for my little Armenian friend, since his nose was at least twice as big as mine.

I wrote her one of my extra-specials and, as could easily have been foreseen, she answered and wanted to hear more. After a couple of months, a really hectic correspondence evolved between us, and I was perfectly sure that the lady in question was definitely the author of her own scripts. They weren't positively stupid, those letters that she sent us, but let us say generously—they were . . . artless.

After a while, Aslan showed me a couple of photographs that depicted Googie in several aspects of outdoor summer activity, and I must confess to you that I found her appearance only very vaguely enticing. And then, as invariably happens with me, I became rather involved in this letter-writing business. I mean that I am incapable of pursuing anything, no matter how seemingly nonsensical, for any length of time, without trying to squeeze some kind of meaning out of it for myself. So my letters got more and more passionate as time went on, and I not only tried very actively to seduce, but I even came pretty close to raping this dame, via the United States mails. She, in her turn, went along with my pace pretty steadily, and then, sometime in the early spring, she even suggested that we meet somewhere, on neutral territory.

Now, get this thing straight: she had already met my Armenian friend the summer before—and, I daresay, had found a certain tepid interest in stringing him along and even throwing him a couple of doses of pretty hectic necking; but once his letters started coming her way, she had a sudden feeling that she might perhaps have overlooked something in him. Those torrid missives of mine had opened altogether new vistas of his personality for her, until she was not only willing but rather eager to take another, closer look at him.

I'd like at this point to tell you a little something about musicians.

The jazz variety of the species I have always considered the sexual proletariat of the nation. That is to say, I always felt that these prematurely balding, never properly shaved, moist-eyed creatures went about the country deflowering a good many moonstruck virgins, so that these girls might later contentedly settle down and get married to steady, hard-working businessmen.

The sex life of the genus longhair is a little more difficult to describe. They are softer and, at the same time, a great deal more devious in their emotions—and since there are quite a number of foreigners among them, they generally tend toward vacillation and introspection in moments of crisis. At least, that's been *my* experience with a lot of them.

Hence, when this Googie letter asking for a rendezvous arrived, my musical pal went into a sort of Asiatic trance for a while. He couldn't immediately make up his mind. It sounds silly, I know, but that's the way it was.

You have to consider also that this Aslan person was a

148

cellist, which is to say that for some twenty-five years, for at least six hours a day, he had been holding an extremely seductive-looking contrivance between his hot knees. Just look at a cello! I think it is the sexiest thing going. I wouldn't be surprised if they had to wear brassières. In addition to which, a cello only talks when you want it to. Maybe all this doesn't make much sense—but I'm only trying to explain to you all the special conditions that perhaps contributed to his chickening out of that possibly culminating event of his life.

The solution to his dilemma was suddenly made miraculously simple for him—that orchestra of his was going to go away on a long concert tour—to Europe, Australia, and who knows where else.

I wrote Googie a letter to that effect, decrying the terrible cruelty of fate, but I did hold out a lot of fat hope to her—for the future. Also, since Aslan had disclosed to me that his inamorata had a small, heart-shaped mole on the seventh rib of her right side, I closed my last letter to her with a poem celebrating this reportedly highly seductive little blemish. Here's the poem, as well as I can remember it:

> *The heart-shaped mole*
> *Upon your seventh rib*
> *Would overwhelm*
> *The arrogant and glib*
> *And give them cause*
> *To wonder,*
> *As only the thunder*
> *Of vast events*
> *Could make them pause.*

And that ended the correspondence.
About three years had gone by when one day, in Wood-

stock, which is an art colony up in New York State, I went to a party and landed on a couch with a couple of girls, only one of whom I had ever met before. Her name was Rosie Kalmack, and since she was already pretty plastered, she made quite a big fuss over me.

"I want you to meet my best friend!" she screamed at this other doll. "I want you to meet the chosen father of all my unborn children, Alex King . . . ! Alex, I want you to meet my other best friend, Googie Cleland!"

So *that* was Googie! She was great. She was the *greatest!* She had a wild figure, like something out of a painting by Franz Stuck.* High-breasted, narrow-waisted, green-eyed—the works! I couldn't imagine how in hell this walking lime lollipop had ever gotten herself involved with somebody like Aslan Hagoopian. You can't ever figure dames, can you?

Well, to tell you the truth, although she had certainly given some kind of tumble to that sawed-off Armenian, *I* seemed to get strictly nowhere with her. I talked a blue streak into that dusty, hamstrung couch we were sitting on, and all I got was just an open-eyed stare. And then, when I figured it was all hopeless anyway, and after I'd taken a couple of shots of some pretty terrible home-brew, I suddenly leaned over very close to her and said: "The heart-shaped mole upon your seventh rib would overwhelm the arrogant and glib . . ." and all the rest of it.

She nearly passed out. Her mouth hung open so far, she looked like a TV singer with the sound track gone dead.

I let her have it for all it was worth. I copped out completely. I told her that *I* was her correspondent, and that she had no reason to waste her time on the doorman when the head of the firm was eager and waiting.

It was great to watch her. She blushed way the hell up into

* That's an artist who was popular in Central Europe when I was a kid.

150

the roots of her lovely chestnut hair. She almost bawled, she was so shaken.

"Googie," I said, "you must pose for me. You've got the most extraordinary coloring I've seen in years."

I assure you I wasn't handing her the usual artist come-on, either; she absolutely gassed me.

She came to my little country studio the next day—and the next—and nearly every day for the rest of that summer—and everything was just fine and dandy. Or almost. You see, she did have one rather serious fault. She was somewhat careless about things. She could never keep anything quite straight in her mind. I don't mean she'd just mess up quotations out of books and stuff like that—most women are pretty terrible about quotations—but she couldn't even make up a sensible grocery list, and if *I* did it for her, she was sure to bring home the wrong things. It was amusing once or twice, but after a while it seemed to get absolutely out of hand. She'd give money to the wrong people—pay the carpenter instead of the bakery man, order things on the phone that she'd later refuse to accept, and so on. It was a mild form of imbecility, I suppose. I don't mean this in a funny way. I finally concluded she was just some sort of serene idiot, and although this adequately explained her involvement with Hagoopian, it really didn't sit any too well on my mind.

One day after she'd posed for me in a little arbor right in back of my house, she lay down on an air-inflated mattress I had bought for her, to take a sun bath. By the time I'd cleaned my palette, she'd fallen asleep.

I stood and looked down on her and marveled at her incredible endowments—the fabulous planes, colors and linear convolutions of that enchanting, prostrate figure. Long-legged, high-breasted (as the Jews would say, she had *broigestige bristlach*, which, freely translated, means her breasts were angry with each other and looked in different

151

directions), the sun had tanned her skin into pure honey from Hymettus.

Quietly I lay down beside her and inhaled the sweet enchantment of that precious moment. Then, quite by accident, my eyes landed on her famous mole.

I'd seen it often before, of course, but I'd never really taken time out to look at it really close up and at my leisure. It was heart-shaped all right, but it was certainly not on her right side. It was on the *left*. I counted her ribs. That is to say, I passed my hand ever so gently across her side and, although she gave a soft moan, she did not wake up. I counted three times. That mole of hers was planted right smack on top of her fourth rib. In short, it was either the *fourth* rib or the *ninth* rib, depending on which end you began to count from but it was most certainly not the *seventh* one.

I suddenly recalled my poem: "The heart-shaped mole upon your seventh rib. . . ."

It would throw my meter completely the hell off if I had to change it to *fourth* rib. You can plainly see that I absolutely needed two syllables in that word.

I found myself getting quite angry with Googie. I was sore at Hagoopian too. *She* was a nitwit—that was plain enough. She didn't know left from right, and she couldn't even count her own ribs correctly. But *he* was a musician; he had to know how to count; counting was the most important part of his business. Of course, he probably hadn't had much experience adding up the ribs of seductive females—but *she* was most certainly an incurable dummy. There was no use disguising it from myself any longer. Her looks successfully deceived everyone. That breath-taking shell of hers covered nothing but sheer mental stultification. Only her body had magnificently matured. Inside her head there was only the depressing ferment of a stale bread pudding. I was quite certain of that now.

I got up, stepped carefully over her sleeping figure, and walked into the house. I packed my belongings into a couple of suitcases and sat down to write her a note. I told her I had to get back to New York on an urgent matter and that I would get in touch with her in a few days. Since she was officially supposed to be living with Rosie Kalmack anyway, I was presenting her with no immediate outward problems at all.

When I stepped out on the porch I took one more look at her wonderful heart-shaped rear end and walked quickly out of the house and down to the bus station.

I never wrote to her, but I ran into her about six years later. She was as silly and exquisite as ever. She was glad to see me and couldn't quite seem to remember where she had last seen me.

"I follow your career in the newspaper columns," she said. "I understand you are illustrating books now."

"Yes," I said. "As a matter of fact, I've made some drawings for a new edition of *Manon Lescaut*—and my Manon was taken from some sketches I made of you some years ago."

"How nice," she said. "You know, I was divorced, and now I'm remarried again. I'm married to a cellist, Aslan Hagoopian. Do you know him?"

So, the kid had finally made it. I certainly think they deserved each other. I just wonder what they talked about after they were through looking at that mole of hers.

The story I have just told you is absolutely true. I am free to tell it because all of the people concerned in it are now dead. That is to say, at this moment, I am the only survivor.

153

I IMAGINE a whole group of people, mostly women, I expect, will come to my laying out chiefly because they feel they know me intimately, since they have frequently seen me on their television sets. It happens to me all the time that people smile at me in the streets or in restaurants, and I automatically smile back at them, for I understand perfectly well that they have simply become the victims of a common modern hallucination. It is an audio-pictorial identity transference, a teleportation phenomenon, which gives them the illusion that since my voice and image have appeared in their living rooms, I must of necessity have come to know them too. I've gotten quite used to it, and it really is no inconvenience to me. What is a good deal less pleasant is the fact that endless listeners and viewers make deliberate and sometimes quite frantic attempts to participate actively in my private life.

This can be a real hardship.

It seems that in my various television appearances I often speak on the subject of love. In fact, just the other evening, I said: "Love has always been my most effective way of escaping from the world and, in the final analysis, the only way I have ever been able to find of *accepting* the world."

Two days after I'd made this statement, I received several hundred letters—among them the following:

DEAR MR. KING,

What do you think of honeymoons? Should they be long or short? This is of the utmost importance to me, believe me. My whole life's happiness may depend on your answer.

FAITHFUL FOLLOWER

I wrote back:

DEAR FAITHFUL FOLLOWER:

I think all honeymoons are very dangerous and a really clever bride will manage to postpone hers until at least the third year of her marriage. Don't you see—every human life has a rhythm of its own, and when two such previously un-affiliated rhythms are suddenly brought together and even especially isolated, as during a honeymoon, a frightful dis-harmony is very likely to be the result. Madam, believe me, you're much better off just to see him only after working hours, for the first few years anyway, when both of you are too fagged out—*you* from selling tickets at the movie house, and *he* from wrangling with tons of wet dishes at the cafe-teria. When you both finally get home, half dead with ex-haustion, you'll have neither the time nor the energy to be too critical of each other. I think a protracted honeymoon is the straight route to the divorce courts. All you'll discover on your honeymoon is that you and your husband actually have quite a lot in common and that the two of you might even have become the best of friends, if only you had never met.

Let me give you an actual salutary example out of my own experience:

Some time ago a young couple whom I happened to know quite well were spending their honeymoon in some fashionable beach resort on the Riviera, and by their very special choice had gone to this place, deliberately, during the off season, when no distracting outsiders were likely to intrude on this memorable intermezzo in their lives.

Nevertheless, when I had occasion to pass within a few miles of their retreat (I was on my way to Italy), I decided to phone them one afternoon at their hotel.

The minute they heard my voice, they both frenetically insisted that I come over at once to pay them a visit. Naturally, I told them that I felt very self-conscious about barging in on them in their blissful sequestration, but they wouldn't let me refuse, and the bride, particularly, seemed almost tearful with disappointment when it became plain to her that I was absolutely adamant.

"*Please*," she finally said, "*please*, Alex. I have a very special reason for asking you. You will be doing me a great personal favor if you come. *Please?*"

"All right," I said, "I'll stop by for half an hour at teatime. Thirty minutes, that's all."

"Thank you," she said. "I'll never forget it."

So, later that same afternoon, I drove slowly along the seaside in search of them, and the place was so completely deserted that I had no difficulty in spotting their two lonely figures when I was still nearly a mile off. As I stepped from the car, Julia (that was the lady's name) leaped at me with such evident signs of joy that I found it a great relief that Martin's (the young husband's) eyes were fortuitously averted.

156

"I'm so *glad* to see you," she murmured breathlessly. "It was most wonderful of you to come and terribly kind, considering that you're probably anxious to get to your friends across the border."

"Come on, now!" I said. "What are you giving me? You're on your honeymoon, aren't you—you're not looking to have company, are you?"

"You know," said Martin, rather sheepishly, "it's really terribly isolated here. Neither one of us has ever been here before when the season was over. All I can tell you is, it's absolutely deadly."

"You *see?*" said Julia. "And don't you forget that Martin, at least, has *me*—but whom have *I* got?"

That's my little story, madam, and since you are presumably yourself a woman, I expect you to be particularly understanding and appropriately moved by the uncensored, anguished cry that Julia gave on that forlorn beach on that sunny afternoon in the south of France.

All I can tell you in conclusion is that I unhesitatingly postponed my own trip by a week so I could spend it with them, and, what's more, I have ever since considered that this public-spirited action on my part was materially conducive in subsequently making this into a particularly successful marriage.

Very sincerely,
etc., etc.

I sent off this letter, and a couple of days afterward my correspondent sent me another note, which I have not yet answered. She said:

> My problem, Mr. King, is a little bit special. You see, my boy friend wants us to take our honeymoon now—and get married later on sometime. What do you think?
> Please advise.

Since I know quite a few people who are of some importance in the various arts, it is quite likely that my funeral will not be lacking in a certain smart, quasi-social atmosphere. This being granted, it is fair to assume that Thyra Kurtz will put in an appearance and, if my expectations of dirty weather prove to be fulfilled, she is sure to be wearing one of her thirteen pastel-colored raincoats.

Thyra is one of the few people whose rise from total obscurity to comparative eminence was achieved without any detours or significant setbacks, and yet, as far as most people would judge, without any particularly unique qualifications on her part. Which only means that the judgment of most people is generally quite wrong.

Thyra certainly *had* something, from the very beginning.

That beginning, as I myself was able to observe, was down in Greenwich Village, where she worked as a part-time hostess in a chain restaurant. She was twenty years old then and, as far as I know, totally without visible family ties or any sort of formal education, excepting of the most rudimentary kind. But I must admit that, from the very start, she was a very careful and consistent reader—which, coupled with her incredible memory, served her brilliantly in lieu of any empty academic degrees. I am fully aware also that, at the moment, I am describing the basic backgrounds of several highly successful female go-getters of my own lifetime; but Thyra was far from typical, even among these generically very easily identifiable predators.

She and I came to know one another during those very early days in the Village, and although there was never any real intimacy between us, she did come to visit me three or four times at my studio. On several occasions I dropped in at her place of business too, and while I dawdled over my meal I would have ample time to quietly observe her. She was trim, dark-haired, almost athletic in her young slenderness; and she was certainly a great eye-relief among the flagrant improbabilities of blondness that fluctuated all around her. She had cold, dark, almost Asiatic eyes, and I remember that she was the only woman employed there who used make-up with any sort of sparing discretion.

In other words, she already physically prefigured a good many airplane hostesses who have since come to marry some of the highly solvent passengers on the various airlines. And, frankly, that's exactly what I expected of her too. I thought she would be taken in tow by some well-heeled customer who would simply add her to his dinner tab and employ her thenceforth as a permanent hostess in his own establishment.

But that's not what happened. At least not quite—and not yet.

First she was made manager of the branch of the restaurant she worked in, and during the time I lost sight of her—approximately two years, I think—she somehow managed to transform herself into a food and diet specialist. She edited a syndicated newspaper column on this recondite subject, and her endorsements became potent factors in putting over a lot of canned and packaged edible merchandise.

And that's when our paths happened to cross again. She had grown enormously chic in the interim and carried herself like a potential cabinet member in the republic of Ruritania. She had become a person to conjure with in the multiple-billion-dollar food business of the nation, and then, at the very height of her success and notoriety, she married Malcolm Kurtz.

Kurtz, as far back as anyone remembers him, was always middle-aged. That is to say, he was neither bald-headed nor paunchy, he was simply anonymous. He looked like the synthesis of everybody who has made a great deal of money and, in the process, has lost all of his identifiable human features.

He was the despair of photographers and caricaturists—in short, he was a truly modern phenomenon. Hans Holbein and El Greco never had such a problem.

And now came the next phase of Thyra's life—she began to write. She had always written her own food columns, of course, but at this point she began to write—poetry. What's more, it got printed, was bound in book form, and was featured in the catalogue of a well-known publishing house.

These poems, by the way, were of such a tepid and trivial nature that no one ever said very much about them, one way or another.

Her publisher, Ray Wharton, was a pretty close friend of mine, so I saw a good deal of her at his home during that winter, but at none of our frequent meetings was I ever privileged to meet her famous husband. It seems that at this critical epoch of his life, Malcolm Kurtz's interests had become so multi-faceted that he had finally added to his ambiguity of features a corporate personality which manifested itself exclusively at board meetings. He had finally become so important that he was practically nonexistent.

It didn't take too much guesswork on my part to figure out that Ray Wharton, my publisher friend, was replacing the anonymous husband in most of his essential roles. Consequently, it was no great surprise to me when, the following season, Ray published a second book of hers—and this time it was a book of prose poems, illustrated with line drawings by the author. This opus was entitled *Sunset Thunder*.

Unfortunately, this little thunder roused no particular critical echoes either, and in a short while I observed that Thyra had moved her peripatetic radiance into another orbit.

She left Ray and took up with John Bertold, the theatrical producer. Time and time again I observed her at Lindy's and at Sardi's, wearing emerald-stippled, horn-rimmed glasses—

riffling through playscripts—while sipping milky, Pernod-looking drinks through a straw.

She *adored* the theater. She felt she had been *born* for it. She told me so herself, one afternoon, over a cup of tea at the old Ritz on Forty-sixth Street. We hadn't met there for that purpose—we simply happened to bump into each other by accident. I had had an appointment with someone who wanted me to help in the rewriting of a play originally translated from the German, and after our business had been concluded, I had stayed on for a while by myself—when Thyra suddenly manifested herself at my table.

"I'm here to meet Dotty Ryan about a script," she said, "but if you'll give me a cup of tea, I'll sit with you till she shows up."

"Please," I said. "I'm delighted at the chance to talk to you. I haven't seen you since you've become stage-struck. How did it happen?"

"I'm not stage-struck," she said. "I just think that there are special periods in the world's history when the only authentic utterance worth making or worth listening to—must be made dramatically. What's more, I feel that such a time is right now! Anybody with anything to say is going to use the stage or the movies. That's the only way a significant mind can have any sort of impact on our society. We have no reading public . . ." and so on.

I looked carefully at her. She was completely sincere and even quite impassioned in her critical exordium, and I only wondered from what *man* of her acquaintance she could possibly have absorbed all this stuff. Not from her present boy friend, Bertold, that was certain, because he functioned practically on the outer fringe of the underworld and used the theater only to finance his one really serious interest, which was the race track. So it must be somebody else, somebody extremely articulate—and reasonably hep too.

161

She had hardly aged in the last decade—if anything, she looked more youthfully vibrant than when she had served as a hostess down in the Village. Her expensive, brilliantly tailored clothes did her no harm, of course, and the best beauty salons and the daily attentions of a personal maid had also contributed their share, no doubt. She was very good-looking; she had a fine figure, a lovely complexion, intelligent eyes and impeccable hands. And yet, there was something indefinably astringent about her. There always *is* about really ruthlessly ambitious women.

For a woman to be truly seductive a certain frivolous and even hoydenish undertone must somehow come through the outward façade—and the dames with the relentlessly tough drive in their souls generally lack, not only a sense of humor, but a sense of animal playfulness as well.

I think that about describes her shortcomings.

Thyra's laugh always came a little too late, and always manifested itself only by her teeth. Her eyes remained constantly alert and speculative, like the eyes of an auctioneer—or an appraiser—or perhaps a weight-guesser at a county fair.

At any rate, she rambled on until Dotty arrived, and then they marched off together into another room. After they had left, I saw that Thyra had forgotten a magazine she had been carrying. As I absent-mindedly turned over the pages, a large caption caught my attention. It was a piece entitled "The Theater—The Absolute Forum," and it was written by Jack Vorland, a rather brilliant new director.

Thyra moved into Vorland's life at some considerable cost to his family; that is to say, his wife and child had to scoot back to Boston where they had originally come from, and since he was a sensitive, basically very kindly man, this retaliatory gambit on his wife's part didn't help him much in his work either.

Thyra was, of course, writing plays at that time, and although one of them was brilliantly cast and directed by Vorland, the critics found it only mildly interesting. Some of them even wondered how so gifted a director could have permitted himself to become involved with such tripe.

Her next play, which was done by Horace Easton, an older and shrewder hand, fared hardly any better.

From Horace she moved on to someone else—I've forgotten this digit on the hand of fate, since I went abroad that year and didn't get back for almost eighteen months. On my return I discovered that Thyra had taken to sculpture, and yet, even two months after I was back in New York, I heard not one single famous name in that field associated with hers.

I must take time out to explain that Thyra was not such an altogether great anomaly as she would seem at first glance. Not in all directions, at least. I've known quite a few women like her—but for various reasons most of them are wanting in the sufficiently ruthless momentum to make their megalomania properly effective. In a country like ours, in which there is no established aristocracy, The Arts seem the most logical chisel, or crowbar, by means of which a resolutely ambitious person can still hope to gain entrance into that enchanting world where the ego can sun itself in the limelight of public attention and admiration, to the point of nausea.

A lot of rich people I know don't buy any paintings from anybody; they make their own. They write their own poetry and, if they've had a little musical preparation, they write their own theme songs too. It represents the ultimate greed of the psyche—gone hog-wild. They don't have too much difficulty with their home-brewed drivel either, since endless numbers of sycophantic hangers-on—not to forget the ever-present hordes of social vermin that accumulate around their festive tables—are always ready to flatter them and lull their occasional misgivings back into comatose self-approval. Of course, very, very few of them are as single-mindedly desper-

163

ate about their ghastly productions as Thyra finally came to be. *She* was something pretty special even in that rather highly specialized field of maniacal self-promotion.

One day George Grosz and Miguel Covarrubias came to my house—and after we'd talked the pros and cons of the art racket over and over for a few hours—we decided that it might be a very good idea if a few of us got together and started a gallery of our own. Just the people we liked. I had already exhibited in a joint show with George Grosz and Frans Maserel in Paris, and we thought that such a new venture in this country might attract a lot of interest and perhaps create a worth-while forum, where even some young and lesser-known people might, after a while, get a fair and decently sponsored presentation.

I probably blabbed about this to a couple of friends, because two or three days later, some of the New York papers carried a few special items about it in their gossip columns.

Actually, nothing ever came of this boozy plan of ours—since not a single one of us was prepared, or fit, to do the necessary organizational work that such a venture requires.

What *did* happen was that I had a call from Thyra.

"I hear you and your friends are starting a new gallery," she said, in that almost uninflected metallic voice of hers.

"Oh, we're just kicking it around as a possibility," I said. "Nothing definite yet."

"Because," she said, "I've had that very same idea for the past six months, and I've even discussed it at some length with Foujita and Chris Orton. I was just wondering whether, perhaps, it would be a good idea if we joined forces, or something."

"Who is Chris Orton?" I asked. "I don't think I've ever heard of him."

"He's the best English sculptor around, at the moment,"

she said. "I don't know anybody within screaming distance of him that is half as good. I tell you what—why don't you drop by my studio next Friday, and I'll cook you a little dinner—and then I can show you some of his stuff, and some of my own most recent things too."

"Where is the studio?" I said.

"It's just a dear little house, near Washington Square, that I've done over into a real workplace. Malcolm is away so much of the time that I thought I'd get away from our huge apartment and have a sort of *pied-à-terre* for weekends, and stuff. Come early—so we'll have lots of time to talk. We'll be *très intime*, so don't bother dressing."

I was curious about her because, in some strange way, I'd always found her rather fascinating—not as a woman, but as a significant manifestation of early-twentieth-century capitalist decay, if you like. So around seven-thirty the following Friday I drove down to Washington Mews and knocked on her door.

She opened it for me herself—and—just as she was standing there, on her highly polished threshold, she could have been a full-page photographic ad for any of the women's magazines on the country's newsstands. Her hair was an absolute coiffing masterpiece of carelessly work-tossed locks; her flowered chiffon frock was like woven ice cream; and she wore a pale-blue chamois leather apron with gloves to match.

"I've been doing a little housework for a change," she said, shedding her gloves. "Generally I like to use all the daylight I can for my *job*—but I've taken a little breather today. I hope you're hungry; dinner will be ready in half an hour."

I looked around. This little workshop of hers had a twenty-eight-foot ceiling, and the interior decor had obviously been created by one of the most talented modern designers loose in the land. The couches, the tables, the chairs—all had such

165

evidently decent and ingratiating proportions that the silly sculpture she had inflicted on that noble room seemed doubly vulgar in its intrusive juxtaposition to all those handsomely functional pieces of furniture.

Actually, she never really got around to asking me point-blank what I thought of her work. She referred to it, once or twice, rather obliquely, as if its intrinsic worth were a sort of a *fait accompli* between us. I again had occasion to marvel at her astonishing good looks, which were so impeccable and at the same time so strangely genderless and so completely unappealing to my particular taste.

But she was certainly informed. She was like a walking compendium on the latest trends in world aesthetics, and it was pretty plain that she had sifted her information from some of the most erudite and discriminating minds of our day. She was certainly no bore.

After a time she said, "Let's eat now—shall we?"

"Fine," I said. "Do you want any help?"

"No, no, please, you just sit still. I've had everything in the oven for hours—because I like things to cook slowly and for a long time."

The dinner turned out to be an enormous surprise. With her dubious past as a dietary adviser, I had expected to be served some baked sunflower seeds topped off by a milkweed salad with gooseberry dressing; but I couldn't possibly have been wronger. The meal was an epicure's dream, and the service that accompanied it was sheer perfection. She was adroit, she was efficient, she was gracious and, best of all, her many thoughtful, minute services were rendered with an air of the most complete and casual self-effacement.

She certainly had her points.

I mellowed considerably during that dinner, and by the time she served us each a small brandy I even caught the whiff of a rather seductive breeze coming toward me from her direction.

It is funny, but this unexpected shift in the nature of my appraisal of her instantly changed my visit from a casual browsing expedition to a rather charming and even slightly risqué venture into an area of possibly delicious enticement.

And then she suddenly sneezed and, holding her napkin to her nose, she said, "Would you be a darling and get me a hanky from the next room?"

It goes without saying that I instantly jumped up and marched off into her bedroom.

It was a royal courtesan's dream—with an enormous canopied bed, frothy pillows, and a dressing table that mirrored everything sixfold.

"You'll find it in the top drawer of the little chiffonier," she called after me. "It's the one on the right side of the bed."

I pulled out the drawer—but I saw no handkerchiefs, only female undergarments of the flossiest texture. It looked like nothing so much as a nesting place for some baroquely pampered hummingbirds.

"I'm sorry," I said, "but I can't see anything that looks like a handkerchief."

"Try the second drawer!" she said.

This time I found a collection of lace-encrusted handkerchiefs that would have turned a museum curator into a thief. I picked up the top one—probably woven by an unusually amorous and gifted spider during the height of the mating season—and brought it to her.

That short visit into that bedroom of hers materially abetted the spell of enchantment which had begun so imperceptibly at the dinner table.

Before long we were sitting on a couch together—I was quietly caressing her ankles, and she was slowly telling me about her dreams. I can't quite repeat to you coherently what these dreams were all about . . . about art and beauty, I think, and how wonderful it would be to make the world more aware of these significant matters. You must not blame me for being unable to report more accurately our soft-spoken, postprandial communion, because something entirely new had entered our hitherto casual relationship—I had suddenly discovered that Thyra Kurtz was one of the world's most desirable women!

Ineluctable as the arrival of the equinox came the moment when we were lying side by side on that small sofa with our lips glued together in a seemingly unappeasable hunger for some sort of earthly fulfillment. I had no further thoughts left. Like a diver submerged in seas too profound for his safety, I was the victim of something that experts in such nautical matters call, depth rapture.

After several aeons of this searching bliss, she whispered into my ear, "Would you like to stay?"

"Yes," I said. "I would like to stay forever."

She gave a small girlish laugh, one that I would never have supposed could possibly have been alive in her—and slowly, almost drunkenly, we both tottered to our feet.

She left me alone in the studio for a few moments, and when she returned she was wearing a pseudodemure night-dress that had surely been designed by a court eunuch with a fabulously retentive memory. She took me by the hand and led me toward a huge Chinese chest that stood between two tall windows at the farthest side of the room.

"Lift the lid," she said.

I did as she asked, and spread out before me, inside that trunk, were seemingly endless pairs of expensive men's pa-jamas. They were all carefully ironed and neatly folded between sheets of tissue paper, and I stared at that collection like a complete idiot. I consider myself a reasonably sophisticated man—but the sight of all that multiple-colored night haber-dashery absolutely floored me.

"Find your size," she said, "and put them on." She took my face between her palms and gave me a kiss that was almost as much fulfillment as it was promise. Then she left me and drifted back into the bedroom again. Actually, she *filtered* back, leaving the stupefying aroma of flowering *achineel* on the supercharged air.

The moment she was gone I sat down on a stool and started to do some heavy thinking. I thought about the evening that had just passed—about all that dreadful sculpture—the won-derful dinner—the incredible bedroom—the lacy handker-chief—the brandy—the kisses—and the terrible drive that made her want to be associated with people of some accom-plishment even if it killed everybody.

"She is like something out of mythology," I finally decided. "She turns people into swine, like Circe." It was a very corny, banal thought, of course, but for various highly complicated reasons I was not really at the top of my form.

Finally I got up and walked, fully dressed, into the bed-room. She was lying under that huge canopy like Undine —like Sisterzia the Gentle—like golden-haired Rapunzel— waiting to be gently ravished by her predestined knight.

"I'm sorry, Thyra," I said, "but I've got an absolute phobia about sleeping in any but my own pajamas."

"A phobia???" she said.

"Yes, a sort of complex. I'm conditioned by long years of habit. You see, I always sleep in black Shantung pajamas, be-cause my mother gave me such a pair when I was only eight-een years old, and I've had them copied over and over again, ever since. I'll just hop in the car and I'll be back in no time."

"Don't be silly," she said. "There is every kind of make and size in that chest; why, there must be at least thirty pairs in there."

"I looked at them all," I said. "There isn't a single pair of black Shantungs with green piping, that my dear mother originally picked out for me, in the lot."

I said all this very jauntily, like a willful little boy who has always had his own way in life.

Her head sank deeper into the pillows, and her nose seemed to grow perceptibly longer.

"My God," I thought, "if I don't get out of here fast, she'll suddenly fly over my head, and I'll have black bat wings beating about my ears while she'll try to dig her poisonous claws into my eyes."

"I'll be back in a jiffy," I said. I turned around, walked quickly into the studio—and out into the street like a man pursued by furies.

As I drove along Fifth Avenue, I noticed that I had the salty taste of blood in my mouth. I had bitten into my lower lip, as men on the edge of imminent disaster had been known to do. I suddenly grew deeply depressed. "Joseph and Potiphar's wife all over again," I said to myself. "My life is full of classical clichés. What a life! Why did I back out? Why? Why? Why?"

I knew damned well why; because she was just trying to use me as she had used all the others; because for years she hadn't ever given me a serious tumble—until my moment to be of service to her had come along. That's why! And now, to hell with it all.

I went home and got out a pair of my black pajamas (I really had three pair of the kind I had described to her), and, after packing them into a box, I went to the phone and called up my friend Pete Nakaras. Pete was a florist, over on Lexington Avenue, for whom I had once done a small kindness, and who in his turn was always glad to be of help to me.

"Pete," I said, "I want you to make up a fine bouquet of just yellow and white flowers. Mimosa . . . lilies of the valley and stuff—a real boudoir bouquet. Now then, please send somebody up here with it right away. I'm sorry it's so late, but it's a kind of emergency. Another thing—I'm going to give your man a small box to take along with the flowers and deliver it all down to Washington Mews tonight. Let him take cabs all the way—right? Thanks. Give my love to Maria."

Then I wrote a note and put it inside the box with the pajamas. It said:

> DEAR THYRA,
>
> I became suddenly ill on the way home. Isn't it heartbreaking? However, accept a little token of thanks for the wonderful dinner. I am also sending along my pajamas, so you can place them along with all the others in the beautiful Chinese chest.
>
> Some day they may come in handy.
>
> My best greetings to you.

CHAPTER ELEVEN

A S YOU READ THESE PAGES you can plainly see how
foolishly prodigal I have been with the raw material of my
life. I think it must be plain to everyone what a bad householder I really am and with what reckless improvidence I
scatter the wealth of my experience without the slightest
regard for the rules of thrift and profitable investment.

Here, in these comparatively scant pages, I serve up the
peculiar and fascinating lives of some thirty-five or forty-odd
people, and yet it must be obvious that, with just a little
common foresight, all these exciting documentary riches could
easily have served to make at least twenty or twenty-five
books of six or seven hundred pages each. These tomes might
have been sold to some enterprising Hollywood producers—
even before publication, perhaps—and this, in its turn, could
have netted me the basic increment for a substantial estate.

Also, the eventual movies ensuing from these enterprises would have borne so little actual resemblance to my books that, through these amiable celluloid distortions alone, I could have received the love of untold millions who don't even suspect that I am alive.

But, I suppose, that's how it is with people who live recklessly—they won't ever learn.

At any rate, there is always the consoling possibility that I may not perish of any of my multifarious ailments after all; I may just wind up *laughing* myself to death over all the wonderful chances in my life that I have managed to miss.

Which brings me back to my funeral, and to another person who probably won't be able to attend—because, chances are, she will be in jail again.

I'm talking here about a most remarkable girl called Roberta Stanton, of whom I first became aware in the Public Health Service Hospital in Lexington, Kentucky. We were both patients at this place; that is to say, we were both there to be cured of our chronic drug addictions, and since it was the rule of the institution that men and women could not communicate with each other, it was quite impossible for me to talk to her during the entire, long period of our sequestration.

Nevertheless, human ingenuity being devious as well as relentless, we did manage to correspond with one another pretty consistently, despite the stringent interdictions of the local authorities. Roberta was in an unusually fortunate position to facilitate this traffic between us because, as her special work assignment, she happened to be in charge of a couple of small children for one of the officers at the hospital. I, on the other hand, as chief contributor and staff artist for the institutional newspaper, was privileged to roam pretty freely all over the place, and so it was not too difficult for me to amble quite casually within pretty close operational radius of

Roberta and her infant charges. These children—girls, by the way—were generally disporting themselves on the various well-kept lawns of the hospital, and Roberta would simply insert her letter to me in the rubber panties of one of these little ones. When the freight-bearing youngster, full of high spirits, would run exuberantly across the grass in my direction, I would find occasion to lift her, playfully, high into the air—and, incidentally, to disencumber her of any of her contraband messages. My replies would go back to Roberta by the very same means, and it goes without saying that I acquired something of a local reputation as an extravagantly devoted lover of all childhood. By the way, nothing ever went wrong with this novel form of mail delivery; I would only like to suggest that nobody at Lexington, either now or in the near future, ought to risk trying it again.

The reason I had written Roberta in the first place was that she enjoyed an astonishing reputation for wit, kindness and good spirits among all the hospital personnel that had ever had any contact with her. The doctors were particularly loud in their praises of her.

"She is the best influence among the female patients in the whole place," Dr. Pregman once told me.

"How come?" I said. "What does she do?"

"She encourages, and finally persuades, even the most unco-operative patients to take psychotherapy. She invents little ingenious competitions among them—she keeps up their spirits—she is full of good sense—and all I can tell you is that every time she is discharged from here, this place becomes an absolute shambles. We are simply desolate without her."

"How often has she been in here?" I asked.

"About twelve times, I think," said Dr. Pregman.

"Does *she* take therapy?"

"Yes, every time she comes back."

"Funny, isn't it," I said, "that such a great influence for

174

good on the other patients in this dreary place should be quite unable to manage any kind of a life for herself on the outside."

"It is fascinating," said Dr. Pregman. "I wish I could devote a few years to deciphering this particular enigma. What is even more amazing is that she is quite well-read and not unaware of this strange dichotomy in her character."

"I think she's very good-looking too," I said. "What does she do on the outside?"

"What can a woman drug addict, without means, possibly do on the outside?"

"She is a prostitute?"

"Naturally. What else?"

I talked about her to one of the chief guards around the place too. He told me that in the past year she had encouraged the girls in her sector to lay out garden plots in the spring, and that the morale level among these women had risen to new, unprecedented heights. "She is a real little mother to those tramps," he said, "and yet, according to her record, she's quite a tramp herself."

"Maybe she's all right as long as she's away from men," I said.

"Must be," he said. "She always gets into trouble the minute she hits the street."

So, naturally, I wrote to her.

In an institution of that sort the grapevine carries everything worth knowing, and it stands to reason that Roberta was pretty well aware of my predicament too. I was a multiple recidivist at the hospital, like herself, and I too, in various ways, was something of an influence for the good among the men in my division. I gave French lessons—I held classes in English literature—I wrote articles and drew cartoons for our paper—and I certainly spent a good deal of my time in purely altruistic pursuits.

Roberta answered my letter eagerly and at once, because she knew I had managed to make a pretty good living on the outside, and so she felt quite reassured that I wasn't just looking for an easy way to become her pimp, after both of us would be discharged from the institution.

This, indeed, is the chief, and very good, reason why the hospital authorities forbid any sort of contact between the sexes down there. Too many of my fellow collegians had always been procurers and panders on the street, and they were certainly not above recruiting a suitable stable for themselves during their months of intramural confinement.

At any rate, Roberta answered my letter very pleasantly and very intelligently, and she particularly asked me for a reading list of books which she might obtain at the institutional library.

I wrote to her pretty consistently after that, and I must say, very proudly, that neither one of us ever befouled those letters of ours with sentimental drivel or facile endearments of any sort.

I'm certain that we became very fond of one another in the course of time, and I can assure you that the arrival of the harmless notes from that dear girl gave sudden point and meaning to my otherwise desperately shadowed existence.

I suppose the human heart is truly lost if it cannot hang onto some fragment of a dream, or a sliver of meaningful purpose, somewhere. During this, my third, visit to Lexington, I had so completely lost contact with the real world that I wrote almost no letters to anyone at all. When mail distribution time came—at around four o'clock every afternoon—and even the raucous voices in that coarse place were suddenly muted by the loving, human influences which filtered through to us from the outside, I never bothered to ask whether anything had arrived for me—since I had long before, voluntarily, withdrawn from all contact with the few people who were still vaguely concerned with me.

It was Roberta alone who nourished my frustrated spirits and my atrophied heart during those sterile months and, as she later confessed to me, it was the contents of my letters which gave her the strength to face her own oncoming discharge date with a certain amount of hopeful resolution.

Let's get this thing straight: she never, even for one single moment, expected to build any part of her future around me. Nothing could have been further from her mind. Quite the contrary. At no time did she indicate that she ever expected to see me on the outside, and I was so well aware of her feelings that I never made the vacuous suggestion that we *might*. And if you wonder about all this, it is only because you haven't the vaguest idea how the other half feels.

The so-called criminal classes, or even the tarnished fringes of society which are adjacent to them, lead lives that are as completely circumscribed by behavioristic codes and shibboleths as the most exclusive aristocracy. Roberta, within the focus of her modest self-appraisal, knew perfectly well that my correspondence with her represented no sort of commitment on my part at all. She knew that I was neither a pimp nor a professional thief, and my graduation into the ranks of drug addiction was bound to remain an eternal enigma to her. She was fully aware, of course, that sometimes even rich or intelligent people became ensnared in such a life, but the folk mores of her class had indoctrinated her to believe that such sordid immersions into the mire were due to some decadent streak in their natures, some quite untypical psychic blemish, which still, in no way, made them fellow members with the real old settlers, who had arrived at their degradation legitimately, through a lifelong proximity to the moral sewers of the world.

To Roberta, I was a learned man who had one day decided

177

to go slumming and who had, somehow, through some incalculable lesion in his will, become entrapped by a vice that possessed some peculiar compensations for his momentary needs.

I don't mean to say that she was able to reason this all out in such minute and painstaking fashion; she just felt that, even if I had returned to Lexington three times—that outside—in the world—somewhere—certain people would be accessible to me whose own lives had always been untainted by even the slightest tinge of dishonor.

I daresay, in some ways, I must have puzzled her quite as much as she puzzled me. After all, I too seemed to get along wonderfully well *inside* the institution. I managed excellently without drugs of any kind, as long as there were solid walls and barred doors and windows around me. But the minute I hit the street, I instantly fell back into the arms of morphine again, because, for some undefinable reason, I had somehow lost the almost instinctive method of procedure by which men, over the millennia, have learned to parcel out their freedoms.

It was her case *exactly!*

But, to her, the similarity was only superficial. She had been born and reared as a child of the most bitter poverty, and as the oldest of six children she had known, very early, the dreadful humiliations and shameful compromises that a slum child accepts as the basic order of its existence. The first time she had received payment for the use of her body, an unavoidable routine of such barters loomed, at once, relentlessly before her.

Whatever the reasons for *my* drug addiction might be, she was unquestioningly convinced that these reasons had nothing whatever to do with *hers.*

She even ignored the fact that I had been medically addicted in the course of a painful major illness, and she was

178

quite right in dismissing this seeming extenuation, since she knew perfectly well that I must have liked the euphoric side effects that narcotics had for me or I could have rid myself of them as easily as thousands of other accidentally addicted people had done.

She looked to me with little hope and no calculation; all she expected of me was a certain detached, paternal kindness, which would last the duration of our stay at the hospital.

You see, she was almost twenty-five years my junior, and as far as *she* was concerned this was the greatest factor of safety between us. You must consider that in her highly codified environment her serious involvement with so much older a man would have been absurdly offbeat, and altogether inexplicable, unless the man were very rich and simply represented an obvious target for easy exploitation. To bridge such a gap of years takes an enormous somersault of the imagination, which the underworld is simply not prepared for. In that rigidly conformist gutter fraternity, this age differential only becomes tenable if it applies to an out-and-out sugar daddy.

Roberta never saw me in that sort of role. She cherished and esteemed me, uncritically, because, like *all* prostitutes, and *most* women, she had a desperate admiration for people who were well informed—or could pass as such.

It was, in its own peculiar way, an ideal relationship.

I'm happy to report that it was in no way tarnished when we finally did meet, in New York. I had discovered that she was working as a waitress in a dingy restaurant over on West Forty-eighth Street, and one day, during lunch hour, I dropped by and sat myself down at one of her tables. The poor thing was as flustered as a debutante whose orchid has just been clumsily decapitated, but by the time I was through eating she had managed to regain some of her composure.

I noticed that she had lost quite a bit of weight since leaving

Lexington. I asked her about it later, in the grim park in back of the Forty-second Street library, where she had come to join me.

"Yes," she said. "I always lose weight when I get out of the hospital. You don't look any too good either. Are you *clean* now?"

She meant, was I off drugs.

"Yes," I said. "Two months now. And you?"

"It's tough, but I'm managing," she said. "It's this job that gets me down. You see, my record keeps me from working in any of the better places, and the tips aren't really worth picking up."

As I sat there looking at her, I marveled by what strange and cruel dispensation of fate this girl had to suffer a daily confrontation with disaster. She was quite pretty, and her clothes, though certainly cheap, were in very good taste and becoming. She had naturally wavy light-brown hair and a clear, fair complexion that made her brown eyes so deeply luminous they seemed like dark mirrors of pure candor.

"You got a job?" she asked me.

"I'm doing some free-lance writing," I said. "I'm fixing somebody's play, and they've given me a pretty good advance."

"You can make it," she said. "You've got talent, and junk doesn't do anything for you anyway. You ought to get married again. You need somebody to look after. I'm the same way myself, I guess. I got myself a cat. I never had a cat before, and I'm telling you a cat is really something. She's so clean, and they're not supposed to get as close to you as dogs do, but this one sits up on the window and waits for me to get home. She jumps right up on my shoulder when I'm getting her supper ready, and I tell you that animal is more company to me than a lot of people I've known."

When we parted, I gave her my address. I was staying in the apartment of a friend who'd gone off to Hollywood on a movie job, and I told her to call me if she was ever at loose ends.

"Maybe you'd like to go to the Museum of Art with me some Sunday afternoon," I said.

"I'd like to," she said, "but generally I'm so pooped when the weekend rolls around that I just have strength enough to wash and iron a few things for myself."

"Well, anyway, keep it in mind," I said.

She must have, because, about three weeks later, she phoned me. "I'm taking you up on your offer," she said. "Would you mind if we went to the other museum instead?"

"Natural History?" I asked.

"Yeah, I guess that's the one," she said. "I was once there, with my class, when I was just a kid, and they gave us some post cards that I kept for years and years."

"Fine," I said. "Let's meet at the Seventy-seventh Street entrance."

Later, after we'd walked ourselves flat-footed and dizzy through the various museum exhibits, I took her to a very good Austrian restaurant right nearby.

"It's been a lovely day," she said. "Just lovely. It must be wonderful to have lots of time to spend looking at such things and learning all about them."

"You're still a very young woman, Roberta," I said. "Why don't you try to take some courses, in the evening maybe, and learn about things?"

She looked at me suddenly with cold and detached appraisal. There was nothing warm in those dark eyes of hers then, and the corners of her mouth twisted into something that looked very much like a dress rehearsal for an oncoming sneer.

"Yeah," she said. "I ought to study in the evening, oughtn't I? Night school—that's really gonna be my big stick, ain't it?"

I impulsively took her hand. "Roberta, dear," I said. "You know I didn't mean to give you any advice. I've had plenty of it myself from people who didn't know what shook. I wish I could help you. You're such a valuable person; I know what you can do—what you've done—with some of that hopeless trash down in Lexington. I just wish somebody could do as much for you."

Her face relented. She patted my hand reassuringly. "I know you mean the best—for me. It's just that everything seems so hopeless. I drag everything with me wherever I go. I'm not just fighting off each day; I have to duck my old pals that keep coming around and telling me not to waste my time trying to be square. It's as if every piece of dirt I ever handled had a life of its own and came back to nag at me. You say I did a lot of good for some of those kids in Lexington—well, why don't I get a job in Lexington? Why couldn't I be an occupational therapist down there, or in some other institution where they need that kind of help? You know why I can't? I've got a record as long as your arm—that's why! Oh, hell—I guess some lives are like riddles that haven't got any answers. Mine sure is one of them."

"You're not a Catholic, are you?" I asked.

"No—I'm just nothing, I guess."

"It occurred to me, Roberta, that you could have been a great abbess in some cloister—somebody that builds churches and monasteries—and finally becomes a saint."

She laughed so hard she had to lift her little veil to wipe her eyes.

"You *are* nuts, aren't you?" she said. "A saint, eh? Well, now I've really heard everything."

182

"No, you haven't," I said. "Some of the most famous saints in the Christian calendar led lives that weren't any less sinful than yours has been. I'm serious, Roberta. I'll lend you some books about it, if you don't believe me. Even Mary Magdalen, the friend of Jesus, had once been a courtesan. It is written in the Bible—"

She suddenly became quite serious. "I mustn't listen to you too often," she said. "It's much too high and boozy for that small brain of mine. I know all about the Magdalen; I just never saw the connection. At any rate—you've just got too rich a brew on tap for me. If I listened to you often enough, I'd lose my bearings altogether. I better go home now, and do a little ironing; besides, Emily, my cat, is probably getting hungry."

"How come you called her Emily?" I said.

"Because I knew a librarian by that name once. She was a little bit of a puffed-out body, and she used to recommend books to me. She was one of the few people, when I was a child, who was real nice to me. When she died I went to her funeral, and I got the stuffing beat out of me by my father. Later it turned out she'd left me fifty dollars in her will—so the old man took me to Coney Island, and he got so drunk I spent the night in the police station. Anyway, I've got another Emily now."

I met Emily five weeks later when the janitor of Roberta's building brought her around to my apartment. He brought her in a cardboard box and handed me a note. It said:

DEAR FRIEND,

I'm off to the dry cleaners again. I don't have to tell you how I feel—you have been through it yourself, often enough. I hope you can give a home to Emily. If you cannot, please drop her at the Bide-A-Wee Home. Who knows, somebody may take a shine to her. I will call you in about five months, maybe.

Your grateful friend,
ROBERTA

Emily lived up to her reputation and became my darling for the next four and a half months. Roberta took her away from me, after that, and I missed that cat so much it made a real dent in my daily existence. A short while later I once more became entangled with the dope chimera, and I had little room in my life to ponder the difficulties of cats or any other endearing beasties. In short, I mislaid Emily and Roberta, along with many other facts and fancies along my slimy and bedeviled road—and I just landed myself right smack back in Lexington again.

When I emerged, after six months this time, one most significant change *had* taken place in the catastrophic routine of my days: Margie was waiting for me at the entrance gates of the institution.

She said, "I've saved up quite a bit of money—enough, I think, to take us both to Thailand."

"To Thailand?" I said. "What for?"

"So you can go on taking dope legally," she said, "or, at least, without too much trouble. I can get jobs singing in the cafés in Bangkok—and—maybe you can draw some quick portrait sketches of tourists in the saloons out there, and we'll earn enough to get by on and have some kind of a life together, no matter what else may happen."

That's what she said. Well, you know I didn't take her up on it. We're just managing the best we can—right here—among the local heathen.

Now that I come to think of it, the most consistent and tireless funeralgoer of my whole acquaintance is Marellie

Krohner Ebenheim. Actually, she could call herself—and sometimes does—Marellie Krohner Mittlauf Spendisch Hartwig Lazar Ebenheim. The Marellie Krohner is what she started out with, the other five names she married, buried, divorced or abandoned.

Her first husband, Mittlauf, was a sculptor; the second, Spendisch, was a composer; Hartwig was a playwright; Lazar disgorged novels; and Ebenheim preached psychiatry. The first and second—she buried; the third and fourth—she divorced; and the fifth she just walked out on.

You don't really have to bother keeping all these not terribly vital statistics too clearly in mind, since they never were any too clear in hers either. I remember that when she talked about her past bedfellows and board providers, she very often got their names, their professions, and even their different tenures of duration so mixed up with each other that, finally, she just referred to them simply by numbers and ignored the date sequences of their various accessions to, and retirements from, public office completely.

On closer consideration, I must admit that, perhaps, her life was not one long ritual of joy and high ecstasy after all. You see, she had a rival, a most formidable rival too, in no less a person than the well-known Mrs. Mahler Werfel Gropius—a lady who had been married, successively, to the distinguished composer Gustav Mahler, the enormously popular novelist Franz Werfel, and the world-renowned architect Walter Gropius.

Now then, just consider poor Marellie's bitter moments whenever she came around to tallying up the score of her *own* hits and misses in the marriage game—and you can understand that she had more than reasonable cause to be bitterly annoyed with the dirty, underhanded dealings of Destiny.

The years had not dealt too kindly with her either. She

185

had become a waddling, terribly nearsighted, bolster of a woman—wearing queer blouses, strange jewelry, and pretty alarming hats.

"My husband number two," she once said to me, "was twenty times more talented than Mahler—but he absolutely ignored popularity. He simply refused to play the game of musical politics. He was a real artist, not a finagler."

"You think Gustav Mahler was a finagler?" I said.

"I know nothing about *him*," she said. "He may have been the most straightforward and honorable of men—but I'm sure he had friends who jumped into the breach for him. Number two had nobody but *me*, and a very few loyal believers. Do you know that Dollfuss' nephew came to his funeral and wept right into the open grave, before everyone? He had to take off his glasses three times. The people were just astonished. When he shook my hand he said, 'Austria will never recover from this blow.' He was right; it never did."

But no matter how bravely Marellie jabbered on about her gifted ex-mates, the sad truth that, somehow, in the world's eyes, they had never really *made* it, just soured her days.

"My number four," she said, "won the Eibenschuetz prize in Liechtenstein in 1939, and even Goebbels, when he heard about it, said, 'I cannot believe that such a talent can belong to a decadent Jew.' What good did it do him? The war interfered with all his publishing plans, and his temper became finally so unmanageable we simply had to part, for both our sakes. I still love that man, to this day. Among the five geniuses I was married to—he was the one who had the true Renaissance temperament. He could cook, he could sew, he was a great writer, and his *petit-point* chair backs fetched two hundred dollars apiece at Druot's right after the war. His next wife realized a fortune on his embroideries alone."

Actually, Marellie was not too well off financially because

she had speculated very badly with the little money she had managed to accumulate from her five unsuccessful husbands.

After walking out on the psychiatrist, she became involved with a pansy interior decorator, and she invested almost all her ready cash in this creature's Third Avenue antique shop. Her partner, whose name was Boyce Binyon, spent a good deal of her investment on a new wardrobe, since he felt this was basically essential in a business that dealt almost exclusively with *nouveau riche* snobs. Somehow, his velvet vests and high-button, cloth-topped shoes failed to lure the suckers into the store—only other pansy interior decorators showed up, and the place was always a-gurgle with their falsetto laughter and steaming with the odor of hot chocolate. The antique ash trays in the joint were generally full of brownie crumbs, while the cigarette butts mostly landed up in the display windows. It was a real hangup for poor Marellie.

"How could I have made such a mistake in that Boyce person?" she wailed. "He seemed such a clean-cut type—I would have trusted him with my life."

"Didn't you notice that there was something queer and effeminate about him?" I said.

"God in heaven—I'm a European woman—I'm used to men who aren't so athletic," she said. "Very few men look like baseball players in Vienna—or even in Paris, for that matter. How could I possibly have known such a thing?"

"He always had gold buttons all over himself," I said, "and you surely must have noticed that he painted his fingernails and dyed his hair."

"Ah, you sophisticated people have it easy, talking," she said, "but a poor simpleton like me just fell into the pit. What am I going to do now? He has spent all my money on silk underthings, and the store is just like a morgue. It is as if the plague had hit it. The dogs in the street won't even pee up against our windows, as if they felt that just to come too near to us was already bad luck. I'm going to lose my mind if something doesn't happen soon."

You know what finally happened?

She got a legal divorce from the psychiatrist and married Boyce Binyon. When I asked her about it, she said, "I figure, as long as he spent all my money anyway, I might at least have the use of some of those elegant kimonos he bought."

"And what are you both going to do about money?" I asked.

"I'm going to get rid of the stock in the store, at any price," she said, "and now, in my old age, I'll just have to go to work."

"Work at what?" I said.

"I'm going to join the Actors' Studio," she said, "and I'll go on the stage. Other people have done it! I'm not too proud."

And that's where we left it, for the time being.

CHAPTER TWELVE

I EXPECT that Katherine Loder will probably show up, simply because we still have many memories in common that the passing years have certainly not been able to erase. The last time I saw her was nearly twelve years ago when we went to see a movie in Newark, New Jersey, together, but I am sure she thinks of me as often as I do of her, which is at least ten or twelve times a year.

Katherine was one of the sensationally publicized debutantes of the early twenties and, in a thoroughly fragmented, fissiparous society like ours, it was not at all surprising that we came to know each other rather well.

She first impinged on my consciousness through a friend of ours named Julian Kyrtoll who was very much in love with her during the time of her greatest notoriety. Julian had a wealthy family background, but he certainly didn't know

Katherine until she became the pin-up girl for his classmates up at Yale. I mean, they had no social bonds or antecedent relationship that predated her emergence into the tabloids and the rotogravure sections of the Sunday papers. Every weekend, during those lively years, insectlike swarms of undergraduates from all the Ivy League colleges used to swoosh regularly into the social life of the season's outstanding debutantes. You'd see Katherine at various restaurants, night clubs and theatrical premières, accompanied by at least half-a-dozen flop-eared fledglings from Yale or Princeton, who not only looked a good deal alike, but whose conversational gambits really required interclassroom asterisks to be thoroughly appreciated.

She was "Gorgeous Kate" to a lot of boys who bought corsages for her out of money that was originally intended for a new set of tennis rackets or an imported English bicycle, and Katherine carried herself through all this rush and hubbub with a poise which was astonishingly mature.

Julian told me that he first fell seriously in love with her when he saw with what unbelievable tact she managed to control some of his more extroverted and rather presumptuous classmates.

"She has inborn authority," he said, "and even the most foolish coxcombs around her find themselves shamed into some sort of grace. I understand her family made all their money in liquor—well, there certainly is nothing beer-saloony about *her*. I think I'm going to devote the rest of my existence to her happiness."

Those were strong and, to me, even alarming words, because long before Katherine had ever happened to him, he had shown a certain dangerous emotional instability which rather worried me. Julian was a tallish, pale-eyed, pale-haired young guy with a very shiny, knobby forehead, who some day planned to become a playwright. Meanwhile he wrote a lot of swollen prose which he fancied to be poetry, drank quite a bit of gin, and had, only the year before, fallen violently in love with a young married woman of my acquaintance and had, in the process, managed to make quite a nuisance of himself to both the husband and the wife in this matrimonial right angle.

He brought Katherine around to my studio one Sunday afternoon, and it was easy enough to see that she was in some ways rather amused by his pseudo-Byronic posturings, but it was equally plain that she certainly had no intention of letting his potentially frenzied amorous proclivities run roughshod across the orderly lawn of her existence.

In a little while—I suppose when he became a good deal more persistent and possessive in trying to find a featured place in her life—she finally had to get rid of him. He never told me anything about that, but the symptoms were clear enough, since he suddenly proceeded to revile her almost without letup.

The next installment of this little episode I read about in the newspapers. Julian had been arrested for climbing into the fountain that is located on Fifth Avenue between Fifty-eighth and Fifty-ninth Streets, with a guitar around his neck, intending, as he told the police, to serenade the statue of the nude goosegirl who disports herself in that highly refined and solvent spot.

(Maybe she isn't a goosegirl at all, but that's what I have been calling her for so many years now that I can't just give up that long familiar title on such short notice.)

Katherine and her family occupied a huge apartment at the Plaza, and this fountain was clearly visible from their windows, so it took no great deductive capacities to figure out for whose benefit this serenade was really intended.

At any rate, the cops threw Julian into the clink, and a few days later he was remanded for observation to a state sanitarium out on Long Island—Pilgrim State Hospital, I think.

After three weeks he was allowed to have visitors, and that's when I called on him. He was installed in a good-sized room along with three other people, and when I arrived they were quietly playing cards. It is always a little embarrassing to call on anybody in a laughing academy, but after a while we managed it all right.

Later on, a doctor dropped by—a friendly young man called Ferdinand Feigl, who, before he left his patients, asked if he might see me privately for a few moments. I stepped out into the corridor with him, and he tackled me straight off.

"I'm in a deep quandary about your friend," he said, "and I wonder if you could help me out."

"Yes?" I said. "What seems to be the trouble?"

"It's just a puzzle to me how he got out of the strait jacket, and I thought maybe you could tell me."

"Is he supposed to be in a strait jacket?" I said.

"Not now," said Dr. Feigl, "but when he first came here he was very violent and unmanageable for over a week—and every time we tied him up, he'd somehow manage to set himself free. It was positively uncanny. I thought that maybe he's practiced yoga or something—maybe he's an escape artist in his spare time. Do *you* have any idea how he managed it?"

"No," I said. "I don't think he's even particularly athletic."

"Athletic! He's about ten pounds underweight right now," said the medic. "Well, I'm sorry I bothered you. If you ever do find out, I wish you'd let me know."

"I will," I said. "I hope he'll cop out to me . . . you know how it is with psychos. They're pretty secretive sometimes."

But he wasn't a bit secretive—he told me at once how it all had happened.

"You remember the Six Spirits of Joy?" he said.

"Sure," I said; "They used to work over at the Whammy Club—on Fifty-second Street."

"Right!" he said. "Well, they're here now, all six of them."

"I'm not too surprised," I said.

This Spirits of Joy group consisted of some colored kids who pretended to be an orchestra. The only two instruments among the six of them were a kazoo and an ocarina; the rest of them just thumped with their fists, or with folded newspapers, on various-sized suitcases and leather hatboxes. The most talented one in the group, Oscar Branzil, used to get some really wonderful rhythmic effects by just swishing a couple of whisk brooms across the top of an old ash-can cover.

"So what *about* the Joy boys?" I said.

"Only this—that they all happened to be working on the maintenance staff as orderlies, on the floor where the unmanageable patients were stashed. I was lying there with my face to the wall, tied up like a parcel, when I heard somebody—somebody who was obviously supposed to be sweeping the floor—beating a kind of crazy rhythm up against the woodwork. I thought to myself I'd really finally lost my mind, because it sounded exactly like Oscar Branzil.

" 'Oscar!' I said. 'Oscar! Is that you?'

" 'That's me, all right,' he said. 'What are *you* doin' in here, Julian?'

" 'I'm learning to play the accordion around my back,' I said. 'Come on, Oscar, in heaven's name untie these strings and get me out of this damned sack, will you?'

"He did, of course. Later, when Dr. Feigl showed up, he nearly had a fit. They tied me up even tighter this time, but in half an hour another Spirit of Joy—I think it was Manuel this time—showed up, and he cut me loose too; and so on and so on—till all six of them had had their turn. By that time,

193

Feigl was absolutely staggered. He offered to give me the freedom of the room if I told him how I'd managed it—but I just took advantage of my privileged status as a nut and clammed up on him. He let me go free anyway—because he isn't really such a bad sort at heart."

And that was the simple solution to his miraculous multiple liberations.

I didn't originally plan to tell you this long, irrelevant story about Julian at all—it was really meant to be only a sentence in brackets in the strange tale of Katherine Loder's life—but, as you can see, things somehow seem to have gotten out of hand somewhere along the line. So I might as well tell you the rest of this crazy yarn too.

The Six Spirits of Joy had landed in the loony bin for having perpetrated a peculiarly malevolent act of vengeance. They had been working in some fleabag over near Eighth Avenue and, in the course of time, had become friendly with one of the mounted policemen who cover that neighborhood; as a matter of fact, they had become friendly with his horse. They used to feed it baked apples almost every day. Don't ask me how they discovered that that particular horse had a sweet tooth for such special delicacies—suffice it to say that they used to swipe baked apples out of the kitchen and slip them to the nag, which generally stood in front of their door while the cop was mooching around the neighborhood trying to find some suitable comforts for his own person. And then, one day, they suddenly got a parking ticket for their beat-up Chevrolet, and this ticket, to their amazement and disgust, was made out by that special friend of theirs, the mounted cop. They couldn't have been more furious. . . . So the next baked apple they served up to the horse had a strong doze of laxatives in it. The rest is official criminal history. After the horse had ruined every fender and windshield in the neighborhood, the cop smelled, among other things, a rat, and this venomously subversive plot was, after a while, discovered and appropriately dealt with. The judge who sat on the case considered the six defendants mentally unstable, and so they too landed in the Long Island hospital, just in time to play Good Samaritan to my friend Julian. He, incidentally, after he got away from clinical duress and observation, went to another university, out in the Middle West somewhere, and the rest of his life, as far as I could determine, has been without further official blemish of any sort. He is an assistant D.A. at the moment, and I think he's even grooming himself for some kind of elective political office next fall.

Katherine Loder's life became a good deal more muted after the intermezzo Juliano, for, although she had had nothing directly to do with his landing in the booby hatch, it is never possible to keep yourself completely out of any published mess once the newspaper columnists have somehow managed to lasso your name into contact with it.

Her people took her to Europe that winter, and I'm sure she created quite a stir wherever she happened to land, because she was not only an heiress, she was almost impossibly beautiful. She was divinely tall, red-haired, with that fabulous color of skin that comes to its greatest perfection in some particularly fortunate redheads. Her eyes were green and gold-flecked—and—her brows, her lashes, her hands, her wrists and her ankles could easily have made the reputations of at least half-a-dozen other fashionable debutantes.

When she returned from abroad, we met from time to time, and on a couple of occasions I had dinner with her at her home. Now then, among all the multifarious blessings that Katherine happened to be endowed with, the one her family would have dispensed with most readily was her unusually active and inquisitive mind. I gathered, during my brief visits at her house, that she was in many ways, and on frequent occasions, a good deal at odds with the lot of them, and I'm certain that a huge collective sigh of relief must have gone up from the Loder clan when Katherine, at twenty-two, became engaged to, and eventually married, Howard Thorndyke, a very promising young architect.

I lost sight of Katherine for the next four or five years, but I did read occasional items about her in the newspapers. She was, in the traditional manner of other young society matrons, quite active in various civic and charitable enterprises. When her daughter Cecile was born, I recall that I sent her a most affectionate congratulatory note.

However, for quite a long spell after that, we had no sort of communication with each other whatever.

I think it was sometime in 1927—after my return from Europe—I was very broke but had been lucky enough to find a cheap studio on West Eighth Street. When I went down to collect my mail, on the second day after my arrival, I saw Katherine Loder's name on one of the letter boxes. And, to my extreme surprise, it was coupled with another name that I was quite familiar with—the painter Maurice Verneuil's.

I remember how desperately anxious I was to believe that this was all just a mad coincidence, and that there was merely another woman, by the same name, involved in this whole crazy pattern. But when, later in the day, I questioned my janitor about it, I finally had to give in and admit that there was hardly any doubt but that it was *my* Katherine, indeed, who was living with Maurice Verneuil in a one-room kitchenette apartment on the fifth floor of our building.

It would have seemed a distasteful situation to me, even if any other woman had been involved in this business, because it happened that I had some rather highly unpleasant advance information on the character of the aforesaid Mr. Verneuil.

196

The following morning, Katherine herself knocked on my door and instantly resolved all my turbid speculations about her.

"I left my husband," she said, "because my life was so boring and so meaningless that I thought I would have to commit suicide to get out of it at last. Luckily, I met Maurice —I think you know him—don't you?"

"Not very well," I said. "I just talked to him a couple of times—at parties—and that's about all."

"Maurice is an artist," she said. "And each day of his life is like an impending adventure. It is the only way I can function without losing my mind."

"What about your child?" I said.

"She's with my mother-in-law, and when she gets a little older and goes off to school, I'm hoping I'll be able to see her regularly, now and then."

"Can't you see her at all now?" I asked.

"No," said Katherine. "Howard made it very tough for me. He stipulated that I'd forego any share in the child if I wanted to get out of my marriage. Since I was teetering on the verge of absolute disaster, I had to agree. I just hope I'll get around to solving it all, somehow, after a while. I've got to go on hoping, don't you see, or I wouldn't be able to live through the next twenty-four hours."

"What about your family?"

"They pretend that I'm dead. I had a little jewelry and a small bank account when I left, and that's what has kept Maurice and me going for a little while—but—I suppose I'll have to find myself some kind of a job pretty soon, or we'll both be in a mess, sure enough."

It is interesting that it never occurred to her that Maurice might also go to work. It never occurred to her because he was, nominally, a painter—and I'm sure she considered his labors a quasi-sacred calling. There are lots of women like that; I have known quite a few of them in the course of my life.

A couple of days later I went to visit them, and this visit depressed me so dreadfully that I made a vow never to cross their threshold again. Their room was as sparsely furnished and measly as most of the other places in the building, but their poverty was made particularly poignant for me by the little touches of beauty that poor Katherine had so vainly tried to effect in their grim surroundings.

Maurice was what, in the parlance of Lexington, would have been called "a cool stud." He was six feet tall, dark-haired, and rather attractive in a slovenly sort of manner. His eyes gave him away, of course; they were pale-gray and hooded, and seemed to derive from a particularly relentless form of predatory animal. He wore his locks artistically long, and although he forwent the vulgarity of sideburns, his lean-jawed face actually seemed to cry out for them. The relationship between Katherine and him was not only palpably obvious, it was bound to be very painful to any but the most obtuse bystander. He patronized Katherine shamelessly and unceasingly, as only such a cheap chiseler and artistic fraud as himself ever could have done. He patronized her for being tidy, for being thoughtful, for being well bred—and—for being all the things he could never aspire to become. To be with them for any length of time was an absolute ordeal. I think she was aware of this too, to some small extent, but since she was incapable of seeing him for what he really was—a heartless, unimaginative, ungrateful wretch—she could never properly evaluate the depth of loathing he actually aroused in me.

"He is a sadly wounded person," she told me later on. "His people have treated him terribly, and for years now he's seen artists with a fraction of his talent taken up and publicized— while he had to live like *this*."

198

As the weeks went on, I saw less and less of her, because I made strong and deliberate efforts to avoid any sort of meeting between us. One morning when I had to leave the house rather early, around seven-thirty, I think, I saw her standing on the corner of Sixth Avenue and Eighth Street, carrying quite a large package. I ran up to her and tried to relieve her of it.

"No, please!" she said. "I'm managing very well. I only have to go two blocks with it to Moretti's. I've done it before—it's really nothing!"

"I'll carry it to Moretti's for you," I said. "I'm going in that direction anyway—"

She seemed absolutely terrified by my offer. "Please—! Please—!" she said. "As a dear friend—you'll do me the kindness and let me go alone—please?"

So I let her go—and, in less than a week, I quite accidentally discovered both the nature of her burden and her mission to Moretti's.

My neighbor, the sculptor Joe Watanabe, had me in for tea one evening, and in the course of my visit he offered me some delicious fudge. "It's the best fudge I've ever eaten," I told him. "Where'd you get it?"

"From Katherine Loder," he said. "She makes it all the time and packs it in pretty colored papers and puts it on sale at the Village novelty shops."

"Where does she make it?" I asked.

"Up in their room. She puts little printed sayings into each bag and, just lately, over Easter, she sold over a hundred boxes at Moretti's alone."

"Does Maurice help her with it at all?" I said.

"Oh, Maurice," he said. "You know him better than that. He just makes fun of her."

Yes, I could imagine it only too well.

The following weekend I myself had a big batch of drawings to finish for a publisher friend, and since it was very hot and it was already one o'clock in the morning, I left my hall door open on the chance of catching a little air. After a while I suddenly had the feeling that somebody was watching me, and when I looked up, there was Maurice standing in my doorway. He smiled at me patronizingly.

"Working at such an hour?" he said. "I've told Katherine time and time again that you had no philosophy of life at all. None whatever!"

"Get the hell away from here," I said. "I've got just enough philosophy not to bend this poker over your disgusting skull —because I think that's just exactly what you'd like me to do. . . . You'd like to wear a martyr's bandage so you can go on sponging on poor Katherine with even greater impudence than ever."

"Don't you worry your little head about that, my bourgeois friend," he said. "I can see envy—cold, green envy— eating your heart out every minute of your life. You're just full of undigested bile because Katherine never gave you a tumble. Ah well, that's how it is. . . . Reconcile yourself to your mediocrity—and learn to housebreak your jealousy, pal."

I jumped up, ran to the door and banged it with all my might into his face. I heard him dashing down the stairs, and a moment later his footsteps echoed out in the silent street— and, I must say, *this* didn't surprise me in the least, because I knew his reputation only too well. I think I've forgotten, so far, to mention to you that he was, among other things, also a most abysmal coward.

Anyway, that's the last time I ever saw him. I moved from Eighth Street up to Seventy-ninth, opposite the museum, and nothing is easier than to lose people in New York by putting such a distance between yourself and them. I did hear about Maurice and Katherine from time to time—very unpleasant stories, mostly—and so I did my best not to think about them too much.

Katherine I saw twice more in the next fourteen years, and both times it happened in the Forty-second Street public library. The first time I even took lunch with her at a nearby Horn and Hardart's—she refused to eat anywhere else with me—and since she finally fully understood my disgust for her boy friend, she never once brought up his name during the two hours that we were together. She was working for a costume designer, she told me, and she planned to perfect herself in this work and hoped, later on perhaps, to be able to join the rather stringent union for this profession. The next time we met, she was herself designing costumes for an amateur group of some kind, and she urged me to come and take a look at their production. Unfortunately, I had to go out of town on a job just then, and I didn't see her or hear from her again until the following spring, when she phoned me and asked me to accompany her to see some kind of a movie over in Newark, New Jersey.

I was delighted to hear from her, of course, although it certainly sounded like an extremely strange request. To me, Newark is just a ghastly, sprawling industrial slum, tastefully surrounded by some mephitic swamps.

"Why Newark?" I asked her. "Isn't it playing in Manhattan somewhere?"

"It might be," she said, "but I can't take a chance on it. Somebody phoned me and told me it was playing just one more day in Jersey, and I'd like someone to go with me. I thought of you—so, if you can spare the time—"

"I'm very happy you asked me," I said. "Where shall we meet?"

"Let's meet at the Ninth Street entrance of the Hudson Tubes," she said.

"Let's take a taxi," I suggested.

"I'd really rather not."

"All right," I said. "I'll meet you at two o'clock sharp."

Katherine looked much older and very much thinner too, but her color and her smile still fell like silent benedictions on me.

We got to this movie house out in Newark and proceeded to suffer through an absolutely hideous picture. I think it was something about a French nobleman who had lost his memory, or some such malarkey. It couldn't possibly have been worse. I sat beside Katherine in that evil-smelling darkness, about as ill at ease as I've ever been in my life. When this masterpiece about the amnesia victim finally ended, there came a Terrytoon short—and this in its turn was followed by a month-old newsreel.

It showed some kind of a ship launching. A very pretty young girl was holding a bottle suspended on a rope, and when, after a couple of tries, she finally managed to slosh a lot of champagne all over herself and a little over the prow of the ship, too—Katherine suddenly grabbed my arm and said, "That's Cecile—that's *my* Cecile!"

I stared hypnotically at that beautiful young creature on the screen and tried to find some resemblance to Katherine. There wasn't any. She was just a slightly self-conscious, taffy-haired elf, laughing in the morning sunlight—as if life, from now on, was going to be nothing but just such a series of froth-blown galas. After we sat through a few more news shots, we finally got up and tottered out into the streets of Newark again.

"Howard's people are all in the shipbuilding business," Katherine said. "I haven't seen Cecile since she was a baby. You know, she is only a few years younger than *I* was when I first met you. Remember?"

"Yes," I said. "You're still very beautiful, Katherine. Your daughter is beautiful too, in quite a different way."

"I hope she'll have a happy life," she said.

"Did *you* have a happy life?" I asked.

"Yes," she said. "I have all the happiness I want. I know you don't believe it—but you can take my word for it—I never knew what real happiness was until I met Maurice. I've had a wonderful life with him. Years ago I used to worry about the fact that his true gifts weren't recognized. Now I no longer care. He's going to have an exhibition at Millray's, up on Madison Avenue, next month—and—I can assure you I can barely get myself to think about it. It matters so little. Nothing matters except the things in your heart. Goodbye, dear friend, and thanks for coming with me. I wanted so much to see her that, when someone called and told me they were showing this ship launching, I thought of you at once. I knew you would be happy for me, and sad for me too, as a real friend should be."

On the way to the tube station, I stopped at a florist and, despite her protests, I bought her a small bouquet of white winter violets. Finally, she even let me pin them onto her jacket.

And then she stepped off the sidewalk and, there, in that dreadful neighborhood, with the street full of slush and muck, she took the sides of her wide tweed skirt into her work-worn hands and made me a profound curtsy—the kind of curtsy a debutante makes when she is received at Windsor Castle.

And then I saw Newark, New Jersey, suddenly transformed into accidental splendor, because I was looking at it through a misty curtain of tears.

Let me confess that I was deeply perplexed by Katherine's life story, but in many incalculable ways she actually ran true to a certain frequently recurring, not terribly pleasant, feminine behavior pattern whose phenomena have been observed and extensively written and sung about during many centuries.

You see, I have always had the highest hopes for women, because no matter where you happen to encounter them, they are always the aspiring individuals of any community.

And yet?!?

And yet, they are also, paradoxically enough, the ones who are, in many ways, the most truly primitive members of the human race too. I have often observed it and pondered the matter quite fruitlessly, and now, at the age of sixty-two, I am still at a loss to account for it on strictly rational terms.

Here is the way it finally shapes up in my mind, as a well-intentioned guess.

I think that in the very beginning there was only rape. I mean that the relations between the sexes were originally activated by simple, brutal coercion. Later on, heaven only knows how long after, there probably came the earliest patterns of at least partial conjugal partnership—and—finally, after all these catch-as-catch-can devices—mankind at last settled down into its first crude forms of systematic domesticity.

I suspect that in the deep subconscious of a good many women—sometimes the seemingly most unlikely ones too—there still persists the memory of those early dark days that witnessed the very beginnings of human society. Actually, this is the only way I can explain the number of women who find themselves unaccountably drawn to certain male exponents whose crude and selfish approach to all aspects of life is only too obviously apparent. That this appeal actually does exist is not something we can argue about—it is only too evident to anyone who is willing to see it. It happens every day, all around us, no matter how many romantic connotations may be marshaled to mitigate the deplorable basic facts. I have a strong feeling that the roots of this condition are definitely bedded in the murky swamps of prehistoric female masochism.

It is as if a profound atavism of the psyche suddenly took command of the modern nervous system and, in one black moment, overthrew ten thousand years of domestic idealism.

In considering such a man—a man without any concepts of genuine male protectiveness in his character—a man without a shred of chivalrous imagination—a man whose behavior promises nothing but hardship, abuse, suffering and ingratitude —in considering such a creature, the Austrian writer Peter Altenberg identified him generically by the name "Flugerl" (pronounced *Floogerl*).

If you have read my translation of *Evocations of Love*, you know all about him, of course; but if you have not (more shame to you), then you might as well absorb this distillate of his small bouillon cube upon this subject right now.

THE FLUGERL
(*A psychobiochemical mystery*)

THERE is no man alive who can claim with any certainty that he will ever escape a "Flugerl." I daresay there are men who *think* they can, but they are just a lot of self-deceptive idiots who have never truly encompassed the fantastic omnipresence of this potential disaster.

You see, the Flugerl is a ghost that haunts the nervous system of your beloved. It may well be she can manage to hide her dangerous whims, her foolish impulses, and certainly her treacherous intentions, but the Flugerl is something that takes possession of her like a blind power of nature. It is a force of wild and uncontrollable urgency, and once it becomes rampant, it throws all conventions and all proprieties into a garbage heap. It is indeed as if nature, suppressed or regimented, suddenly demanded its atavistic, primordial rights.

The Flugerl is of many types, of course, but there is one

large, generic resemblance. All the Flugerls are just as relaxed as a cat with a damaged mouse.

In short, the Flugerl is a man—not necessarily handsome, very rarely accomplished, and hardly ever rich.

But, still, he has something.

He generates the exact critical wave length with which to upset the moral and psychic equilibrium of your mistress or wife, and she becomes aware of it the moment he enters a room, even if her back is turned toward the door.

There is no real weapon against a Flugerl, except a rapid and unceremonious withdrawal from the premises where he is rampant. Taking the girl with you, of course.

Remember, this calamity may befall you anywhere at all—in a restaurant, on the street, in a bus, in a train, in a department store—anywhere at all—and, before you know it, the damage is done. She is committed before she herself knows what has happened to her, and you are suddenly in touch with one of the truly dark powers that hover malevolently around us in this world.

There is only one occasion when I stood my ground. I gave the Flugerl in question an unprovoked slap in the face.

I'm sorry to say, this doesn't always work. As a matter of fact, it is liable to arouse a sudden spasm of justified womanly sympathy which is bound to lead to inevitable emotional involvements.

No! My best advice to you is, run, and make a fuss about it later on.

To me it is not a bit surprising that Altenberg, who knew so much about the relations between the sexes, should have cast his discerning eye so profitably into this dark side of the human psyche and have come up with a specific character definition for one of the most enigmatic manifestations of *homo saphead*.

CHAPTER THIRTEEN

Wᴴɪʟᴇ ɪ ᴛʜɪɴᴋ about all these curious matters, it comes to me that, among all the female oddballs who are likely to show up at my incineration, the one most likely to cause a certain amount of astonishment will be a plushily upholstered, quasi-Victorian leftover called Mme. Clementina Perrault. She manifests herself mostly in velvets and satin brocades, but beneath that deceptively dated façade of hers there beats—as I know—the heart of a shrewdly competent executive.

She likes rainy days too, and I remember when I first dropped into her cozy little spider trap, some years ago, the water was coming down in sheets across her heavily leaded, bottle-bottom windowpanes, over on East Fifty-sixth Street. She was delighted that I had braved the wretched weather for her sake, and instantly poured me a stiff glass of Armagnac, by way of a blood circulator.

I had read somewhere that Mme. Perrault baked cakes for Presidential inaugurals; also, for more than ordinarily stupendous coming-out parties, as well as for certain commercial superspectaculars of a particularly decorous and restrained nature. The article, which had appeared in the house organ of a large flour mill, I think, had inspired me with a deep longing to meet the lady, and so I had phoned her at once to arrange for an interview that very afternoon.

As I've already told you, it rained like Niagara when I crossed her doorstep, but Mme. Perrault looked as tidy and edible as a freshly baked brioche. A brioche encased in a velvet jewel box. She was a short, fashionably stout woman, with carefully marcelled hair; and on the front of her formidable bosom there hung a large gold-framed cameo displaying Leda and the Swan in an ambiguous but discreet act of intimacy. Actually, this trinket seemed more like an oval raft not too securely anchored on a sea which was occasionally agitated by a quite formidable undertow. She must have been around fifty years old at the time, but her skin was as smooth as the satin bow in her hair, and her inept-looking, beringed hands gave no clue whatever to her remarkable capacities as a business woman.

Before I had started out from my home, I had put an extra ten-dollar bill into my pocket with the intention of buying some kind of a small cake from her—one of her lesser efforts—a sort of curtain raiser to the amiable relationship that I hoped would come to rich florescence between us. I had in mind a mere three- or four-pounder, one garnished with currants and filberts and with perhaps a modest filling of sugared cinnamon or gooseberry jam.

Well, there weren't any cakes around that place of hers—

all she had visible were a few genuine French antiques that her customers were obviously expected to sit on.

"You are disappointed not to see any pastries?" she said, giving me an Old World smile of indulgent commiseration.

"Frankly, yes!" I said. "I know that you make rather big ones, for banquets and things like that, but I thought you might also have something for more run-of-the-mill occasions like a five o'clock tea, or a Kaffeeklatsch, for instance."

She pointed to an elegant little sofa. "Please sit down," she said, "and let me explain our situation to you. You see, we are out-and-out specialists. We make *only* large cakes—cakes that are expected to serve at least one hundred and fifty or two hundred people. *These*, as a matter of fact, are really our *small* cakes. What we prefer is to create pastries for supreme gala occasions—occasions when anywhere from one to three thousand people are expected. You understand?"

"Yes," I said. "I'm just wondering how you do it—I mean, how do you bake such a monster . . . ? How do you move it? And how do you keep it from falling apart? There is no end to the questions I'll have to ask you. . . . How, for instance, do three thousand people help themselves to their share of cake?"

I could see her face crinkling into jubilant puckers in her readiness to answer me. "It is all a matter of careful planning," she said. "My grandfather designed festive pastries for Napoleon III, and my father catered to Monsieur Fallières, to Monsieur Tisserand, and to Monsieur Clemenceau. You see, we have been the outstanding experts in this field for almost a century."

"When you say *we*, do you mean your husband—your family—? Who is involved in all this with you?"

"My husband is dead," she said. "Been dead for twenty years this coming March. Although not born into this milieu, he was a genius, both in planning the designs and in estimates. I shall never cease to miss him. Unfortunately, I am the last of my line. I have no children—and my nephews and nieces have not had the right feeling for it, I'm sorry to say. They lack the proper approach."

"And what *is* the proper approach?" I asked.

"It is to think of it all like an artist who has been commissioned to create a masterpiece for a great patron. I will show you some photographs and then you will understand better."

She went over to a Louis-the-Something escritoire and produced an old-fashioned, plush-bound picture album; then she sat herself down beside me and showed me the first example of her art. It was nothing but a corny, head-on photograph of the Petit Trianon.

"It was twelve feet high," she said, "six feet deep, and seventeen feet long. There was room inside for ten musicians, and after all the cake had been eaten you could see them all playing, inside, right through a silver latticework of interwoven laurel leaves.

"Here is one"—she displayed a picture of a cathedral—"here is the one my papa made for the bishop's fiftieth anniversary. It was commissioned by the city of Lyons and weighed two thousand kilos.

"Here is one we made for a Texas jubilee, which was attended by twenty-five hundred guests. . . ."

And so on, and so on, until my poor head was full of serenading crickets.

"Madame," I said, "you still haven't explained the eating part of it. How is *that* done?"

"It is very simple, really," she said. "The cake is pre-cut into suitable slices—and each piece has a narrow silk ribbon depending from it. When the cake is ready to be served, each guest pulls his piece of ribbon—they take turns approaching the structure, of course—and when they pull, each slice falls neatly into the plate that is held below it. That is all."

"And who," I said, "designs the structure of these cakes in the first place? Do you? Does the customer? Or what?"

"We have a staff of architects, of course," she said. "Also we have three men traveling all over the world, constantly, copying suitable designs for us. You see, not everything is suitable. The Taj Mahal, for instance, is a great problem. It *could* be done, I suppose—but it presents formidable obstacles. *Formidable!* Our chief concern, of course, is good taste, in every direction."

At this point there was a knock on the door, and I got up.

"Please don't leave," she said. "I think I know who it is— and you might learn something by listening to how we deal with our clients."

She went to the door, and when she opened it I at once recognized the late Walter Chrysler, Sr. I had never met him—but an illustrated biography of him had been appearing in one of the national magazines, and so I was quite familiar with his face. He had obviously been there before and had merely called to settle the final details for the baking of a gigantic cake for his daughter's impending wedding.

"I'm quite satisfied with all the arrangements," he said, "and your people can come over to take the proper measurements any time after the next weekend. There's just one thing I thought of that might be no great hardship to *you*—and would please *me* very much."

"Yes?" said Madame Perrault. "What is in your mind? Please feel free to make any suggestions."

"Just this—I'd like very much if the cake—instead of representing a building—could rather have the shape of a Chrysler car—one of our latest models that will be coming off the assembly lines just a few days before the wedding. What do you think of that idea, Madame?"

"It is a very pretty idea," said Madame Perrault, suddenly growing several feet taller and talking to him from quite a long distance away. "But, you see, unfortunately for us, Mr. Chrysler, we don't make *anything* after the *eighteenth century!*"

As I told you, she was quite a cat, and we became very good friends in the ensuing years—so good, in fact, that she once gave a job to a friend of mine, Phyllis Raab of Boston.

Phyllis will probably come by the funeral parlor too, if she happens to be in New York. We've known each other a couple of decades, and I've always been deeply devoted to her. Once I was even more than just devoted to her but, for various special reasons, nothing permanent ever came of it.

I had known Jason Raab, her husband, long before he got married to her. He studied architecture here in New York, and we used to meet every once in a while at parties or at a dinner table in somebody's house. He must have been around forty when he fell in love with Phyllis and married her, up in Boston, where both of them originally came from. A little later he got a good job with a big building firm in Massachusetts, and a couple of years after they were settled in their new home I happened to be in their general neighborhood, and so I dropped in to see them. Actually, as I remember, I stayed with them for a whole weekend.

I have some hard-boiled theories about middle-aged bachelors who marry women much younger than themselves, and most of these theories are really just post-mortems to unavoidable disaster.

You see, when a man gets to be forty or thereabouts, he is pretty well settled in his ways. That's just common sense, ain't it? Well, this settling process of his *excludes*, in most cases, any sort of steady female companionship. I mean, he doesn't have somebody hanging around the house all the time, and the chances are he never finds hairpins on his night table and powder puffs on the bathroom sink. These are trifling matters, of course, provided you're used to them. A bachelor of forty is either an unmanageable slob, or he is a hopeless prig on the subject of his precious environment and his cherished belongings. In either case, his young wife is going to have a hell of a time with him.

And that's exactly what poor Phyllis had, as I could clearly observe during that whole disastrous weekend I had with them. Jason was wildly in love with her and this, as far as I could see, made it all so much worse. He tried to control himself. . . . His voice was unnaturally low, and his smile absolutely frozen in its artificiality, as he chided her gently about uncorked lotion bottles, exposed cold-cream jars, and topless tooth-paste tubes. He was absolutely seething inside as he softly inquired for the whereabouts of his safety razor, and I think he was on the point of tears when he asked her why the mouthwash had landed in the refrigerator. Well, *that*, or nearly as much, can happen between people of the same age too, I suppose, but a younger man, being less rigorously routinated in his habits, is bound to commit a great many fluffs himself, and so, if he has a reasonable sense of humor, it all winds up without leaving too much stored-up rancor in his heart.

Not so with the bachelor of forty. Not a damned bit of it. He finally gets so that he is convinced that she is doing it all just to get a rise out of him. He simply can't believe that those rubber bands of hers weren't deliberately planted in his bedside ash tray, or that those bobby pins weren't purposely, with malice aforethought, dropped into his slippers. Finally, the marriage, if it lasts that long, becomes just one continuous monitoring action, with police overtones and inquisitional side effects.

Another thing, a bachelor of forty has had a lot more experience than a girl of twenty—that is to say, he's had a great many more chances to make a complete and effective ass of himself—hence, it stands to reason he will look with compassion, if not contempt, on anything his young wife tries to do on her own. He knows all about everything that she's ever going to undertake; he knows all the hazards, the pitfalls and the comeuppances that are headed her way; and, what's more, he predicts every disappointing step on her dismal road with sounds of muted but triumphant rancor.

In short, as I said before, living with him is pure hell.

And so, after a while, Phyllis started to visit some of her relatives in New York for longer and longer periods—until—one day—she wrote Jason an eight-page letter explaining why she was never going to go home to him again. He came after her, of course, since he was sure she would return to him at once if she clearly understood how much he really loved her. Except it didn't work out quite that way. She'd had enough of it.

"He is just a sort of top sergeant, really," she said to me. "He has no way of showing affection except in its most crude and immediate form, when he wants to sleep with you. I can't imagine what sort of women he must have known before he got around to me—but I'm sure he must have paid them. He certainly hasn't the vaguest idea of how to make a life with anyone, excepting a servant maybe. Well, I'm finished with it. I tried it for three years, and he hasn't learned a thing, and he's almost made *me* forget that human beings don't have to live together just because of biological necessity, like two coupling animals. I'd like to see the shimmer of a little courtesy and grace in my life—and if I can't have it, then I'll just live alone, that's all."

Good words, all of them, but in the meantime she needed a job. Mme. Perrault hired her as a secretary-researcher, and

214

they took very well to each other, right off. Jason kept writing Phyllis every week, and at least once a month he came down to New York trying to persuade her to change her mind. Finally he applied for a divorce, and I think I've never seen Phyllis quite so happy.

The day she got the news she called me up, and I took her to the theater and later we went up to the Savoy Ballroom in Harlem to dance. I took a real good look at her that night, and I decided that Phyllis had more than just ordinary attributes to attract the attention of a truly discerning man. It is true, she was only blond and blue-eyed, but she had a beautifully minute, aquiline nose and a figure that could very easily have caused some of the minor wars of the ancient world.

Before I realized it, *both* of us were anxiously waiting for her divorce to become final. Meanwhile, we saw a good deal of one another, and although I was as old, or even older, than Jason—*I* had been married to somebody ever since I was a child, so I had no difficulties whatever in making allowances for the small, chronic foibles that seem to assail most of womankind.

Everything was going along great until one Friday afternoon I had a phone call from Boston. It was Jason, asking me to take luncheon with him the following day. Ordinarily I would probably have turned him down, but since I had an undeniable sense of guilt toward him, I accepted, like an idiot.

Of course, I couldn't help speculating pretty freely on why he had called me. Had somebody tipped him off that I was spending a lot of time with Phyllis? Was he going to reproach me about it? Was there going to be a blowup—or what?

When we met at the restaurant, it was instantly clear that he knew nothing at all about the new *rapprochement*. Not yet. Jason had many failings, but deviousness wasn't one of them. He could no more have hidden his suspicions, if he'd had any, than he could hide an active boil on his nose. No, all was well, as far as it went. What he really had in mind was to ask my advice about getting Phyllis to go back to live with him again.

"I think you're her closest friend, here in New York," he said, "and I think she takes a great deal of stock in your opinions. Now then, I'd like you to tell her that I'm still terribly fond of her, and that I'd do anything, within reason, to make this marriage work."

"You have to tell her that yourself," I said. "It's really between the two of you, isn't it? I don't see how an outsider's word can carry any more weight than your own."

"She's a strange girl," he said. "You see, she's taken it into her head that I'm impossible to live with, that I'm finicky and pedantic—and, yet, anyone who knows me will tell you that that's just sheer nonsense."

"She's lived with you three years, hasn't she?"

"Two years and eight months," he said. "It's always tough for married people in the beginning. Fred Kobler and Doris separated twice before they finally settled down, and now they have four children and are one of the happiest married couples I know. You know yourself that there is always a period of adjustment. Isn't that true, in every marriage?"

"Three years is a pretty long time," I said. "I think she also feels that you aren't very chivalrous, that you're a middle-aged bachelor who shouldn't have gotten married in the first place."

"What do you mean, I'm not chivalrous? I hold doors open for her, don't I? I help her out of cabs, and I get up from my chair in restaurants when she comes back from the powder room, don't I?"

"I'm afraid there is a good deal more to chivalry than that," I said. "In fact, a man can find endless small things all day that will show his wife that he is romantically aware of her. You don't have to concentrate all your amorous proclivities

216

just on a bed—after all—a woman likes to feel surrounded by attention, even in nonorgiastic moments."

He suddenly became very thoughtful. "I daresay you're right. Of course, I'm not in the habit—and—actually, I don't really see the reason why one should make a constant fuss over somebody who's living with you as your wife, anyway; but, I suppose, there are two sides to every question."

He looked at me with such bovine seriousness at that moment, and he seemed so baffled and stricken, that I couldn't help feeling a strong wave of sympathy flowing out toward that sterile, unimaginative oaf.

"Women are different from men," I said. "They live almost entirely on their emotions, and they bitterly resent being treated as just a convenience."

Jason fished around in his inside coat pocket and produced a little gold-encased notebook. It must have been a marriage present from someone, although it really looked more like a *bar mitzvah* gift, and when he detached a tiny gold pencil from the front of this trinket, I wondered whether he planned to write a message to Phyllis, with the intention of having me deliver it.

"You've been married several times already," he said, "and that proves that you aren't such a mastermind in the business yourself. Nevertheless, I must bow to your superior experience, if nothing else, and I'd be very grateful to you if you'd be good enough to give me a couple of hints—I mean a few suggestions that I might follow in my behavior with her."

As you can see, the son of a bitch had thrown me a real curve. He was asking *me* to tell him how to hold on to the dame that I was planning to marry myself. Has anybody ever been in such ridiculous messes as I was constantly getting into? Has anybody, ever before, sat at a restaurant table giving advice to a husband on how to woo back his wife while he was busy making love to the same woman himself?

You will look in vain through all of French literature to find its parallel. It just never happened—until it happened to me.

Well, what could I do . . . ? *I advised.*

"In the evening," I said, "just before you sit down to dinner, why don't you put *Eine Kleine Nachtmusik*, by Mozart, on the gramophone and have it play, very softly, all through the meal."

"What recording would you suggest?" he said.

"Get the Viennese Chamber Music Society's," I said. "I think it's released by Odeon Records."

He wrote it all down with his little golden pencil.

"What else?" he asked.

"On Sixty-fifth Street near Madison Avenue there is an English saddlery shop," I said, "where they sell very coarse-grained gloves which are wonderful for rubbing across the body when you are bathing—particularly across the stomach and the neck and shoulder blades. It circulates the blood, and her skin will tingle very pleasantly for a long time afterward. She'll be most grateful to you, I'm sure."

He looked at me as nonplused as if I had talked to him very rapidly in a foreign language. After I had repeated every word over again, he wrote it all down in that golden book of his.

"Yes," he said, "go on!"

"In that same shop they have some tortoise-shell clasps with rubberized edgings which she can fit around her forehead if she ever puts on extensive make-up; it will keep the gook out of her hair. It's very practical."

He made a note of it.

"Also," I said, "I think a couple of times a week you might bring home some flowers. Not every day—you understand—because it shouldn't become just a mechanical habit—and not even on the same days of the week. Although, perhaps, I *would* get a larger selection every Friday, because then they'll brighten the house over the weekend. See what I mean?"

"Flowers?" he said. "We used to get flowers all the time. I had a standing order with one of the best florists in town. We got flowers twice a month, regularly!"

"You have to pick them out yourself," I said. "There are some flowers that are very perishable—like mimosa, for instance. They dry up and shrivel almost instantly—but their color, even in that shriveled state, remains lovely, and the odor of even a few small bunches will pervade the whole house for days. Get African daisies, too—they come in endless varieties; and nowadays, even in the middle of winter, you can get large branches with blooming quince blossoms on them that will last for more than a week or ten days."

The poor sap wrote down this whole rigmarole just as I told it, and as I sat there glaring at him I realized how hopeless and futile it all was. I could just see him, every day of his life, consulting that romantic dossier of his and studying its multifarious instructions like a hitchhiker brooding over a road map.

When he'd filled about ten pages in that ledger of his, he ordered some stewed figs—and after he'd explained their nutritive value as well as their digestive potentials to me—we parted.

I told Phyllis about that meeting of ours, and, curiously enough, it didn't seem to depress her one bit.

"He's hopeless," she said. "He should have learned about all that, not out of a love Baedeker, but by personal experience, long before he ever met me. The best thing is just to forget all about him. He loves his work—his employers appreciate him and pay him well. He's looked up to by other people in

219

his profession, and he has sent his linen to the same laundry for twenty-three years. If that laundry ever goes out of business— *then* there'll be a *real* crisis in his life. Some day he may even find somebody who appreciates all his virtues, and—who knows?—he may be a happily married man yet."

I must say, he depressed me greatly, and I really couldn't just dismiss him from my mind as easily as Phyllis most certainly did.

A month or so after my luncheon with him, he wrote her a long letter saying that he had halted the divorce proceedings against her indefinitely.

"You are at present under a very bad influence," he said. "I did not realize this until very recently, and I think you will make a terrible, irreparable mistake if you should suddenly find yourself free of the bonds that tie you to me. I hope my continued affection for you, as well as your good common sense, will make you change your mind, and you will come back to the home that is waiting for you."

Somebody had, finally, told him all about us, I suppose. Well, whatever his intentions, he certainly succeeded in keeping us from getting married.

I'm not very good at long engagements and—what with one thing and another—the next time I had to leave town, I had a funny feeling that, very probably, Phyllis and I had already had our best days together. While I was away in Haiti, she wrote me that Jason had finally divorced her, and a little later on I heard from someone else that she had gotten herself involved with a guy called Glen Decker. She actually did get married to Glen, about four days before I hit New York again.

All this is ancient history now. The Deckers have three fine children, while Jason Raab is still keeping bachelor hall up in Boston.

I wonder what he ever did do with all the information contained in that little golden notebook of his. Did he finally get around to trying out any of that material on anyone? Does he, sometimes of an evening, alone in his tidy house—open its pages—and muse—speculatively—upon the strange, tangled web of his own feelings—that made him write all that stuff down in the first place?

CHAPTER FOURTEEN

Although he hates funerals, Scobie Clivette is bound to show up, because his fine wife is sure to drag him there.

Scobie, once, some forty-six years ago, went to grammar school and to high school with me, and he belonged to that hard, central core of my earliest friends and adherents, who were never going to settle for anything less than a life on their own terms. By the way, when I say "adherents" I don't mean that they were my vassals or bondslaves—it only happened to work out in such a way that, in the whole group around me, I was the one who had the greatest freedom, to start with.

I was an only child. My father earned pretty good money. I knew exactly what I wanted to be and—also—I was the exclusive member in the whole set who had a steady girl friend, when I was just in my early teens. This last item was an almost unbelievable phenomenon around 1915 or thereabouts, and, you can believe me, it gave me considerable status with all the other kids.

The bunch of us were tied together by a very powerful bond, namely, our great and ever-present fear of becoming just a lot of wage-earning mediocrities. All those boys of fourteen and fifteen (most of them first-and second-generation immigrants) had sworn to themselves to, somehow, become significant members of society, and, failing this, to wind up as out-and-out bums—that is to say, to become, at any cost, at least significant human failures. They were seriously determined not to settle for just the drab, mindless life which was vegetating in smug contentment all around them.

So, it naturally happened that a good many of them turned out to be eccentrics, rather early in their years, and, unfortunately, acquired no special distinctions later on to balance these personal oddities. Others, who did have certain demonstrable scholastic attainments, but who were closely tied through affection or gratitude to their doting families, awaited the time of their eventual liberation, with bloodshot eyes fixed firmly upon the horizon.

Scobie Clivette belonged to this latter group. His mother and two older sisters dedicated their lives to brushing motes and cobwebs out of his path, and his apple-cheeked, benign father, who was a bookkeeper, nourished only one dream in his bosom—to see the glorious title of *Certified Public Accountant* added to his only son's name.

Well, after a while it all happened just the way they had dreamed it, and everything should have been *matzobrei* and blintzes from then on. But a really devoted family group always has something to worry about, and the next thing that lay like a huge anvil across their communal awareness was their ceaseless worry that Scobie was never going to get married.

I must admit he was pretty hard to suit. I myself introduced him to a couple of likely chicks, and all I got out of him were a lot of grimaces and groans. Of course, I understood his problem much better than his parents and his sisters did—I really *knew* the reason he was leery of getting married.

You see, Scobie, who had started in as a world-beater, like all the rest of us, happened to have such a natural knack for figures that, before anybody got a chance to realize it, he'd become a licensed C.P.A., with quite a bit of cash of his own in the bank. And this hung him up, plenty. In his heart, as I perfectly well knew, he was really a Karamazov, but his suits came from Hart Schaffner and Marx. A dichotomy, obviously. Now, the question was, how to resolve it? Through a marriage, of course, or so at least it seemed to him. He'd have to find some very special life partner—some uniquely gifted individual—whose mere existence would at once lift him out of the commonplace matrimonial concerns which had already stultified the burgeoning aspirations of some of his most promising friends.

It was quite a problem. You see, in the nature of things, it was really not very likely that some great concert pianist or world-renowned actress was ever going to throw in her lot with him. His life was pretty well circumscribed by various honest, or swindling, bookkeepers—and he spent most of his time in petty arguments with laundrymen and tailors who maltreated his haberdashery and his clothes. I didn't really see how in hell it was ever going to be resolved.

But, man knoweth little—and God is great.

One day he came to see me, in the middle of the day—already a most unorthodox sort of happening—and it was clear to see that his face was draped in unmistakable patterns of profound joy. After a few minutes of some unavoidable, meaningless palaver, which is the eternal handicap and frustration to all true human communication, he finally blurted out to me the uniquely significant purpose of his visit.

"I've met a very nice girl," he said. "I met her a couple of months ago, and I want to introduce her to you."

"Fine," I said. "Why don't you bring her to dinner to-morrow night?"

"That won't be possible," he said. "You see, she works till quite late, and then she's generally too tired to go anywhere."

"All right," I said. "We can make it next weekend—Saturday night or Sunday afternoon, maybe."

I could see something was wrong with that, too.

"I tell you what," he said. "Why don't you come with me to see her tomorrow, around four o'clock in the afternoon? Would that be all right for you?"

"Sure," I said. "Shall I pick you up, or what?"

"No, I'll come by with the car—you see, she lives out in Coney Island."

The Coney Island bit surprised me a little, but, of course, I agreed to go with him. You see, I couldn't quite repress a certain inbred, Manhattan snobbery about it all, and, I daresay, I hadn't ever expected him to fall for a dame that lived in a place with such tawdry associations. Not that there is anything basically wrong about the Island—it just somehow always stood in my mind for sandy ice-cream waffles and wet behinds. However, I puzzled no more about it, and since it was already around the middle of June, I even thought we ought to go out there by boat.

"No," he said. "You can't ever figure the boats. Their schedules aren't too dependable, and I'd like to make sure we get there at five. She'll have a little time to talk to us at five."

I'm not going to pretend that I wasn't highly intrigued by all this schedule business. After all, what could this dame possibly be doing that would make her time so precious that she couldn't even swing a few hours over the weekend?

Meanwhile, I kept my trap shut and awaited the coming denouement with becoming civility and composure.

Let me tell you at once, he really surprised me. First of all, after we'd parked the car on the Island, he steered me straight over to the Museum of Strange People, which was the biggest freak show on Surf Avenue.

"She work in there?" I said.

"Yes. That's why she can't get away weekends," he said, "since this is nearly the height of the season."

"I see," I said. But I didn't really see anything at all—because I had actually expected him to introduce me to the girl cashier of this joint, but he just bought a couple of tickets and steered me right inside. He obviously knew his way around, since he walked straight to the rear of this huge place, and when he got to a platform that bore a luridly illustrated placard, designating this as the habitat of Rita the Leopard Girl, he suddenly stopped and turned around to face me. All I can tell you is that he seemed as excited as a kid who is about to get his first bicycle, and even in that dim light I could see that his expression was beatific to the point of imbecility.

"I'll call her," he said. "She's really very shy with strangers, but I've told her all about you. Please be nice to her." His dark, calflike eyes suddenly turned sodden with potential misery.

Fortunately, I'm a man who adjusts easily to unexpected situations, so I really had no trouble taking that look off his face. "I'm nice to everybody," I said. "After all, who the hell am *I*, anyway?"

He put his hand gratefully on my shoulder, and I don't think he'd ever felt closer to me in his whole life.

Then he called her.

She looked very good in her little black satin bodice, and he'd been perfectly right about her—she *was* shy. Her skin was rather fair, and sprinkled all over her legs, her arms and her face were irregular-sized, dark-brown blotches. When

226

she came a little closer to us, I noticed that these spots were even slightly raised. She would have been a real beauty without those pigmentation blemishes, and I could easily see why Scobie had taken such a dive for her.

Of course, she was quite ill at ease with me, but, even so, she gave a pretty good account of herself and told me she was getting a lot of reading done, between shows. She was doing Jane Austen, I think. All in all, she was really quite charming during the few minutes we spent with her—but I could hardly concentrate on what the both of them were saying for the constantly gnawing thought in my mind: *What are his poor folks going to think about all this?*

One is bound to have trouble with one's kinfolk, no matter who in hell you happen to bring home as your bride—but Rita the Leopard Girl was really putting it on a bit strong. Even *I* had to admit that.

When we hit the street again, Scobie noticed my almost somber preoccupation, and of course he misinterpreted it completely.

"I take it you are miffed at my glaring error in taste," he said. "And, curiously enough, I picked you as the only man among all of my friends who would be sympathetic and understanding about this whole thing."

"I am, Scobie," I said. "I think she's a charming young woman. I was just wondering about your parents and your sisters—"

"I'll have to start living my own life sooner or later," he said, "and, as a matter of fact, it is pretty late for me, already —as you perfectly well know. But I, somehow, have the feeling that you, too, aren't entirely enthusiastic about my choice. Well, let me tell you, it just goes to show what a deep streak of bourgeois prejudice is still alive in a lot of us. These freaks, as they're called, are, to me, like the pantheon of ancient Olympus. They are the cloven-hoofed, spotted, striped, wing-footed, curiously marked gods of classical Greece who have come down in the world to be gaped at by yokels in the market place. I had hoped that *you*—above all people—would catch not only the picturesque but also the undeniably tragic qualities inherent in such a tableau. I'm terribly disappointed in you, Alex. I would never have expected it of you."

"Oh, boloney!" I said. "It has nothing to do with me—and you know it. I'm not your father, after all. I'm prepared to be best man at your wedding, if it comes to that. But you do know perfectly well how this is going to affect your family —and you. They'll commit mass suicide when they hear you're going to marry a leopard girl. I think you ought to stop yacking away at me about Mount Olympus and try to figure out some rational way how this whole thing can be solved without breaking everybody's heart. Come on, now, pull yourself out of Homer and Aeschylus for a minute, and let's see if something can't be done to make it all socially feasible without too many tears and heartbreaks. How long, by the way, have you known Rita, anyway?"

"Two months," he said. "I saw her picture in a magazine, and I flipped for her at once. I met her mother a little while ago, too; she used to be a schoolteacher in Connecticut, but two years ago she needed some kind of an operation, and that's when Rita decided to go to work in a show."

When I got home from Coney Island, I fixed myself an ice bag and went to bed. The schnook really had me worried. He was in a pretty bad mess, that's for sure.

A long time after all this had happened, it occurred to me that we poor mortals can only see and savor such a small sliver of the pie of life, that only someone situated high above the whole dish could be in a position to estimate the true relevance of all the ingredients involved. If I had known all this before, I really needn't have worried so much about it all, because certain forces, much greater than my limited imagination could ever have conceived possible, were already quietly at work to bring about an altogether surprising conclusion to this seemingly unsolvable dilemma.

One of these forces, the strongest single one, surely, proved to be—mother love.

In short, Rita's mother, with a surprisingly girlish kind of voice, phoned me, a couple of days after the Coney Island visit, and asked if she might call on me.

I had her over the following Sunday afternoon, and, as Shakespeare might have said, she did indeed such a tale unfold, as few mortals on this earth have ever given ear to.

Her name, by the way, was Ernestine Goodwell, and she was a sprightly, bright-eyed woman—who seemed to have landed in my living room straight after quitting a New England town meeting.

"The reason I am here," she said, "is because I think those children care a good deal about one another, and it would be a great shame if any harm came to them, simply because of a slight misunderstanding."

"There is really no misunderstanding," I said. "The whole difficulty centers around the fact that certain people, like Scobie's parents, for instance, are likely to have strong and seemingly insurmountable prejudices against circus performers; don't you see?"

"You are being very tactful," she said. "But Rita isn't really a circus performer—she's a leopard girl in a freak show—and that's where the whole misunderstanding comes in. You see, Rita took up this terribly unpleasant work because I had been very ill, and we ran into awful debt—paying doctor and hospital bills—you understand—? You see, my daughter originally used to work in a research laboratory, for a very small salary, until two years ago, and, what's more, she'd never had any spots or splotches to exhibit—in the first place—until this terrible emergency came along."

I jumped out of my seat as if someone had run a long needle up my rump. "What's that?" I screamed. "What's that you're telling me—? She had no splotches—well, how in heaven's name did she *get* them?"

"She got them from eating six raw tomatoes every day," said Mrs. Goodwell. "Tomatoes will do it to her every time."

My face must have been really something worth seeing, because my polite little visitor finally couldn't contain herself any longer and just burst out laughing.

"I'm sorry," she said, "but you really look like you ought to have a strong cup of tea."

"You mean she brings those splotches out on herself *purposely? ! ?*"

"Yes," she said. "We always knew she was sensitive to the acids from tomatoes—and—from certain berries, too. And then, when we were so worried about our finances, she started to experiment with the tomatoes, and, before I knew what happened, she was getting seventy-five dollars a week as the leopard girl at the Danbury Fair."

I gave the old lady a big hug and a kiss—and I think I even did a little jig of pure delight, right there in front of her. But my joy didn't last more than just half a minute, maybe, because I suddenly remembered that Rita's removable spots were, actually, only half the problem. There still remained Scobie's maniacal desire to mingle with the outcasts of Olympus and to escape from the mediocrity of his middle-class success by ravishing an authentic, exiled goddess.

I tried to explain this to Rita's mother, but it was all just a little too much for her. She had done her share—she had explained away the objectionable leopard spots—and she was, obviously, unprepared to go into the schizoid ramifications of her prospective son-in-law's psyche.

I did, finally, make one thing clear to her—I convinced her of the necessity of getting Rita out of that freak show, at once, and of stopping her from eating any more tomatoes.

"She has a contract, though," said Mrs. Goodwell, "and it still is effective until September 30, I think."

"Well," I said, "if she suddenly loses her spots, she won't be worth anything to them. They'll be only too glad to let her go."

"That is true," she said. "I'll talk to her about it this evening after the show."

"Fine," I said, "and please tell her to call me."

When I talked to Rita, on the phone, the following day, I didn't have the least bit of trouble making clear to her what a great problem she still had on her hands.

"I was afraid of that," she said. "He always talks so strangely about ancient Greece, and everything, and I'm sure it will upset him no end when he finds out that those spots of mine weren't real."

"I wonder," I said, "whether it might not be better if *I* were to tell him all about it. You see, Scobie is, by nature, a very rational man, and, as far as I can remember, he has never been able to resist listening to a sound argument in all his life. And I've got plenty of sound arguments, believe me."

"I don't know how to thank you for all the trouble you're taking," she said. "But I'm sure you know how deeply grateful I am; and my mother, too."

"Forget it," I said. "After all, Scobie went to grammar school with me, and I assure you he's done quite a bit for me, too, during all these years. He's one of my oldest friends. I'll see him tonight, and I'll call you around noon tomorrow."

I couldn't possibly have been more wrong about Scobie. He not only didn't pay the slightest attention to any of my sound arguments, he absolutely blew his top. Worse than that, he

231

wept real tears all over my fine, handmade Kerouan rug, and wound up by cursing me roundly, and loudly, as a co-conniver in unsavory conspiracies against his most sacred emotions. When he finally left, he gave my front door such a bang that an old African mask fell off the wall and broke into six pieces.

I had never in my life seen him in such a state. He was inconsolable. He was irreparably wounded. She had deceived him! She had toyed with his heart as if it were a ten-cent Yo-yo! He was through with women forever!

I had the unhappy task of transmitting the gist of this sad condition of affairs to poor Rita. She was, of course, appropriately shattered.

"I don't know what I'm going to do," she said to me tearfully. "I'm going to quit my job with the strange people, anyway, because I'm so heartsick I just have to go away for a while, to pull myself together. Just a minute, Mr. King. I think Mother wants to say something to you."

"Yes?" I said. "Hello, Mrs. Goodwell. I'm sorry I've had to tell such bad news to Rita, but—"

"Hello, Mr. King," she said. "I wonder if I might have the chance to talk to you again; just for a few moments, privately."

"By all means," I said. "Come here this afternoon, if you like."

"Fine," she said. "I'll be there in a couple of hours."

When she arrived at my house, I must say, she seemed to have pretty good control of herself. "Well," she said, "it is certainly quite understandable that the poor boy's feelings are quite mixed up, right now. But I'm absolutely certain that he is very fond of Rita and that all he needs is just a little of the right kind of help."

"I'm afraid that this isn't going to be easy to give," I said, "because he's so mad at everybody—he just won't listen to reason."

"Maybe reason isn't quite the thing that is wanted," she said. "Tell me, Mr. King, would you be good enough to let me meet him here, in your apartment? I know we've already trespassed on your kindness more than enough, but I'm sure you'll forgive me when you consider that my daughter's whole happiness may be at stake here. You know that a mother will try for her children when everyone else has already given up hope."

"Please feel free to do anything you like. If you'd like to meet Scobie here, you can arrange to have him come to my studio, which is right on the floor above. You arrange whatever seems best to you, and I'll be only too glad to help. Frankly, I'm not too optimistic about his coming—but I'll certainly ask him."

"You don't have to ask him," she said. "I'll write him a nice note and, after all, I don't think he is the type of man who is likely to be rude to an old woman like me. *Is* he?"

I wasn't really too sure, but I said nothing further about it. "Call me any time you like," I said, "and you'll be free to use my studio any time he's willing to talk to you."

"Thank you," she said. "I'll pray to the good Lord to reward your great kindness to us."

To my great surprise, she did call me, about five days later. "He's agreed to meet me at your place tomorrow at one-thirty," she said.

"I'm very happy to hear it," I said. "There is a separate entrance—and I'll leave the door unlocked. You won't, either one of you, have to see me at all. Scobie knows all about the studio; he's been there many times before."

Just to make sure that there would be complete privacy, with the smallest possible chance of embarrassment for anyone, I went out to have lunch and dropped into a movie the next afternoon; that is to say, I left my house around twelve-thirty and didn't get back until around nearly five.

As I walked down the block leading to my house, I saw *Rita* and Scobie coming toward me, on the opposite side of the street. They were walking arm in arm, and the both of them were so oblivious of their surroundings, they didn't even once give a glance in my direction, and they passed me by as if I were just a lamppost. The most important thing of all, I haven't told you, yet.

Rita was completely without spots—and she looked absolutely sensational.

What had happened? ! ?

Scobie told me all about it, later that evening. "That little Mrs. Goodwell is just a shrewd old finagler," he said. "You know, that cunning old woman never came near your studio at all. It was Rita who came—and *she* expected to meet *you*. When she saw *me* there instead, she suddenly started to cry and flung herself at me. So, what could I do? At any rate— we're planning to get married, on my birthday, next November. My family has met her, and they're absolutely overjoyed. So, if you still want to stand up in church with us—"

"I'll be delighted," I said. "I'm glad you've come to your senses. You not only have a lovely bride—you have a mother-in-law who ought to be in our State Department."

When they were off on their honeymoon, a long cruise in the Caribbean, as I recall it, Scobie sent me a picture post card from Port au Prince. He said:

The Gods of Olympus never had it so good. Last night, Rita won first prize at the ship's costume ball. She ate a couple

234

of tomatoes around lunch, and by the time dinner was served, the Leopard Queen was the big sensation of the captain's table. I can't write as often as I would like to—but—you can't blame me—I have nothing but spots before my eyes.

Love,
SCOBIE

CHAPTER FIFTEEN

I TELL YOU who won't show up, even if she has the time and the opportunity to do so, and that's Constance Delorme. The reason for this is that she never properly understood the stupendous sacrifice I once made for her, and the bitter agony it cost me, at the time.

It was in the latter part of 1946 that a friend of mine, Doris Grant, introduced me to Constance, and, I must say, I found her rather dull and unattractive from the very start. Nevertheless, since I was addicted to morphine during that period of my life, my critical tolerance was so elastic it permitted almost every form of human flotsam to accumulate around the moss-covered jetties of my indifference. I suppose I liked Doris just well enough to allow all of her nondescript henchmen and hangers-on to clutter up my already wretchedly hallucinal existence—and so I hardly noticed it when one more not particularly prepossessing face was added to our entourage.

Doris, although tagged as my official girl friend, was not actually living with me. Nobody was living with me, because I had no place to live in in the first place. I floated from one sleazy, roach-ridden hotel to another, carrying a hundred-watt bulb in my coat pocket, since none of the fleabags I infested ever supplied sufficient illumination for me to read by. The places I could afford generally had only a long wire descending from the ceiling with an exposed forty-watt bulb dangling at the end of it. I ate my meals mostly in self-service restaurants—or brought some raisin buns and chocolate milk to my room so I could eat at the behest of my own sweet whim, at any time during the day or night. I managed to read about two books, on an average, between sunset and dawn, and spent most of my waking time scurrying around for likely dope connections. It is a full-time job to find a sufficiency of drugs for an addict and, since I did very little lucrative work, I had the additional anxiety of having to borrow considerable sums of money from all possible and impossible sources to keep myself and my gluttonous addiction in a state of reasonable replenishment.

That was my general condition when I first met Constance.

She was a great big dragoon of a girl with nothing French about her excepting her accent, which was genuine enough. She was some sort of assistant designer in a dress house, and yet she was probably the most tastelessly attired woman I had ever seen in my whole life. Of course, she didn't exactly have a model's figure to start with, but it seemed to me that most of the clothes she wore only helped to accentuate her fat thighs, her flat bottom, her breastless chest, and her thick, squat neck.

A sort of mild horror, actually.

At any rate, Doris, for reasons I never fathomed, had added this lymphatic chickenbrain to our social circle, and, as a matter of fact, it had even been decided that we were to celebrate the coming New Year's Eve at Constance Delorme's apartment. Fortunately, I couldn't possibly have cared less.

I suppose I ought to give you a little more detailed information about my girl friend, Doris, before this grim legend proceeds any further, but, to tell you the absolute truth, it is not too clear in my mind, even now, how, or why, this strange creature ever got mixed up with me, or I with her.

However, I think I *can* supply some sort of small hint that might serve as a possible clue to this desperately arid relationship.

You see, when you take large doses of narcotics, you really haven't any particular need for women; you aren't actually impotent—it is simply that you have no special yen for them, one way or another. But a man like me, who had always been hanging around women, all through the years, went right on seeing them, and even courting them, mostly out of habit, I suppose.

Now then, for such purposes, Doris was the ideal subject. I don't recall whether I have told you this, but a great many American girls, from their earliest adolescence on, go in for such frantic bouts of shameless necking that a great number of them derive about all the sexual satisfaction they need—from the mere manipulation of their superficial erotic zones, alone. Such dolls, when they finally do get married, have almost no appetite, and, sometimes, even a real loathing, for any true orgiastic pay-off. Their poor, bewildered bedfellows are destined to be eternally frustrated in their attempts to find any sort of satisfactory communal climax in their relationships with these chronically manhandled monsters.

Well, that describes Doris, to the life.

She looked like a seething sexpot, of course—dark-haired, dark-eyed, wide-hipped, narrow-waisted, and, like most American girls, rather cleverly made up and adroitly accoutered. In my peculiar, almost neuter, condition, she proved an absolute blessing, and, since she always had fancied herself agitated by certain unnamable artistic aspirations, my general, highly peripatetic bohemianism served her purposes satisfactorily enough, too, I suppose. We were no burden to each other, really.

So, on New Year's Eve, the two of us, accompanied by a small retinue of schlemiels, of both genders, proceeded to troop up to Constance's apartment. We were actually accompanied by Felix Horstmann, Jon Wickoff, Toni Palette, Nanette Gilman, Sherman Dortmund, and Ethel Parker. I'm listing them in this strictly statistical fashion, without any further detailed identificational data, because there was really nothing sufficiently personal or characteristic about any of them to make them memorable to anybody, excepting, maybe, their mothers. I don't mean to imply that they were in any way repulsive or abnormal—quite the contrary. In fact, I had the feeling about this little group that if you'd left the lot of them at any of the millions of New Year's Eve parties that were scheduled for that night, all over New York City, nobody would have noticed that they hadn't been invited in the first place; that's how chummy and run-of-the-mill this job lot really was.

As we were heading up in Constance's general direction, toward Seventy-second Street, I was a little worried because I had only six morphine tablets left in my pocket, certainly not enough to last me until morning. However, I hopefully figured that I might, somehow, manage to escape our little festival long enough to get to a drugstore and cash one of the forged morphine prescriptions which I always carried about my person. "Who knows," I thought to myself, "in the boozily jubilant spirit that pervades such a night, I might even try to get *two* of them filled."

I forgot to mention that this party was also going to mark a significant change in Constance Delorme's life: it was expected—so Doris had told me—that our hostess was going to announce her engagement to Barney Pierce, an apprentice engineer of our acquaintance, who had been nuzzling her experimentally for the past couple of months.

What eventually happened that evening was really most interesting, when you consider that I couldn't possibly have been further removed from all these people, their concerns, and their activities—if I had been living on another planet.

At any rate, when we finally reached our destination—a typical West Side refugee trap—and before any one of us even had had a chance to knock or to ring the bell—Constance flung open the door and—with her face completely smeared with melted mascara—gave an insane, animal howl —and flung herself around Doris' neck.

"Kill me—! ! !" she screamed. "Please, kill me, some-body! ! ! I want to die—! ! ! I want to die—! ! ! I want to die! ! !"

You can imagine the mad consternation among the members of that thunderstruck barnyard. Eyes were plastered solidly up against fogged bifocals—an almost hysterical out-burst of meaningless gibberish and incoherent exclamations— a wild cacophony of conjectures—cluckings—rumblings and neighings broke out all around me and, for a couple of minutes, it was really more like a midnight fire at a circus than anything I'd ever heard before in all of my life.

At last, when the racket had reached its height, it sud-denly, quite unaccountably, broke into an almost religious recitative, as Constance, supported by at least fourteen hands, was nudged and kneaded back into her apartment again. Then it all came out in a rush: Barney Pierce had left town that morning, *in the company of another girl*—!

No engagement—no wedding—no party—no nothing.

You cannot possibly conceive the orgy of sympathetic squealings and barkings that those stultified, inarticulate people now proceeded to wallow in. Also, please consider that this aimless collection of jibbering idiots had, at one stroke, through God's infinite kindness, found half-a-dozen intense and burning foci for all of their wandering, pointless faculties.

They fetched water—they poured brandy—they lit candles—they turned on the radio—they turned off the radio—in short, they had a bigger ball than anybody in his wildest dreams could ever have anticipated. Since most of them had kept their coats on, they started to slosh perspiration around like crazy and, naturally, some demanded that the windows be opened; others were afraid that Constance, in her thin, cotton wrapper, would die of pneumonia; but, at this critical point, Doris—as the chief mourner—took complete command. First of all, she convoyed the stricken, leaking vessel off into the bedroom. When they were gone, the rest of us stood around like a coroner's jury waiting for the corpus delicti to be rolled in. Everybody had stopped talking—they just stared at the floor and shook their heads from time to time, like some cart horses bothered by a swarm of persistent gnats.

At last, after about ten minutes, Doris re-emerged from the bedroom. She was great. You could see she was fit to be in charge. She was the only one among us qualified to bear this soul-shattering burden. "Ethel," she said, turning to a girl who looked like a boiled asparagus with a dead rabbit around its neck; "Ethel—here are the keys to my house.

You all go over there, and I'll join you in a little while. I've got liquor enough to start with, and I'll pick up another few bottles on my way home."

Brilliant! Everybody instantly brightened up. Drama—liquor—dancing—and maybe sandwiches, later on. It looked like the best New Year's Eve party any one of them had ever had. Great!

They started to file out—leaving commiserative messages for the invisible victim—and the general feeling was that Constance was much too noble for this terrible earth, and certainly too valuable for any living man.

"I'll stay here with you," I said to Doris.

"You really needn't," she said. "I'll manage."

"We ought to persuade her to get dressed," I said, "and maybe she'll come over to your house in a little while. We certainly can't leave her here alone."

"You're right," said Doris. She gave me a quick kiss—but, still, a kiss with some real affection in it, for a change. You see, nothing will bring people closer together than the misfortunes of others. They can be real cozy then, for a couple of minutes, anyway.

Doris went back into the bedroom, and I turned on the radio and started to look through a magazine. It was a three-year-old copy of the *National Geographic*, devoted to the wonders of Genoa.

I'd visited Italy for the first time as a small child, with my mother, and I remembered everything about that journey as if it had all happened just the week before. I even remembered the taste of the sugar-coated, toasted almonds that I'd gotten out of a vending machine at the railroad station in Vienna. I have a fiendish memory for tastes and odors, and if I ever want to fall back into time, in an almost nostalgic swoon, I just have to recall how I used to pluck leaves from the old walnut tree in our garden, and crush them between

242

my childish palms, fifty-five years ago. The smell of those leaves comes back to me whenever I close my eyes and will it to be 1905, in the old Kingdom of Austria, when the world was a softly told fairy tale and I was the youngest of three princes. But the truth is, I was actually the youngest and the oldest and the one in between, too, because I was an only child who had an only child's special childhood. It was a lovely loneliness, most of the time, and I hardly ever had any sad feelings about it. I used to go, all by myself, to the big park called Schoenbrunn, and, with a book of Heine's *Harzreise* in my lap, I would sit under the ancient beech trees for hours upon hours, without talking—or needing to talk—to anyone. I used to invent long, elaborately intricate stories about the children who passed me by, accompanied by their governesses, and sometimes I would go to the zoo with a sketch pad and some water colors and make painstakingly detailed sketches of those fabulous creatures that had come into my life from so many distant lands. I found it difficult to communicate with most children, because I thought them rather silly. Also, I constantly had to play down to them, and pretend enthusiasm for their boringly circumscribed interests, and I found this pretty exhausting, after a while. I read everything I could lay my hands on, and the only books that made me absolutely ill were the ones especially written for young people.

When my mother and I returned from Italy, I longed to tell someone about the wonders I had seen on this magical voyage, but after a few failures to set up sympathetic contact with anyone of my own age group I finally gave it up. You see, these wonders carried hardly any dramatic significance at all—I was simply shattered by the color impacts which that thrice-blessed land had strewn before my astonished eyes, and I was just desperately eager to resavor all my travel impressions in the company of a perceptive listener.

It was then that I suffered my first intimations of the true state of man. I concluded, as a very young child, that he was doomed to loneliness in all truly essential matters—and the real pains and the real ecstasies of his life were incommunicably locked in his own heart, forever.

As I sat there in that unspeakably depressing apartment, ruminating on my fabulous past, my throat was constricted by an acrid spasm of sudden self-loathing. I was overwhelmed with shame and regret when I realized how wretchedly I had dealt with all my early treasures.

"I should have kissed her more," I thought. "I should have bowed down to the ground, in all directions of the compass; I should have bedewed the pale chrysanthemums upon her darkened robe with tears of gratitude."

I was thinking of no earthly woman—I was thinking of Destiny, that shadowy, unpredictable lady who had bestowed upon me such a plethora of riches at the very outset of my life. I had taken all these talents and sensibilities as nothing but my just due; I had given thanks to no one; I had taken blindly and spent freely, and not at all like a man who is destined to inevitable extinction. I had behaved as if I had been one of those immortals who may casually renew themselves by merely drinking at the secret fountains from which existence is derived. I had accepted and dissipated my opulent dowry without a single thankful glance in the direction of the fierce and fickle powers which had showered them upon me. Well, I had finally fallen into the bottomless pit where grim repentance had ample time to catch up with me, at its leisure.

I had lived in the United States for thirty-two years. During that period, I had been a painter, a writer, an editor, a playwright, and a lover, of sorts—and now I was addicted to drugs, alone, in this gruesome flat, with a catastrophically jilted girl—not to forget Doris, the Necker—and I was certainly celebrating the coming of the new year as if it marked the final incineration of all my earthly hopes.

At this point, my beloved emerged from the bedroom. She looked quite distraught, poor thing, and I could easily guess what was bothering her. It was already eleven-twenty, and she was terribly anxious to get back home before that herd of cattle had drunk up all of her booze and made a complete shambles of her apartment.

"Why don't you run along," I said to her. "It's all right—I'll stay here with Constance."

Doris looked undecided for a moment. "She doesn't want to leave here," she said. "I really don't know what to do with her."

"You can't do anything, right now," I said. "You go home—and after she's asleep I'll come over, too."

"You're sure you don't mind?"

"Not a bit of it," I said. "We'll have our little celebration by ourselves, later on."

You can plainly see that we were talking like a couple of people in a magazine. I knew perfectly well that my girl friend, before the night was over, would permit any man who happened to be around her, at the right moment, the most lurid and intimate anatomical researches on herself—and she knew, beyond the shadow of a doubt, that I loathed every one of her other friends just as much as I abhorred Constance, and that I certainly had no interest in having a little party with anybody—including herself.

"All right," she said. "You're a real darling to do this for me—but I'll make it up to you, later on."

Another kiss, one less tinted with rapture than the last one —because her mind was flying ahead of her, to the probably already vandalized apartment.

After she was gone, I poured myself out a little bourbon—

not because I cared a damn about liquor but, since midnight was rapidly approaching, I instinctively felt the need to lift some sort of celebrative glass, along with the millions of others who were sure to do so, all over the land, in just a few minutes. As I sat there staring at the liquid topaz in my glass, Constance suddenly appeared in the doorway.

"Would you like a drink?" I said.

"No, thank you," she said. "I've taken some sleeping pills, and I'll go to bed in just a little while."

"Would you like me to turn off the radio?" I asked.

"It's all right," she said. "I'm sorry I spoiled everybody's fun, but—"

"They're over at Doris's," I said, "and you just don't worry about anybody but yourself right now."

"It was very kind of you to remain here," she said. "I'll never forget it, as long as I live. I never realized what a really good and kind person you are."

"Nonsense!" I said. "I never cared much for parties in the first place—and I always prefer to stay home and read. I was reading the *Geographic*, here, just a while ago."

"Oh, yes," she said. "I know you're a great reader. I used to read in France. I never could get enough books into my hands—but now, between my work and my English classes, at night, I hardly ever have time even to look at a magazine."

Just then Guy Lombardo, or somebody a lot like him, blew a thunderous blast on the radio, and everybody in Times Square shouted, "Happy New Year! ! ! Happy New Year! ! ! ! Waah! ! ! Waah! ! ! Waah! ! !"

I lifted my glass, to a remarkably composed Constance, who came over to me and put her hot, wet hands on my face. "Happy New Year," she said—and gave me a kiss.

That's all she did—but I think Krafft-Ebing or Freud could have written several interesting volumes about that kiss of hers. You see, she was a deeply stirred woman, in whom all the basic aims and expectations of existence had been ruthlessly churned up, in the last couple of hours. She was actually at the mercy of all the dark, instinctive forces of life, and her poor, fluttery, frustrated ovaries were blindly searching for some sort of instant, critical catharsis. She didn't know, herself, what she was doing—but, before I realized it, she was holding me in a viselike grip and kissing me all over my face and neck with such a famished look in her swollen eyes that I really got just a little bit scared.

I was very nice to her, of course, and I even kept thinking about literary and historical parallels to this crazy situation. In *Richard the Third*, for instance, the king woos and wins a loving widow at the very bier of the man whose death he has caused. I thought of others, too—but, in the meantime, I had to cope, with some sort of reasonable tact, with the fleshy tentacles of the passionate will to maternity that was threatening to smother me in its fiendish embrace.

It wasn't easy. The big trick, as I perfectly well knew, was to keep standing up, and to use my hands no further down than her neck. Even so, she weighed at least a hundred and thirty pounds, and I had a hell of a time to keep her from dragging me onto a couch, or even an armchair, because once we were settled down anywhere—the rest was only too clearly unavoidable.

Fortunately, morphine does have a few very definite compensations. My mind remained as clinically detached as if I'd been dealing with a rampant lunatic in a psychopathic ward.

"Doris promised to come back here," I said. "She only went home to see that everybody had drinks, and to lay out some cold cuts for them. She's really very devoted to you, Constance, and, I expect, she'll probably spend the night here with you."

Ever so slowly, she finally released her wrestler's hold on me and tottered to the doorway of the bedroom.

247

"Phone her," she said, "and tell her I'm all right."

"Okay," I said, "but I'm sure, no matter what I tell her, she's not going to desert you tonight. That's the only reason she let me stay here at all—because she expected to relieve me as soon as she'd looked after things, at home."

"All right," she said. "I suppose you know what you want." She passed her hand across her face, turned around and walked into the bedroom. "You can go now!" she called back to me. "The door locks itself. Good night—and thanks!"

"Good night," I said. I turned off the radio—shut off the light—took my coat and hat out of the hall closet—and left.

It was after twelve o'clock—the drugstores were closed, and I wouldn't be able to get any morphine that night. There were a couple of all-night drugstores, but I was leery of them, since they were in the Times Square district where, on a night like this, you were sure to find hundreds of detectives milling about. I had taken my six pills shortly after our arrival at Constance's apartment, and now I was just going to have to sweat it out, somehow. "Happy New Year," I thought to myself.

Since I planned to spend that night in a foul little retreat on West Forty-fifth Street, I signaled a cab and told the driver to take me there. I had just eleven dollars to my name—and because I carried no luggage, I would, of course, have to pay my room rent in advance. As we were going along, I noticed that the hackie hadn't lowered the flag to his taximeter—figuring, quite rightly, that a New Year's Eve customer wasn't likely to call this to his attention, or put up any beef about it, later on. When we got to the hotel, he pretended to be furious with himself about this oversight, but I reassured him.

"Don't let it worry you," I said. "Let's not start in the New Year in a bad temper. Here's the buck fare—and forget all about it."

"Happy New Year," he said. "Imagine me woikin' on a night like dis, instead o' bein' home wid my family."

"Happy New Year to you," I said. "Better luck next year."

"Thanks," he said, and he pulled away.

When I got to the desk, in the hotel lobby, I took out my remaining money and discovered that I had accidentally given the chauffeur my ten-dollar bill, and all I had left was a single dollar.

I walked slowly out into the street again, and since my withdrawal symptoms had already begun I steered, at once, over in the direction of Grand Central Terminal. It was the only place I could think of where I might spend the night without running the chance of getting picked up. I also had forty-five cents in change left, and I planned to buy myself a cup of coffee and a newspaper, later on.

It started to drizzle when I hit Madison Avenue, and every once in a while some late celebrant would scream "Happy New Year" into my face as he passed me. Some of those cheerful wassail bibbers were being led around by castrated dogs who were already performing their first defacement of the city for the new year.

One of these mongrels, obviously very badly constipated, was hunched in an absolute agony of constriction at the edge of the gutter while his owner, wearing a clown's peaked cap, was blowing ten-second blasts out of a toy trumpet. The dog was wearing a paper ruff around his neck and sported a conical hat exactly like his boss's. I stared hypnotically at that desperately convulsed beast—when he—suddenly—dropped one tiny, stonelike turd onto the asphalt.

"He's made it!" screamed his master. "He's made it! Happy New Year, everybody—! Happy New Year, mister."

"A Happy New Year to you," I said. "It's starting off pretty good for you, already, ain't it?"

249

"Yeah," he said. "Sure is. I just hope it keeps up like that. I can certainly use a little luck, for a change!"

I expect Tom Ballard to be standing way up in front of the chapel, looking over the house with his shrewd cockney eyes—and wondering what sort of spiel the preacher was going to hand out. Spiels are Tom's specialty, and during the many years of our friendship I've sampled quite a few of his choicest ones. Tom, too, goes back to my early days south of Fourteenth Street, when the both of us lived in small, cold-water flats in Minetta Alley.

I *heard* him long before I ever laid eyes on him—because Tommy was learning to play the five-string banjo, and for many hours each day I heard him practicing "Old Black Joe," always only up to the sixth bar. Somehow, he never managed to get beyond that pitfall, and I think he had the whole captive audience in that house twitching with anxiety whenever that seemingly insurmountable instrumental hazard came along. I asked one of my neighbors, Charley Dean, about him, and he told me that the frustrated serenader was an Englishman—that his occupation was unknown—and that he always had a good-sized blaze going in his fireplace, no matter what the condition of the weather happened to be.

A little while later, Tom himself stopped me in the downstairs hall and ceremoniously presented himself to me. "My name is Tom, not *Thomas*, Ballard," he said. "I used to be a British object—and now—I am an American subject—at the service of mankind. I understand you inquired about me, Mr. King—and I couldn't be more flattered. At present I am studying to master one of the world's most difficult instruments—so difficult, indeed, that nary a single symphony orchestra, anywhere, has, so far, included any of its practitioners among its working personnel."

"Are you planning to join a symphony orchestra when you've finally mastered it?" I said.

"I do have general plans in that direction," he said, "but, for the present, I'm actually planning just to play along the public streets and, perhaps, in certain choice back yards—the ones where the acoustics are particularly favorable."

He was a card, that was sure, and he certainly looked just right for his role, too. He was about five foot three, sandy-haired, and deceptively plumpish. I say *deceptively* because I saw him strip to his skin once, and he proved as tough and as agile as an old-time wrestler at the height of his form. The liveliest parts of him were his pale-gray eyes, which were full of bubbling wit, and their restless sparkle effectively belied the deliberately torpid manner of his movements. He had only a fragment of a cockney accent left, after fifteen years in this country, and he told me, one day, how hard he had worked to rid himself of it.

"People had trouble understanding me," he said, "and since this is a world of instant communication, I couldn't afford to tune out. Could I?"

The stuff about the permanently blazing fireplace proved true enough, too.

"I had some years in my life," he said, "when I was completely denied the benefits of even a bit of warmth for human comfort. I never got over it. I sometimes get up in the middle of the night and put on another log, just for the joy of savoring the privilege of doing so. It's like an addiction, don't you see?"

Since I found him a most rewarding companion, we saw a good deal of one another, over the next few months, but no matter how seemingly familiar our communion, I still hadn't

251

the vaguest idea how he managed to make a living. One evening after I had brewed us some mulled wine (it was the middle of December, and his fireplace happened to serve a more useful purpose than merely to compensate him for past deprivations), Tom fell into an unusually reminiscent mood and told me a few things about his past, in the old country.

"It was after the First World War," he said. "There was massive unemployment, and thousands of men used to roam up and down the land, looking for work. Most of them still had their army overcoats on, but there were a lot of young ones among them, too—kids in their teens who couldn't get a job near their homes and had struck out and joined one of the passing gangs that marched through their towns. They were a desperately sad lot, *I* can tell you, since I was one among them. We'd generally hit the road shortly after sunup and start marching toward the next town, and somewhere about midway we'd meet another mob coming from the direction we were headed for—and, believe me, we never stopped to greet any of those men, or to ask them any questions, because we knew all the answers ourselves. There was no work anywhere—and we didn't expect to find any—but we wanted nothing to interfere with our marching. We'd marched for years in the bloody army—and I suppose we'd gotten used to it. Except, in the army, somebody had fed us, with some kind of regularity, and now the only thing we could look forward to was a meal of thin, tasteless soup, in the various county workhouses where they put us up for the night. We used to do a little wood chopping and cleaning around those workhouses, and early the next morning, after a cup of gray-green coffee, we'd be off and hit the road again. This went on, month after month, until I finally used to envy the dogs that barked at us in front of the farmhouses we passed. It was a time of black, black despair, I can tell you. And then, one evening when we hadn't managed to strike a town at all, we camped out on the highway. We'd managed to catch a skinny rabbit that afternoon, and now we were all sitting around a huge fire, waiting, with tin cans in our hands, for our share of the rabbit flavor. I'll tell you one thing about those marchers—they never sang any songs at all. Not ever. They just sat around that fire like a lot of unburied corpses, and hardly anyone ever said a word. While we were waiting for the cooking to get done, suddenly a pale, skinny youngster, who had joined us a couple of days before, lifted his eyes from the blaze and turned to an old paddy who'd tramped the roads of the country all of his life —long before any of us had started marching—and said, 'Ain't there any way out of all this? Do we just go on like this forever? Ain't there any way out at all?'

"The old paddy looked at him for a moment and said, 'There's three ways out of this, son. There's the hospital, there's the jail, and the best of all is the river.'

" 'It's a bloody lie!' the kid screamed. 'I tried to get the coppers to pinch me last week—I went into the police station and showed them some stuff I'd stolen off a barrow, and the damned coppers just laughed at me and whacked me across the behind. It's a lie about the coppers!'

" 'I told you,' said the paddy, 'the river is the best. It puts an end to all of your problems.'

"I tell you, Alex, I sat there in that darkness, and I became afraid as I've never been afraid before in all of my life. I'd spent some pretty scary nights since I've been fourteen years old, but that old tramp over the fire frightened my great appetite right out of me. I got up and, holding on tight to the cigar box that contained my personal effects, I marched straight off into the darkness. You know what else I did? I opened my luggage and took out my razor—it was a straight, old-fashioned razor—and threw it way the hell off into the bushes. You see, I had always shaved every day—because I thought it might help with a job; also, it was definitely a morale factor. But, hearing that tramp talking about the three ways out—I was suddenly afraid to be alone with that razor. I'm sure it is hard, for people who have never felt it, to understand what real despair is really like. You suddenly begin to think of death as a kind of a friend. Well, I marched all through that night and, being off by myself, alone, I must have strayed off the road, because when the sun came up—I suddenly saw the sea. I looked over the heath, and there it was. And then I *really* got scared. I'd always heard that England was an island, but it hadn't mattered to me much, one way or another—but when I actually saw it, with my own eyes, I nearly passed out. It was an island, all right. There was water all around me, and I was trapped like a bloody rat. I turned my back on that water and marched straight away from it. When the sun was a little higher, I passed a shepherd, a Scotsman, who was having a bit of some bread—and when he looked at me, he offered me half of it—without saying a word. You can just imagine what he must have seen in my eyes.

"I was dizzy with fatigue and hunger when I came to the outskirts of a town, where a couple of young men were doing a little cricket practice. When I came closer, they asked me if I would mind doing a bit of bowling for them. That's like pitching a ball for a batter. Well, I did it. I bowled for those two youngsters until the whole landscape was spinning around me like a drunken carrousel. And then a young woman came off a nearby porch and she brought down a trayful of small tea sandwiches. They offered me some, too, of course, but when I looked at that tray I realized that if ever I stretched out my hand toward it, I'd have to take all those sandwiches—every last one of them—and shove them all into my mouth at the same time, even if I choked on them, or had to throw them up all over the lot of them. It was a terrible crisis of mortal temptation. I did take a gulp of the tea the young lady had handed me—then I made a quick getaway. When I felt I was out of their sight, I even started to run—and that run led to the best thing that had happened to me in many months. You see—I'd all night long been walking toward London, and when I ran along that road, a lorry stopped and gave me a lift. The driver, who must have guessed my condition, gave me half a meat sandwich, and when he let me off, where he was making his delivery, I was in the very heart of the town—the business section, you understand—and I felt like a dirty blot on the landscape. I walked just right near the edge of the gutter, so I'd be out of the way of people who were properly dressed and had an aim and a meaning in life. I hardly dared raise my eyes from the ground, when suddenly somebody grabs me by the arm and shouts, 'Tom Ballard—as I live and hope to have twins—! Tom Ballard, you old reprobate, what are *you* doing here?'

"I looked up, and there stood a man who'd tramped the road alongside of me, the winter before. His name was Dick Ransom, and I certainly hadn't expected ever to see him again. 'I just landed here on a lorry,' I told him. 'You seem pretty spry,' I said. 'Looks like London agrees with you.'

" 'It does,' said Dick. 'I'm making a good living as a retail merchandiser. See?'

"And then I first noticed that he had a shallow box strapped across his front, with some cutout paper dolls in it.

" 'I'm selling monkeys on a stick,' he said. 'I clear ten, twelve shillings a day at it, and I'm even thinking of getting married. I'm good at it, Tom, and I'm through marching the roads forever. Look here, boy, I'll buy you a bite to eat —you look like you could use it—and then I'll introduce you to Ma Hertwig, who'll fix you up with some merchandise, and you'll go into business, too.'

" 'Oh, Dick,' I said, 'I'm a dummy from dummyland—and

you know it. I couldn't give away freshly minted government money—I'm such a dull-mouthed clod.'

" 'Nonsense!' says Dick. 'You don't know what you've never tried. Of course, monkeys on a stick might be too great a test for your powers, right off—but I'll get you a tray of matches—that's the stuff for a beginner. I began that way myself.'

"Well, what can I tell you, Alex? That fine lad fed me a good dinner, and after he took me to Ma Hertwig's, and she strapped a tray filled with matchboxes across my chest, and the two of us went back toward Piccadilly Circus. I can't tell you what a great, big helpless lummox I felt like—beside that lively Dick, who kept jabbering encouragement at me, all the time we were walking. To tell you the truth, it was the bright daylight that really got me down. I wouldn't have minded starting in the dark—but the clear light, in which people could look at me and plainly see me, was what gave me the scairdy bejabers.

" 'Listen, Dick,' I said, 'I'll go just around the corner—it's no sense in my standing here trying to get customers alongside of you—right?'

" 'Nonsense,' says Dick. 'Competition is the greatest thing for business. We'll stimulate each other. It's the great secret of all commerce—as you'll discover in a twinkling. Now then, post yourself right here, and I'll be standing twenty feet further on, in front of the bank.'

"How can I ever describe to you the condition I was in at that moment? I stood on that crowded corner, that damned tray around my neck—knowing that Dick's eyes were on me every moment that passed. I started to sweat so hard, the water ran into my eyes, and, having no handkerchief, I had to wipe myself with my coat sleeves. I was on the verge of starting to bust out crying, when I suddenly found myself jabbering something. I was muttering just like a ventriloquist, barely moving my mouth. I was in such despair that I didn't really care what I was doing, or what came of it all. But my voice, on its own volition, must have become louder, because a young man stopped in front of me—threw some coins on my tray and took a box of matches. I wanted to run after that lad and embrace him; instead, I looked toward Dick, and there was such a smile of friendly joy and encouragement on his face, I gave him a knowing wink, and even tipped my greasy hat to him. And then—I was off. I mean, I was really off. How shall I explain it to you—? I suppose you realize that there may be a potential ski jumper living in Ceylon who will never be able to demonstrate his skill because he happens to live in the intense tropics. There might, for all we know, be a champion tennis player forever lost among the Eskimos, for sheer lack of physical opportunity. Well, that just about describes me. You see, Alex, I'd really always had it in me—I just never suspected it until that blessed afternoon in Piccadilly Circus. I was a born retail merchandiser—one of the best in the country—but if my golden opportunity hadn't come along—both I—and the world—would certainly have been the poorer for it. By sundown my tray was nearly bare of matches. I ran after people and shouted: 'Here are a thousand marvels of combustion, yours for only a penny —here are fresh matches to light the fragrant cigarette—the good cigar—the cheerful hearth—ladies and gentlemen—for only a penny. Bring home these remarkable scientific marvels this evening, and see the triumphant smile on the face of your beloved child as he blows out the flame after you have, at one masterful stroke, ignited the oven that bakes your succulent apples. Ladies and gentlemen, all these two hundred master-pieces of combustion cost only one penny! ! !'

"I had to go three times that evening to refill my tray, and when I was finally through, I had earned two shillings and sixpence, clear. I was in business for myself, and I had dis-

257

covered my vocation. I stood silently in the dark and put my thumb to my nose and twiddled my fingers into all directions of the United Kingdom. You see—the paddy on the high road had been quite wrong. I had found the *fourth* way out."

"It is a wonderful story," I said. "And did you go on selling matches from then on?"

"I sold monkeys on a stick before the week was out," said Tom. "I branched out, and I plunged into every form of portable merchandising. In less than two years, I bought a lorry—a truck, I mean—and fixed up the interior as living quarters for myself. I had a dart board, and prizes, and toured all the market fairs, all over England. When I came to the United States—I simply had to come, because business in the old country is really much too limited—when I arrived here, I bought another truck, much bigger and infinitely better equipped, and that dear vessel, named Esmeralda, is anchored for the winter up near Van Cortlandt Park. The minute the first robin gives his first inaugural chirp, I shall take you up there and show the darling to you."

"You go away for the summer, is that it?"

"I see the land," he said, "and I enrich the communities I pass through. I leave patented tape measures, guaranteed silver polish, toys and knickknacks for the children—and a large assortment of advice and help for all sorts of household emergencies. For certain special communities I have even stocked some forms of literature: dream books—books on numerology—and books on letter writing and everyday etiquette. There is a dart board, too, of course. In the winter I study the banjo—with the hope of enlarging my general usefulness some day."

"You have a beautifully complete life," I said. "I'm sure many people would envy you, if they knew how well you were managing."

"Ah, they might, at that," he said. "It wasn't always popcorn and jelly beans for me, though—not by a damned sight."

"The unemployment was pretty terrible, all over the world," I said.

"I had a tough time of it, even as a kid," he said. "I left home when I was fourteen, and there were plenty of thumps, and a very few laughs, until I was a grown man, on my own."

Another time he told me about his childhood, too. "My father worked in a wretched draper's shop," he said. "The sheriff was always at the door, and we had boiled potatoes too often to mark the days apart. I was an only child, so my folks let all their frustration and spleen out on me. Then my father got sick, and he took it into his head that my mother was in love with the postman. No amount of weeping, of breast-beating, or of just good common sense could cure him of his mania. He would have died sooner, but he clung to life with absolute desperation, because he wanted to spoil my mother's fun. He finally died one night, and when we came to his room in the morning, his hands were clenched so tight about the bedposts, they had to cut the posts and bury them with him."

"What happened after that?" I asked.

"My mother married the postman," he said. "I don't think she had ever really cared a damn about him, until my father started to harp on it, and turned her mind in his direction. That's when I left home. I couldn't stand that my father had been so right about her. I felt the whole world was just a basket full of vipers. It took me ten years to get over that, and by that time I was twenty-four and ready for either death or transfiguration."

"Well, you made it," I said.

"I did," he said. "Thanks mostly to my natural gifts—and to despair—of course. Let's never forget, or overlook, the

strong propulsive powers of despair! It doesn't always have
to lead to matrimony, you know—it sometimes leads straight
to glory, and sometimes even to a quiet heart."

Thinking about Tom's childhood reminded me of my own,
here in New York. I certainly had some weird experiences as
a job-seeking teen-ager. I remember, in the summer of 1915,
I answered an advertisement for a switchboard operator in a
law office down on Nassau Street. I hadn't the vaguest idea
of how a switchboard functions, but the whole idea of working down among the skyscrapers, in the heart of the financial
district, simply fascinated me. To tell you the truth, I was
scared green by all that heartless, self-sufficient architecture
down there, and the sight of it had haunted me for all of the
sixteen months I had been in the United States. You see, the
ship that brought me into New York harbor had docked
right in that general neighborhood, and I'd never gotten over
the cold austerity of that first—overwhelming—visual shock.

When I arrived at this law office on Nassau Street, there
were about half-a-dozen applicants already ahead of me, and
three more arrived after I got there. I don't know what
qualifications all these other boys might have had; suffice it to
say that, after the whole gang of us had been interviewed,
I was the one that they picked to serve as a switchboard
operator for the joint. When I say *they*, I just mean a young,
blondish, rather good-looking secretary, who was completely
bamboozled by my youthful eagerness and loquacity. At any
rate, after she'd made this highly fateful decision, I very
honorably copped out to her and confessed that I didn't know
a damned thing about switchboards. She was quite a bit
taken aback, of course, but since she was only a few years
older than myself, I suppose she was still pretty warmhearted
and heedless, on her own account, and so she offered to

come in earlier the following day to teach me at least the rudiments of my new job.

When I got to the office at seven-thirty the next morning, Gladys Tobin (that was this angel's name) was already there, waiting for me.

Now, then—I don't believe there is anything in this whole world more difficult than the running of a switchboard. I want you to know that ever since that morning in that law office I have been consistently polite and thoughtful to all switchboard operators—and I only marvel how these callously underpaid, hard-pressed people don't flip their lids more often than they do. I am a reasonably intelligent man, and I'm really not too clumsy about mechanical contrivances —nevertheless, after about an hour and a half in front of that blasted apparatus, I was ready for the wringer. Gladys did her damnedest for me, too, and she even rigged up a sort of little graph for me—which she pasted up against the board panel so I could instantly check every one of my connections for accuracy. Of course, I forgot to mention to you the most important thing of all: there were sixteen lawyers—distributed in various cubicles around that floor—and a great many of their names happened to sound a good deal alike, too. For instance, there was a Steinman and a Steinberg, a Weingarten and a Baumgarten, a Pressburger and a Weissberger—and all the rest were Levi, Cohen, Vogelman, Schlossberg, Greenbaum, Hammerstein, Teitelbaum, Rosenfeld, Wechsler, and Robichek.

Before Gladys finally left me to go about her own duties, she also informed me that I was in charge of all the stamps and the petty cash around the place.

"Here in this little box," she said, "are stamps of all denominations, and if anybody wants any, they have to pay you for them. There's three dollars' worth of change in here, and that ought to last you for a while. Tomorrow morning you can drop into the bank downstairs and get yourself enough change for the day. If anybody owes you any money, write down in this notebook all these transactions—and here is an *Argosy* magazine that you can read when you're not busy. And now, good luck and chin up!"

I daresay there have been some writers in the glorious past history of literature who might have been able to justly render the events of that day in my life—all I can tell you is that no one contemporary with myself could possibly have done it. It was too big a subject. It covered too much ground and involved far too many people. In other words, I won't be able to give you a real account of everything that happened, either, but I'll try to indicate to you some of the most salient points, anyway.

First of all, the moment six people at the same time started to ring for attention, I just plugged in any of those crazy sausages wherever I thought they might do the most good, and to hell with the system. Now that I come to think of it, I was probably the first Zen Buddhist switchboard operator in the Western world. I was guided almost completely by intuition. After a while, I hardly lifted my eyes from the *Argosy* magazine—I just plugged in and pulled out like an expert communications man caught in a frenzy of creativeness. I felt like Stokowski conducting the "Ballet Mechanique."

It was wild.

Of course, there were certain sobering distractions. A couple of men with black mustaches, who looked sufficiently alike to be identical twins, suddenly rushed into my cubicle —and one of them just shoved me off my chair, right on to the floor, while the other one made some lightning readjustments in the connection patterns on the board. Before they both left, they glared balefully down on me, and I think one of them, the one nearer to me, even lifted his foot in my

262

direction, as if he had it in his foul mind to give me a good kick. There were other adventures, too, but they were really minor, until court recess time came around and sixteen infuriated lawyers landed on top of me, demanding my blood. It seems I had, in my morning's mild endeavors, managed to connect certain people who hadn't spoken a word to each other in thirty years. I had plugged the district attorney for New York County in with the janitor of our building, and one of my major efforts had been to give the senior senator of our state a chance to have a few words with the manager of a beauty parlor, who had called to verify a hair-setting date with one of the girls in our office.

Well, those sixteen furiously frustrated legal minds stood around me looking like a Jewish college of cardinals that has suddenly discovered a ham bone in the matzoball soup. For once, they were absolutely stumped. Not by my performance—but—by my attitude. I was all blandness and good nature, and I even recommended one of the stories to them, out of that magazine I had been reading. They finally retired to hold a caucus, and in the end I was informed, by Gladys, that they were prepared to let me finish out the week, provided I concentrated exclusively on the stamps and the petty cash—and kept my paws strictly off that switchboard.

All I can tell you is that I became friends with everybody in that office during the next few days, and a couple of those hard-boiled characters even invited me to their homes to meet their children. When I finally left, on Friday, they gave me a box of chocolates and issued me a reference which proved so potent that, on the strength of that document, I became traffic and communications assistant for the U.A.C.N.Y., which was the United Aluminum Company of New York. I lasted there for the rest of the summer, because I was too big a figure to do anything myself. I never went near a typewriter, a stamp or a switchboard—I simply supervised the menials who were involved with these trivial things—and when I left in September, to go back to school, everybody was heartbroken to see me go. They gave me a fulsome reference, too, and you can see what an inept manipulator I really am when you consider that, with all my powerful credentials, I could easily have become Postmaster General of the United States, or eventually even head of the Federal Communications Commission.

I never fully realized my great potentials. If you want to know, *that* has been the true bane of my whole life.

Gladys, by the way, wrote to me right after my first book was published, and when I phoned her over in Jersey, where she now lives with her lawyer husband and her two grown-up sons, she burst into tumultuous tears the moment she heard my voice.

"I knew it was you," she said, "the minute I got to the part where you'd painted Chinese murals in a kosher Jewish restaurant. I said to my husband, 'Warren,' I said, 'that's the same boy who was our switchboard operator. He became a legend in our office, and we never had anyone at that board after him that caused so much comment.' "

As you can see—she is still the same dear girl she had always been. I certainly like to think she will manage to show up at the funeral parlor—because she would be one of the very few people there who could truthfully say she knew me—when—!

CHAPTER SIXTEEN

I THINK it is quite likely that a few representatives of the underworld will quietly come by to condole with my widow, too. I expect that among them will be a fair representation of drug addicts, of pickpockets, a couple or so of strong-arm men, and, inevitably, a decorative, but very decorous, bevy of assorted prostitutes.

I've never in my life had any sexual dealings with prostitutes, and this not because of any moral grounds—but on exclusively aesthetic ones. I don't much care for cafeteria food, either. I mean, I have always found that love, or asparagus, has to be freshly cooked to have really any sort of flavor at all, and Cupid waiting for a customer while hovering over a steam table just wasn't *my* idea of a rich and savory existence. But I've been great friends with whores ever since I was a teen-ager, and I can tell you one thing about them—I've hardly ever found one among them that was really completely dull. In fact, some years ago, after I came out of Lexington for the first time, I concocted a little truism for myself—namely: There are no smart crooks and there aren't any really stupid prostitutes. I don't know what it is about their undeniably sordid lives, but, somehow, it seems to sharpen not only their wits but, strangely enough, also their general awareness. I've had some great gab fests with streetwalkers, in my time, and I can tell you they're a lot more fun to be with than any group of debutantes *I* ever met—or any group of girls at a fashionable prom, for that matter.

I came to know my first prostitutes when I was about fifteen or sixteen years old. It happened through a neighbor of mine, a Negro doctor whose name was James Wales, who specialized in treating venereal diseases. During those years, before any penicillin was sloshed around so freely, getting cured of a dose of clap was a major calamity and costly as all hell. This Dr. Wales had hired me to illustrate a booklet for him which concerned itself with the advanced degenerative phases in the realm of the social diseases. Although my designs were only going to be reproduced in black and white, I was so fascinated by the color possibilities of this lurid subject that I made most of my pictures in full color.

Of course, we became great friends after that. Although the good doctor's clients were mostly whores, he often assured me that venereal diseases, according to his certain convictions, were actually far more rampant among the so-called respectable classes.

"Don't you see," he said, "a prostitute has to keep herself clean or she'll soon be out of business. Also, she knows a good deal about most of the superficial manifestations of gonorrhea and syphilis, and so she can much more easily tell if one of her clients happens to be infected. The great spreaders of these sicknesses are the *Charity Broads*, the ones that sleep with you for nothing. The nymphomaniacs and the heavy social neckers that get carried away at parties or in the rumble seats of automobiles—*they* are the really dangerous and persistent carriers of infection in our society. They give the disease to their boy friends, and these fellows eventually pass it on to a sometimes careless or overtired prostitute. I've been in this business thirty years and, I assure you, I'm convinced that most of these venereal diseases are carried by members of reputable society. What's more, when they get it, they are much more likely to keep it—and to pass it on, too—since they are frequently too ashamed to seek out a doctor. A whore, on the other hand, goes straight to a medical man the minute the first symptom appears. And that's just common sense, too, since *she* can't afford to get a bad name in the business. A rep like that simply ruins her."

This Dr. Wales was a thin, very wrinkled, extremely dark man of unbelievable gentleness and remarkable integrity. Most of his clients absolutely adored him, and it was on his home grounds—that is to say, in his waiting room—that I first met some of the most lively, and yet easily confiding, ladies of my life.

I recall that once a pretty, young prostitute, who was a little hard up for cash, asked him to take out his fee in trade—and I shall always remember the sweet, unsurprised look on the doctor's face as he cocked his head to one side and said, "I'd like very much to oblige you about this little thing, Kitty, but, you see, the trouble is I can't pay the landlord that way."

It is due to my acquaintance with this dear man that I was once saved from a pretty grim involvement with a woman that might not only have damaged my bodily safety but could very easily have marked, and even ruined, my psychic equilibrium as well.

I had come to know the widow of an elderly banker of

some sort, and, although she was years older than I, she seemed not at all disinclined to grant me her ultimate favors. This lady and I had been tampering with each other for three or four weeks, and she finally invited me up to her apartment one evening, and, since she was quite a heavy drinker, she now proceeded to get herself very effectively liquored up. The rest was like program music, of course—literal and preordained—and it was only a question of a little time before she would allow me to make free of her loins.

And then I suddenly remembered Dr. Wales and his many warnings to me about *Charity Broads*.

This woman's name, by the way, was Reina Payton. She was tall and attractive and wore her hair combed up very high on her head, while almost the whole of her large forehead was hidden by thick bangs.

Well, I suddenly had an insane desire for Reina to brush back her bangs and to show me her forehead. I told her so.

"Please," I said. "I'd love to kiss you on the brow."

Now, an extremely strange thing happened. Although Reina was certainly plastered when I'd started talking to her, she was quite sobered up by the time I'd finished that very short sentence of mine.

The rest is so gruesomely nightmarish that I must tell you about it, very quickly.

She stonily refused to consent to my request. When I approached her and tried to force her into it—she suddenly picked a fruit knife off the table, and I could see that she was prepared to slash me with it, if I persisted any further.

Nevertheless, I persisted.

Some urgent frenzy in my heart prompted me to proceed beyond the point of reason—beyond the point of caution, even—and when—after a fierce struggle that toppled dishes and furniture all around us—I finally managed to push back her bangs—I saw one of my most beautiful syphilis illustrations, pulsating in revolting reality, all across her frightfully ravaged forehead.

You can't learn too *soon*—and you can't remember too *well;* that's what *I* always say.

There is a common belief among people that prostitution is the oldest profession. I don't go along with this. I think midwifery is the oldest—though I will agree that prostitution came right after that. The reasons why it originated at all are too manifold for elucidation here—but why, as the years roll along, it still persists, is certainly of considerable interest to me.

Unfortunately, for too many people, the sexual act only becomes poignant if it contains the element of novelty. Also, most men are really not terribly interested in the build-up that every halfway normal woman, and every normal cat, requires before she finally surrenders herself to her partner. In fact, what makes prostitutes so attractive, to most cafeteria-style lovers, is, precisely, their easy accessibility. Also, of course, there are a lot of people among us who are married to women who receive no joy whatever out of the sexual act, and these disfranchised men, naturally, gravitate into the arms of the professionals. There is another point to be considered: even so-called happily married men suffer a sudden upsurge of libido the moment they leave their home territories and are off to New York, or to New Orleans, on some conglomerate business trip, in company with half-a-dozen of their fellow satyrs. Such groups of frolicking Babbitts will, of course, hurl themselves blindly into any available brothel, if merely to avenge themselves for the bitter years they have already spent in sober, solvent boredom with their legally accredited paramours.

And then there are the completely unattached men, the ones who, for one reason or another, never really made it, on a legitimate level, with any dame that was free to choose her own company. There are a good many sadists among these lonely ones, too, who like to savor their power over the unfortunate girls who are compelled to take their money—and, believe me, I've heard a few pretty hair-raising stories about some of their revolting doings.

I've also always been interested in the relationship that prostitutes have toward the panders who leech on them. You see, I've known quite a few pimps in my life, too, since the hospital in Lexington is always full of them. I believe that *they* are the truly pathetic ones in the whole unfortunate pattern of this sordid subculture. I soon discovered that the pimp is not really a man at all—he is a sort of infantile fetish, to whom the prostitute makes constant maternal sacrifices. She buys him clothes and jewelry out of her hard-won earnings and, later, she boasts to her outcast sisters about the enormous expenses that these purchases involved. She stands in shiny-eyed admiration as he passes by her, on the street, and she says to another whore who happens to be along, "Just look at the way that English-draped suit sits on him. Every stitch on that coat is handmade—and it set me back one hundred and sixty-five dollars. Next week I'm gonna get him a Borsalino hat—a black one, with a wide band around it—and—when the other boys see him—they'll just bust their guts with envy."

In short, he is the baby she never had, the baby she can dress and sacrifice for—the child that is incapable of gratitude because he is still too undeveloped to know any better. I can tell you, from personal experience, that criminals are a sad lot—all of them. But the lowest louts among the thieves and professional tough guys I have ever encountered were, nevertheless, endowed with some small, recognizable human attributes, which I found totally lacking only among pimps.

I'm also happy to report to you that I have it from absolutely unimpeachable sources that the Fascist movement in

Italy and the Nazi movement in Germany were largely recruited from—and consistently sustained by—thousands of foot-loose, professional panders.

It figures—doesn't it?

Speaking about the lack of intelligence among criminals, I would like to make just one exception, and that concerns a man who broke his way into my life sometime in 1931. I was living and working in a pretty large apartment over on West Twenty-first Street in New York, and since I was also getting out a strictly homemade and highly personal magazine called *Americana* at the time, a good many strange and seemingly unrelated people used to drift in and out of our flat at various odd hours of the day.

One afternoon, in the early spring, two men suddenly showed up who were neither clients nor contributors of mine; they had simply come around to make some repairs in my wood-burning fireplace. At least, so they said.

Now then, I never in my life heard of a fireplace that couldn't stand a little repairing, so, although I hadn't ordered anybody to come around and look after ours, I saw no reason for not letting them proceed about their business just the same.

First of all, let me describe these two men to you. One of them was dressed like an insurance broker trying to impress a particularly influential client. He had on a black overcoat, a cast-iron-looking Homburg, a white muffler, and gray-suede gloves. He was a man about forty or forty-five years old and had a good shock of grayish hair standing away from his temples. The other chap couldn't have been more than sixteen or seventeen at the most, and he was dressed in some kind of a castoff soldier's outfit—a soldier of the First World War—with braced puttees and all that sort of nonsense. On top of his thick, blondish curls he had on a hat made out of a rolled-up paper bag, and in his hand he carried an enormous, hooked crowbar. Neither one of these two idiots looked like any kind of a workman to me, but, of course, nowadays it isn't really so easy to tell.

At this point, the older one of them, without taking off any of his fancy haberdashery, not even his hat, got possession of the crowbar and, very purposefully, proceeded to poke it up into the chimney. He puttered around with it for a moment or two, and finally he gave an enormous yank with that heavy hunk of steel—and—a second later—about half a ton of bricks and dirt fell straight down into my living room.

Although I was taken by complete surprise, I picked up a large, metal ruler from my desk and started to brandish it quite threateningly around his silly head. As a matter of fact, I had a lot of trouble keeping him in focus, since such dense clouds of soot and dust were swirling all around us that I had to keep my free hand almost constantly before my eyes to ward off potential blindness.

"You lunatic!!!" I screamed at him. "What in hell is the matter with you, anyway?!? Have you completely lost your mind?!? You get this place cleaned up instantly or I'll brain the both of you—you hear?!?"

I can only tell you that nobody in that room, excepting only myself, of course, seemed in the least bit upset by what had happened. The vandal with the crowbar was covered with crap from head to foot, and when he bent a little forward, to look at his ruined shoes, a great load of dirt fell from his hat into his pants cuffs. The other one suddenly looked like Al Jolson in blackface, and his cute blond locks had turned to a dark, ashen gray.

"You have nothing to worry about," said the insurance broker in a calm voice. "When we leave here, the place will be as spotless as when we arrived."

"Why in hell didn't you spread some newspapers around or

272

something?!?" I shouted. "This soot will never come out of this carpet unless I have it dry-cleaned. What in the devil's name is wrong with you guys, anyway?!?"

"Leave it all to us," the older one continued. "It is all old stuff to us. You will have nothing to complain of, I assure you."

"Jack," said the other one, "should I go down to the truck and bring up the sheet metal?"

"Fine," said his partner. "Bring up a couple of good-sized hammers, too."

I was so furious I really didn't know what to say, so I went out into the hall to look for my landlord, just to find out whether it was *he* who had ordered these two madmen to come and wreck my apartment. When I stepped out of my place, I ran into Ben Finkel, a dear neighbor, who lived in the flat right on top of mine, and so I quickly told him what had just happened to me.

"I think there's another man with them," Benny said. "He's standing right in front of my door upstairs, and I believe he's praying."

"Praying?!?" I said.

"Well, if he isn't, he *should* be, because when I just came out of the door, he was standing in the far corner of the corridor, and he had a long string of rosary beads in his hands."

Benny and I stared at each other for a moment, and then I turned away and walked halfway up to the next floor to investigate. Sure enough, there was a really old geezer standing under the skylight in the hall, and he had a string of rosary beads hanging from between his folded hands.

And then the crazy humor of this whole situation finally got home to us, and we both started to laugh. "Come on," said Ben, "let's go up to my place and have ourselves a couple of cups of tea." And that's what we did.

After a while, we got to talking about a lot of other stuff, and, what with one thing and another, nearly two hours must have passed before I got back into my living room again.

Well, I had to confess they had performed very remarkably with the job of cleaning up. Naturally, there were still some traces of soot around, but, by and large, the worst of the damage had been obliterated. I couldn't quite imagine what good they had done my fireplace, but, at that point, I was so grateful that they were gone, I didn't even bother to investigate what improvement, if any, had actually been achieved.

Later that day, I met my landlord, Mr. Firenzi, and I talked to him about my strange visitors. My landlord was a mural painter, by profession, and I really don't think he was any too well equipped for running a building with eight tenants, and, when he'd heard me out, he seemed a good deal more puzzled than usual.

"I have not ordered anyone to do any fixing of fireplaces," he said. "Every good fireplace blows back a little smoke— that's only natural. That's what makes such a nice odor that you can't get when you use steam. That smoke is a test of sincerity, and I think there is nothing whatever wrong with the fireplaces in this building."

"So, who could those people possibly have been?" I said. "They wrecked my house—they covered everything with dirt—and, although they did their best to clean up the mess they'd made, it will take us weeks to get rid of the last traces of their shenanigans."

"I cannot imagine who sent for them," said Mr. Firenzi, "and I'm sure there has been some misunderstanding."

And that's the way it stood, until I talked to Benny again, the day after, and he very urgently advised me to notify the police. I never liked having anything to do with cops, but, since I had two small children running around the house—and heaven only knew what those lunatics had actually been about

—I overcame my instinctive reluctance and called up the nearest precinct station for some help.

The detective who eventually came around to see me turned out to be a wonderfully agreeable man, a Mr. Frank Gavin, an elderly Irishman with a fine sense of humor and an inbred feeling for old-fashioned social decorum.

"It doesn't make much sense, does it?" he finally said. "Did you say there was another one of them—one that never came into the apartment at all?"

"There was," I said. "He was a really old hunk of tallow, with feathery wisps of hair, and a funny hat, like a sawed-off stovepipe, the kind Winston Churchill sometimes wears."

"Anything else?"

"Yes—I think he was saying his rosary, out in the upstairs hall—while his partners were ruining my apartment."

"Rosaries?!?"

"Well, he had a string of them between the palms of his hands, and he seemed to be praying."

The detective raised his eyebrows way up on his forehead and gave a mirthless laugh. "I'm afraid you got mixed up with a pretty smooth customer, if it turns out to be the one I have in mind," he said.

"You mean you think you know this man?"

"The description fits. It sounds to me, Mr. King, like your visitor was somebody called Praying Parker. One of the slickest confidence men in the business. The only thing that doesn't fit is the house-wrecking part; he generally operates without any crowbars."

"You mean Praying Parker, the one who never came into my living room at all, was the leader?" I said.

"That's right," he said. "Seems to me he was looking for something inside your chimney. Let's find out who lived in this apartment before you did."

"All right," I said. "Let's go ask my landlord about it."

But this line of investigation came to nothing. The previous tenant had been a painfully impecunious sculptor who had been so desperately in need of daily funds, it was not very likely that he had hidden any particularly significant swag behind the bricks of his fireplace. Upon closer investigation, it turned out that my mysterious visitors had indeed left a great hole, halfway up the flue; but this cavity gave every indication of being only a recent, and seemingly pointless, piece of vandalism—and that it had never before been used as a hiding place for any secret treasures, either.

It surely was a great stumper for the rest of that afternoon; but, later that evening, Detective Gavin returned to my apartment, and he looked very much as if he'd finally found the proper answer to the entire senseless conundrum.

"I'm not ready to tell you all about it yet," he said to me, "but I think it's all starting to fall into place. Tell me, Mr. King, do you generally go away for weekends?"

"Yes," I said. "We always leave Friday afternoon and come back Monday morning."

"Excellent!" he said. "Now, then, would you mind if I stayed in your apartment part of that time—because I think somebody has been studying your habits pretty closely, and it might be they're counting on you to be absent again the day after tomorrow."

"That'll be fine," I said. "And you couldn't tell me any more about it now, could you?"

"Not at the moment," he said. "In fact, I'm urging you very strongly not to mention any of this to your children—I mean —about my staying here—and so on. Children are likely to blab, and I'd prefer if we kept everything as close as possible."

"Don't worry," I said. "I'll mention it to no one."

276

The following Friday, we left for the country, as usual, and when we returned, Detective Gavin was there to greet us.

"The case is solved," he said, grinning widely. "You see, the building next door has temporarily been leased by some foreign-mission societies, and their funds are kept on the third floor—that would be right on the level with this one. It's as simple as that. Parker, that old rascal, must have wormed this information out of some unsuspicious minister, perhaps, and he made his plans accordingly. All he had to do was gain access to the floor, and the rest was easy as pie. He'd figured out that the fireplace next door adjoined yours, and so his friends made the beginning of an entrance right under your very eyes. On Friday evening they got here, and when they came through on the other side we let them get started on the safe before we finally grabbed them."

"Actually, they were pretty stupid," I said. "They could have arranged the whole thing much better, and could have done a much neater job, too, couldn't they?"

"You're quite right," said Mr. Gavin. "But, you see, burglary and safebreaking are not in Parker's line at all. He works with clean hands, literally speaking, and this time he had to call in some help, and that's where he made his great mistake. Parker's specialty is to run confidence tricks, exclusively, on members of the clergy."

"Any special denomination?" I said.

"No, he's quite impartial. He discovered quite early in life that ministers, priests and rabbis are mostly an unsuspicious lot and, as far as his record goes, which is a long one, he's never in his whole criminal career tampered with anyone excepting men of the cloth."

"Well, I suppose it's always a great risk when you stray from your specialty," I said.

"That it is. Well, now, he'll have quite a bit of time to regret that lapse of his," said Mr. Gavin. "Mr. King, it was a pleasure to know you."

Then he shook my hand and walked out of my life forever. But not Praying Parker. I managed to obtain permission to pay him a visit in jail, and he proved a most well-spoken man, with a truly philosophical sense of humor. He was the only criminal I ever met who articulated not the slightest anti-social attitudes or sentiments, and who considered his career a rather well-rounded fulfillment for most of his early expectations.

"It's the ups and downs of the game," he said. "I was a little too greedy. You see, I actually had enough to retire on, when this thing suddenly came along, and I should certainly have steered clear of it. It had all the earmarks of something that I'm not really in favor of—forceful entrance—safecracking—and all the rest of it. It's not my field. But—that's the way it is."

"I asked Detective Gavin," I said, "whether you had any denominational preferences about the people you deal with—and he told me that he didn't think so."

"He's wrong," said Parker. "By and large I prefer to get involved with Baptists, Methodists and Presbyterians—in that order. The Protestant clergy, as a whole, is less suspicious than the Catholics and the Jews. Also, I think they tend to be more unworldly, particularly in the smaller communities. I try to steer away from the big cities, anyway, because urban life makes *everybody* cynical. Give me the small towns every time."

"Are people in small towns less suspicious?" I said.

"No, much more so. But there is one significant difference: they are most bitterly aware only of the crookedness of city people—and, you see, I'm strictly a home-grown product, to them. As you can judge for yourself, my vocabulary is more than adequate for any occasion, but my pronunciation, my

278

method of locution, is strictly from corn. I was actually born in Brooklyn, but quite early in life I realized that if I wanted to be successful in my special calling, I had better suppress this awful detail in my vital statistics. I acquired a Midwestern accent, and I've been sailing along as a trusted member of society ever since."

"I hope you don't mind my asking you," I said, "but do you personally subscribe to any special form of religious belief?"

He gave me a sweet, understanding smile. "Under the circumstances," he said, "when you realize that I have successfully fleeced clerical members of almost every extant religion —including the Mohammedan, the Buddhist, the Hindu, and, on one occasion, I even managed to beguile the caution of an Eskimo shaman who happened to attend a world's fair—considering all these circumstances, then I think it would be safest to call me just a freewheeling, liberal agnostic."

"Well," I said, "Mr. Parker, I'm certainly sorry for anyone who has to go through life without faith of any sort."

"Oh," he said, "I'm afraid you misunderstood me. I think you've just got to believe in your fellow man. If you didn't, then even a very good thief like me couldn't make a living."

"Another thing," I said, "what made you stand there, out in the hall, with that rosary chain in your hands? Was there any reason for that?"

"Well, yes, you might say there was. You see, I knew your landlord often crawled about that building, and I had reason to believe he was a Catholic. Now, then, I didn't really want to be too far away from my henchmen, either, because, to tell you the truth, I didn't trust them too much. So, there I was, in a strange hallway, where I really had no business—and so I figured that nobody was likely to be suspicious of a man who was quietly reciting his beads. I have reason to believe that human nature is full of imaginative tolerances and often, particularly in certain crucial emergencies, I've counted on it,

279

with some reasonable success. Does that answer your question?"

"Yes. Thank you." And then, without even thinking, I said, "Well, better luck next time, Mr. Parker."

CHAPTER SEVENTEEN

L̲ARIA N̲IEBERT will surely mourn me, because we emptied our hearts to one another, during certain times of stress in our lives, and the memories of those soul-searching sessions are, I am sure, as keenly alive in her mind as they are in mine.

Laria's husband, John, was a patient in Lexington at one of the same periods when I was confined there, and in a little while we became exceptionally close friends. Niebert was a Negro doctor who had been chronically addicted for several years, and he had returned to the Public Health Service Hospital six times before I'd ever met him. On Saturday afternoon, when softball games were played on the recreation field, behind the institution, John and I would stay quietly in our rooms and listen to some serious music that came in over the FM radio. He had a vast knowledge of this field and was particularly sensitive to fine vocal renditions of the classics. He had a beautiful voice, too, and often, in the stillness of the deserted building, he would recapitulate, just for me, some of the noblest efforts we had heard throughout the broadcasts that afternoon.

In due time, I came to learn something of his past, and I can assure you it never puzzled me how or why he had turned out to be a drug addict. He came from very poor people, in Mississippi somewhere, and, because of his unusual athletic prowess, as well as his outstanding scholastic achievements, he had managed to acquire the patronage of some local politicians, and, with their very willful and constantly patronizing help, had finally managed to escape into a medical doctorate. Naturally, his practice, which was government-sustained, was restricted to the Negro slum dwellers, among whom he had spent most of his childhood; and he didn't really mind this at all, since, heaven knows, they were certainly pretty desperately in need of decent medical attention. His real troubles, as an adult, began when one of his ex-school friends promoted him to the attention of some Eastern academic bigwig, who offered him a chance to do some work in a huge research laboratory in New York.

I'm not going to bother telling you the endless, dirty, discriminatory tricks that were played on him by his various medical colleagues, since the subject is far too familiar to every wide-awake individual to need recapitulation here. I will only say that, reconciled as he was to living in the gruesome confines of Harlem, his life was made one long endless horror by the fact that not even the simplest forms of social or communal life were accessible to him during the many hours he stayed around the laboratory. I don't know exactly how John became dependent on drugs, in the first place, but— since I know all about the effects that narcotics have on the human psyche—I simply marvel that *all* Negroes, all over the country, aren't addicted, also. Luckily, no one on the job ever guessed at his predicament, and he had already been to Lexington six times (as a volunteer patient) when he finally met Laria Worth. With her emergence into his life, a new and peculiar agony began for him.

Laria was the daughter of a white father and a Negro mother, which means that, very early in life, she had had to pass through the additional difficulty of a completely ambiguous status as a human being. By the time Laria was nine years old, her father died, and the widow, who had somehow managed to live on sufferance on the outer fringe of a derelict white community, felt suddenly unable to continue in that twilight world any longer. So, she moved to Harlem, too.

Unfortunately for all of us, we have made the Negro color-conscious to a degree where he is just as discriminatory as we are. He has, to everyone's misfortune, learned to assess social value in ratio to the lightness of an individual's skin, and has thereby increased the already catastrophic fragmentation of the socioethnic structure of his people to an almost unimaginable degree. In short, there are snobberies from the dark as well as the light side involved here, which endlessly increase the unspoken rancors and hostilities of an already deeply injured and insulted people. I am not going to go into all the crazy ramifications of this heartbreaking subject—suffice it to say that Laria, while frequently envied for the pale color of her skin, was also subject to relentless gossip and backbiting on the part of the community which looked with distaste and suspicion on any of its members who had become seriously, and openly, involved with any white person. Also, Laria was very beautiful—as certain patrician faces on ancient Egyptian sarcophagi are beautiful—and so her young womanhood was constantly in jeopardy of brutal violation by people who are compulsively urged toward tampering with any sort of physical perfection. For a great many frustrated individuals, beauty represents a needless taunt, and there is something in such lives —lives that have become hopelessly thwarted by lack of opportunity—which wants to lunge out and to damage this seeming reproach to their own shortcomings. By the time she was twenty years old, and working on her first job, in a bacteriological laboratory, Laria had learned everything there is to know about constant, self-preservative awareness in a poisonously dangerous environment. Our slums are our accusers, not only because they breed disease and crime, but because they expose the flowering beauties and talents of some of our best people to the hazards of the most brutalizing physical and psychological circumstances. This shame lives in too many of our towns and cities, and the miracle is that anyone ever actually survives it.

Laria survived it, until she met John Niebert. She became instantly vulnerable the moment their lives crossed, but, having successfully mastered the iron self-discipline imposed upon her by the slums, she was unafraid of committing herself, quite freely, even after he had confessed his deadly drug addiction to her.

"We will do this thing together," she said to him.

And, I must confess to you, that, after I came to know Laria, the chances for his recovery seemed almost ideal.

Since they were planning to get married eventually, anyway, she insisted that they go through with it at once. It was, indeed, an act of high and foolhardy courage, when you consider how small the chances for a narcotics cure actually are. They are negligible in the life of a white man, and in the life of a Negro they are almost nonexistent, because the whole world seems to operate against it. His life is so hemmed in with day-by-day crises that it surely takes some superhuman summoning of incalculable powers to achieve any sort of satisfactory end.

It was typical of John's character that he was very reluctant to enter into any of these plans, but she absolutely refused to listen to his objections, and in due time, they were married. John stayed "clean" for a year and a half. But, when she became pregnant, they began to look around for better living quarters, and then, of course, they instantly ran into the everlasting evasive tactics of real-estate men and prospective landlords, who are desperately afraid that Negro tenants will tend to depress their property values.

As you probably know—and, if you don't, you *should*—there are hardly any decent or livable houses available to Negroes anywhere, even north of the Mason-Dixon line; and the endless barrage of insults and mealymouthed hypocrisies that they were constantly exposed to—in their desperate search for a home—eventually sent John back into the arms of morphine. Laria, shortly afterward, had a miscarriage.

That's when I met him.

As I've already told you, I found him an immensely sensitive and valuable human being, and so, when the time arrived for our respective wives to come to visit with us, we arranged for them both to reach the institutional grounds on the same day.

Laria certainly lived up to everything John had told me about her, both as to her looks as well as her intellectual endowments. Of course, we were not permitted to speak directly to anyone excepting the person to whom we were related, but in the close quarters of the visitors' reception room, it was easy enough to overhear what people nearby were saying to one another, and when our dear ones finally left us, John and I noted with quiet happiness that they went out of the main gate together, arm in arm.

The next day my wife showed up, quite alone.

The reason? Laria had made the trip by bus, which, I think, had taken anywhere from sixteen to eighteen hours. She was utterly exhausted by the time she arrived, and when the two women finally landed at a hotel, in Lexington proper, they discovered that Laria, as a Negro, could not be accommodated with a night's lodging. The desk clerk, a pretty decent sort, according to his lights, advised Laria not to stop over at any of the local places available for colored people.

"They wouldn't be right for you," he said. "I don't think they're sanitary, and I'm sure they're not safe—not for a nice girl like you."

And so, Laria, almost out on her feet, had gone back to the bus station, sadly accompanied by Margie, and had boarded the next coach heading north.

My wife later confessed to me that she had made some sort of a fuss about all this in the hotel lobby at the time; but all she had encountered was just stony-eyed hostility and tight-lipped noncomprehension.

So, that was that.

It was shortly after Laria's visit that I talked to John about the possibility for a confirmed drug addict to live in the East —in Thailand, or some such place, where narcotics, in their purest form, are easily available. I guess he must have written his wife about this, too, because she also began to gather all her resources against the day of his release. John and I got out of Lexington within a few days of each other, and when I met the Nieberts in New York, their trip to the Orient had been all but paid for. I visited them in their home, alone, because Margie had gone off to Nebraska for a few days to see her people, and, shortly after dinner, the two of them sprang their big news on me.

"We should have gone off long ago," Laria said. "We are both competent people with skills that are needed, and I don't think we have a thing to worry about."

"I'm not so sure it will be good for you," John said, taking her hand. "You notice Alex isn't going, although Margie offered to cut out with him."

286

"Alex's problems are quite different," she said. "He can live where he wants to, he can eat wherever he feels like, and nobody has any feelings about him, one way or another, the very minute they lay eyes on him."

"I think Laria's right," I said. "I certainly wouldn't want to submit my innocent children to such a thing. Not if *I* could help it. I know there are plenty of talented and intelligent Negroes who are making it without dope—but—frankly—I wouldn't want my son or daughter to have to undergo a daily ordeal by color. It's really just a little too inhuman for my taste. Not if *I* had any choice in the matter."

John seemed greatly reassured by my attitude, and two weeks later they were off.

We didn't write very often to each other; all I gathered from their scant letters was that John was working in a hospital and, after a while, that Laria was expecting a baby. When their daughter was born, they sent us a beautifully drunken cablegram and told us that her name was Thana, which means "joy." We heard less and less of them during the next two years, and then one day we received a letter from Laria telling us that John had died of cancer and that she and the baby were returning to the United States.

Our first meeting, after she came back to this country, was pretty rough on both of us. "He smoked opium out there," she told me. "Not too much—about four to five pipes a day. He worked very hard at the hospital, and everyone loved him. Finally, when he became very ill—he had cancer of the lung, you know—he started to worry terribly about me and Thana. Then, one day, I told him I was planning to return to the States—and I could see that this pleased him very much. 'I've been very happy out here with you,' I told him, 'because I would have been happy with you anywhere. But, if anything should happen to you, I'd take our child back. Conditions seem to be slowly improving there, and I think she ought to grow up and do her share to make things still better. Some day people will be just people, and their worth will be established by their intrinsic qualities, instead of accidental externals. Thana has her role to fulfill in that sacred cause, and good people of all races will stand beside her while that struggle is still going on.'

"I'm glad I'm back, and I will try to raise my child to be a pride to all Americans; meanwhile, we're looking for an apartment that is decent and fit for people to live in, in a neighborhood that hasn't been precondemned as a special breeding ground for sordidness and for crime. As you can see, Alex, my problem hasn't changed any—has it?"

CHAPTER EIGHTEEN

Every man who loves, and whose love is requited, becomes, at once, a lover of all the world. The particularly lucky ones among us, the ones whose wives or mistresses have the gift of playful make-believe, can, through the medium of their loved one's mimicry and whimsy, come to savor the richness of this earth in the most manifold measure imaginable.

When Margie sings a Spanish song for me, and pretends to be rattling her gypsy castanets in the middle of our living room, it suddenly becomes Easter in my heart, and all Barcelona is throwing lilies down on my blessed head. If ever she attempts to jabber some phrases in my native Austrian dialect —all the phantom doves of my incredible childhood beat their magical wings about my ears.

Of course, not everyone desires or even expects to achieve

these additional blissful addenda out of a relationship with a woman. Some people are made inordinately happy to find that their loved ones favor the same cocktails and cigarettes that they themselves do. In fact, I once knew two young people who nearly got married simply because they were able to wear each other's shoes.

I, on the other hand, expect a great deal more.

Love, all by itself, is quite a lot, isn't it?

But, marriage!?!?

Now, then, you had better listen attentively, and even reverently, because I'm about to tell you a few carefully selected aspects of a truly happy marriage.

My wife has a deep affinity for flowers—for animals—and for all aspects and manifestations of nature, to which most other people are either totally indifferent or only mildly, or sporadically, reactive.

She certainly never had to teach me that when you are in love, all sorts of rainbows are likely to sprout out of common mud puddles—but she did have to revive in me my childhood faculty of infatuation for all the sensory marvels of the world around us—which early endowment of mine, for various unjustifiably trivial reasons, I had permitted to lapse into desuetude.

What I am telling you is that, although I am thirty-three years older than my wife, she has taught me much, and that she is constantly, and sometimes even quite inadvertently, going to go on teaching me a great deal more.

In the beginning, I had brought to her eager and acquisitive mind the answers to certain mysteries and wonders of art and literature which had hitherto been beyond the limited horizon of her short experience. Verlaine, Baudelaire, Rimbaud, Goethe, Heine, Rilke, Herrick, Browning, and Cummings found a newly responsive heart to echo the raptures and austerities of their particular passions and beguilements, and it became a greatly rewarding thing for me to have channeled her avid young perceptions into these fruitful fields of new aesthetic experience.

But, believe me, in just a very little while she began to lead bold forays of her own into this special territory occupied by the greatly elevated minds of this world, where I had had a long and seemingly insurmountable advantage over her. Without any special prearrangement between us, we began to share new and brilliant discoveries, in the realms of intellectual experience, almost every day, and, if the jewel of our current enthusiasm proved especially rewarding, in its multifaceted glory, we even elected it to become *The Find of the Month*.

It stands to reason that human beings, in general, cannot be expected to profit indiscriminately from these peculiarly specialized and highly personal confessions on my own happy married life, but I want to assure you that it can do you no possible harm to get all these revealing glimpses into the working order of a so stupendously successful matrimonial relationship as ours.

Another thing—even if you happen to believe that you have no feeling for poetry at all, and if the height of all poetic rapture in your life has been encompassed by

> *Roll me over*
> *My darlin' lover*
> *While the stars are hoverin' above.*
> *What good is learnin'*
> *When you just burnin'*
> *Forever yearnin'*
> *For the one you love.*

I say that, even in so extreme a case of mental stultification, I urge you very strongly, and most sincerely, to read the poem which follows. Please don't skip any lines—and read it not so much as poetry, but think of it rather as a statement about this earth, made by another human being, who had already fallen to dust many, many centuries before you were born. It is a poem accredited to Virgil and, for almost half a year, it served as *The Find of the Month* in our own household. Margie discovered it for us in a collection of medieval Latin poetry,* and the poem is called "Dancing Girl of Syria."

Dancing girl of Syria, her hair caught up with a fillet:
Very subtle in swaying those quivering flanks of hers
In time to the castanet's rattle: half-drunk in the smoky tavern,
She dances, lascivious, wanton, clashing the rhythm.
And what's the use, if you're tired, of being out in the dust and the
  heat,
When you might as well lie still and get drunk on your settle?
Here's tankards and cups and measures and roses and pipes and
  fiddles
And a trellis-arbour cool with its shade of reeds,
And somewhere somebody piping as if it were Pan's own grotto,
On a shepherd's flute, the way they do in the fields.
And here's a thin little wine, just poured from a cask that is pitchy,
And a brook running by with the noise and gurgle of running
  water.

There's even garlands for you, violet wreaths and saffron,
And golden melilot twining with crimson roses,
And lilies plucked where they grow by the virgin river,
—Achelois brings them in green willow baskets—
And little cheeses for you that they dry in baskets of rushes,

* *Mediaeval Latin Lyrics*, fabulously translated and annotated by the gifted poet and writer, Helen Waddell, was published by Constable and Company, Ltd., London, and is reprinted here by permission of the publisher.

292

And plums that ripen in the autumn weather,
And chestnuts, and the cheerful red of apples.
In brief, here's Ceres, Love, and rowdy Bacchus
—And red-stained blackberries, and grapes in bunches,
And hanging from his withe seagreen cucumber.
And here's the little god who keeps the arbour,
Fierce with his sickle and enormous belly.
Hither, O pilgrim! See, the little donkey
Is tired and wistful. Spare the little donkey!
Did not a goddess love a little donkey?

It's very hot.
Cicadae out in the trees are shrilling, ear-splitting,
The very lizard is hiding for coolness under his hedge.
If you have sense you'll lie still and drench yourself from your
*   wine cup,*
Or maybe you prefer the look of your wine in crystal?
Heigh ho, but it's good to lie here under the vines,
And bind on your heavy head a garland of roses,
And reap the scarlet lips of a pretty girl.
—You be damned, you there with your Puritan eyebrows!
What thanks will cold ashes give for the sweetness of garlands?
Or is it your mind to hang a rose wreath upon your tombstone?
Set down the wine and the dice, and perish who thinks of tomor-
*   row!*
—Here's Death twitching my ear, "Live," says he, "for I'm com-
*   ing."*

I don't recall whether I have ever, anywhere, recounted to you how it came about that Margie originally met me and, finally, even came to marry me. Sometime in 1952 I was living on the upper West Side in a friend's apartment, and this man and his family were away from New York for so many months of each year that most of the time I was the sole occupant of their spacious, six-room home. I talked to my friend about this foolishly wasteful arrangement, and he finally posted some notices in the various music and art schools around town—notices to the effect that students in need of suitable living quarters were to inquire for further particulars at his address.

And so, one drizzly afternoon in early May, Margie showed up on our doorstep, and *I* was, of course, the only one at home to receive her. She loved the apartment at once, but, despite her obvious enthusiasm, she seemed rather reluctant to make any definite commitment about her plans. I hastened to reassure her most volubly about the place, and after a while I managed, rather successfully, to ameliorate most of her unspoken uneasinesses.

"I am the only one who lives here now," I said to her, "but if you wish, you can have a girl friend come and stay with you, without charge, until the family who owns the apartment returns again in the fall. Besides, I am fifty-two years old, and I have eight grandsons, so you needn't worry your little head about me at all."

In short, I hoped to answer all the questions in her mind, and, sure enough, after I had harangued her, very persistently, for about twenty minutes, she finally decided to move in.

The next time she called, she brought along her boy friend, a young musician who was a student in the same school where she eventually hoped to matriculate. It happened that this young man and I hit it off so well together that Margie felt greatly pleased by her choice of a domicile.

And now a really fascinating situation arose between the three of us: you see, Margie's suitor, who was a native of Australia, was determined to return, experimentally, to the country of his birth, to size up the opportunities for a musical career among the possibly art-famished Aussies. I think his plan was to send for Margie later on.

294

I, on the other hand, tried my damnedest to convince that stubborn Antipodite that he had much better take his beloved right along with him, because, as I very cogently pointed out —so highly attractive a young woman was not likely to remain alone for very long. I spent endless hours explaining all this to him, and I even recounted my own experiences, as a young husband and father, to convince him that a wife and even children need not necessarily prove a handicap to a burgeoning career.

It was all in vain.

One fine day he took off for Australia, and I remained behind, to console his forlorn young enchanter. So, I at once proceeded to take her to various theaters and movies, and once I even wound up at the Savoy Ballroom, up in Harlem, with her. The worst of it was that she began, very consistently, to neglect all of her other acquaintances, the ones she went to school with—and—before very long—she seemed to see no one—but me.

All right—so I *was* a grandfather! !

In the end, only one factor actually counted: I was a man. As it turned out, I was a rather sick and much dilapidated man, too, and for a couple of years we certainly had a pretty mixed-up time of it. Margie doesn't altogether admit this now. With the happy gift of youthful rejuvenation, she has managed to revamp even that early, sometimes quite bitter, period of my drug addiction into something full of ecstatic interludes.

At any rate, the great bond between us—besides our love, of course—was our deep conviction that, for various highly complex reasons, we had a desperately urgent need for one another. Although my darling was still very young, she had already experienced certain disillusioning denouements in her own life, while I, racked by chronic illness, and completely sidetracked by my enslavement to narcotics, no longer felt able to find my way back into any form of useful existence.

Well, we both have come through, haven't we?

And, no matter what happens to us from now on, our happiness has already become a contributive factor in that general world harmony to which, I believe, the universe is constantly aspiring.

That's true—isn't it?

The end, of course, is bound to be tragic, no matter whatever else may befall us, because all of human life is forever destined to end in tragedy. And that is precisely why I refuse to avert my eyes from either the joys of today or the inevitable catastrophe that is bound to overtake each one of us on some unpredictable tomorrow.

Talking about marriages reminds me of a wedding I once attended, out in Chicago; it was the nuptial ceremony that bound together the destinies of a certain Francine Calvert and a creature called Barton Plummer.

You have probably heard quite a lot about them throughout the years. She was a multiple divorcee who also fancied herself an interior decorator-journalist of sorts, while he owned and operated a whole flock of highly successful newspapers.

At the time of their marriage, they were both, so to speak, on top of the pile, no matter what you privately happened to think that pile was really composed of.

I had certain small obligations toward the bride, since I had been a consultant of hers some years before, when she happened to have accidentally stumbled into the chartless quagmire of abstract art; that is to say, one of her billionaire clients, even more benighted than herself, had suddenly shown a fancy for this dreary form of wall desecration, and Francine, whom I had known, on and off, for some five or six years, had sent me a despairing SOS the moment this unexpected emergency occurred. I had stood by her nobly and, I must say, quite lucratively, too, during this and some other anxious periods of her life—and so, when she particularly requested me to attend her impending wedding, I couldn't really find it in my heart to refuse her.

I'm not going to bother telling you why I've never had even one really happy moment in the city of Chicago, since that would extend these confessions beyond the ordinary confines of even a very large autobiography; suffice it to say that some of the most depressing moments of my life have taken place in that extremely amorphous and disheveled city. So, when I landed at the Blackstone this time, I made not the slightest attempt to get in touch with any residents of the town whom I might possibly have come to know during my former visits; I simply got undressed, plumped myself into bed, and proceeded to read the first volume of Thomas Mann's *Joseph Legend*.

But, before I'd properly gotten into the spirit of this fabulous work, my phone bell rang, and Jack Marley, a former city editor, who had done heroic service for Barton Plummer some time in the past, apprised me of the fact that we were next-door neighbors.

"Come on in," he said. "I'm all by myself, and I oughtn't really to be left alone here with a whole fifth of Scotch. I promised my wife I wouldn't."

"Why don't you come on in here?" I said. "Leave your booze behind. I don't drink, so you won't even be tempted."

"All right," he said. "Let my virtues be on your head." Then he hung up.

I'd always liked Jack. He had been an excellent reporter and editor, and after he'd left the Plummer empire he'd found himself a couple of easy, well-paying jobs as editorial consultant with some book-publishing houses in New York. I wondered why he had bothered to come to the wedding at all, since I'd heard somewhere that he hadn't really parted on any too amiable terms with the bridegroom at the time they had finally severed their relations.

I asked him about that, of course.

"It's hard to say, Alex, why one sometimes does a thing like that. Actually, I suppose it's because I became so friendly with his mother. She was a really great woman. She was able to help me a lot, too—because she was the only one Barton has never really been rough with."

"She's dead now, isn't she?" I said.

"Yeah, that's true," he said. "That, of course, knocks my alibi right out from under me, doesn't it? I suppose I came mostly out of curiosity. I wanted to see the bride. You know, of course, that ninety per cent of all the eligible females in America have been trying to shack up permanently with Barton for the last twenty-five years. Barton is forty-three now, and he's never been married. What has *she* got he can't get any other way? Do you know her?"

"Yes," I said. "I've known her for quite a while. She's got more drive than a steel drill, and all of her artistic pretensions can't seem to hide it. There is something really deadly about her single-minded purposefulness, and when her steam's up and she's in full charge—I can't imagine anyone in the world who could possibly stand up to her."

"I'm getting a little moody about our little festival here," said Jack. "How come *you* bothered to come and witness all this nonsense yourself?"

"Mostly, I wanted to see the groom," I said. "I've never met him—and so I wanted to get a closer look. Actually, *she* put in quite a pitch for me to show up, and so, I thought—to hell with it—!"

Jack seemed visibly depressed by my little character sketch of Francine. "I'm sorry, mostly for his mother's sake," he said. "She was really a great gal, and hoped against hope that the right wife might, some day, do wonders for her boy. Too bad it didn't work out quite that way."

"How can you tell?" I said. "They might be just great for each other. They might come to full bloom under each other's auspices. We might see wonders yet! Who knows?"

"I guess we might," he said. "I've just got a funny feeling, though, that I can predict their lives as if they had already happened. By the way, did you ever read *Le Chant de Maldoror?*"

"By Lautréamont?" I said. "No, I haven't read it. Wasn't Lautréamont an early surrealist or something?"

"Oh, yes. Almost a century ago he was like the Hieronymus Bosch of the writing fraternity. He had a real nutsy streak, but he was undoubtedly gifted, too. If you'll let me get my bottle of Scotch—and if you're not too sleepy—I'll tell you a brief excerpt out of *Maldoror* that seems, somehow, particularly apropos at this moment."

"Bring on the juice," I said. "You'll have to drink alone, because the most I ever take is a short beer at the height of summer."

"O.K.," he said. "Then I'll just pour myself a single and bring it in here, ready for use."

When he came back with his iced drink, he took a long look at the glass and, without tasting it, put it down on the floor, beside his armchair.

"This Maldoror person is a sort of hero in this book of Lautréamont's," he said. "Actually, I suppose, he is a sort of antihero, the ideal surrealist prototype, who is surprised by little and shrinks from nothing. At any rate, somewhere in the middle of the book, Maldoror has managed to get possession of a defunct lighthouse. I mean a lighthouse that had been replaced by a more recent and accurate one; but, Maldoror, purely for purposes of mischief, keeps his lighthouse going anyway. That is to say, on very stormy nights he purposely keeps the light going, too, just in the hope of leading some ships astray, so they'll founder on the huge rocks in this particularly treacherous part of the coastline. A nice character, as you can see. Well, at any rate, one particularly dirty night, when a fierce storm was raging, he watched from his illuminated eyrie and saw a huge ocean liner break apart on the cliffs not too far from shore. He was absolutely ecstatic when he saw the poor passengers struggling helplessly against the mountainous waves, and he noted with satisfaction that nobody among them seemed able to hold on to a spar or a life belt that might have meant his salvation. But then, suddenly, he observed one lone swimmer, obviously an unusually powerful man, making exceptionally good headway through that turbulent sea, and, by the way he was going, it even looked as if this intrepid man might, after all, manage to reach the shore. Quickly, Maldoror took a knife and a club from a huge oaken chest and rushed down to the beach. He got there just in time, too, because the powerful and desperate man was just beginning to stagger out of the water. But, before he had taken more than just a few steps, Maldoror was right on top of him, and, with one fierce blow, sent this sole survivor back into the watery grave. Meanwhile, the storm started to abate a good deal, and even the sliver of a sick, pallid moon began to appear from behind some black clouds."

"You tell this story very well," I said. "Have you told it often?"

"I haven't even thought about it in more than twenty years," Jack said. "I read it originally in French, and, somehow, when we got to jabbering about the bride and groom a little while ago, old Maldoror suddenly flashed into my mind."

"Go on," I said; "the storm had calmed down, and a sick moon was just appearing from behind the clouds."

"Right!" he said. "And then, in the strange, jaundiced light

300

that came upon this gruesome scene, Maldoror saw three
enormous sharks making their appearance. They were two
males and one female, and the female was the largest of the
lot. It was, of course, a perfect banquet for them, absolutely
ready-made for their tastes, and yet not one of those beasts
made the slightest attempt to sink its teeth into any of the
corpses that were floating all around them. Maldoror wondered about this for a moment, and then he realized that those
three deadly creatures were quietly and slowly circling each
other—undecided about what each of them was going to do.
The males were a little closer together—they had, indeed,
almost formed an instinctive, combined front against the female, who was flicking her tail in ominous swishes every time
the other two showed any signs of beginning their meal. This
went on for quite a few minutes until, finally, one of the males
couldn't resist taking a sort of experimental nibble at the
white elbow of a young woman that just happened to rotate
past him. Well—the moment he took that bite, the sea instantly churned into a raging vortex of foam, and, a moment
later, the two male sharks were gone from the scene and only
a vast stain of black blood indicated the place where they had
been seen. At this point Maldoror began to walk into the
water like a somnambulist who is compelled by emotions beyond his own control. As he sloshed forward, he began, piece
by piece, to shed his clothing, and when the water finally
reached his shoulders the only thing he had left on his person
was his knife. He clenched the handle of the knife between his
teeth—struck forward—and began to swim out toward the
one remaining shark that was now seriously beginning on its
bloody gourmandizing.

"Maldoror was a superb swimmer, and before five minutes
had passed he had reached the main body of the wreck, and, a
split second later, the shark became aware of him. And now a
curious thing happened. The shark observed him out of its

murderous eyes but made no attempt to lunge toward the intruder. Instead, it began slowly to circle around Maldoror as it had previously done around the male sharks. And he, in his turn, now began to circle the female shark, too, constantly keeping his eyes on her monstrous head and biting his teeth with viselike intensity into the knife handle. They slowly circled each other for a few minutes in this insane fashion, by the lurid light of that ghostly moon, and neither one seemed in the least inclined to break the spell of that fantastic, moribund ballet. But, as they were silently, and compulsively, continuing in their rotary spell, Maldoror suddenly got a full, clear look of the monster's eye, and, without any thought or volition on his part, he opened his mouth, and he could feel the knife fall slowly past his chest and his knees into the unfathomable depths below. Also, without realizing it, his circular motion around the shark had ceased, and the two antagonists now faced each other in still, cold appraisal, for the first time. And then, in that icy silence, Maldoror felt himself moved by an emotion he had never experienced before. As he stared at that female shark, it came to him with irrevocable certainty that never in all his life had he seen so much concentrated ferocity as he now beheld in that monster's eye. The shark, too, seemed to have undergone a peculiar transformation. As it gently drifted toward Maldoror, a film seemed to descend over its jewellike iris, and, almost without effort, they now floated together in one glaucous mass and clutched at one another in an absolutely frenzied embrace. You see, each of them had, finally, met an utterly suitable and proper mate."

We were both silent for a moment after Jack had stopped talking, and he slowly bent down and picked his drink off the floor. "Here's to them!" he said, taking the tiniest possible sip out of his glass. "And here's to everybody else who's completely ruthless and coldly purposeful!" Then he put down his almost untasted glass on the floor again.

302

"There's a train out of here in forty-five minutes," I said. "Shall we mosey back to New York?"

"We shall," he said. "After all, if, as I believe, the dynamics of redemption are founded on self-discipline and imagination, then I don't think either one of us has any business here at all. Have we?"

"No, we haven't," I said. "And, what's more, this is the first time in my life I've been to Chicago and really learned something."

In concluding all this talk on marriage, I ought not to overlook another couple of my acquaintance, who came to this country some twenty-five years ago from Argentina. He had been a professor at a university down there and had, along with several of his colleagues, signed some sort of petition or document which the highly sensitive government of that country had considered flagrantly seditious. So, a few weeks later, Diego and Inez Inclan had landed in New York with a small sampling of their most necessary household goods and several large suitcases of polemical manuscripts.

Luckily, both Diego and Inez had quite a bit of English on them when they got here, so, after a while, he obtained a pretty decent job as a teacher somewhere, while Inez stayed home and proceeded most lovingly, and very painstakingly, to translate his immortal works into English. Diego was a tall, long-mustachioed type of Latin, with an enormous parchmentlike brow, while his spouse could very easily have passed for one of the usual plumpish-looking ladies who generally play the roles of duennas in pseudo-South American films. She managed to maintain a remarkable number of her good looks throughout the years, and, since she fancied rather long golden earrings and somewhat elaborate lacy fichus on her tight-fitting satin blouses, I think she was generally considered rather sexy in that small circle that encompassed their modest, bilingual social life.

I met them only a couple of years after the beginning of their exile, and the way I got to know them is rather interesting. It was Inez who originally came to visit me, and the man who introduced her to me was a Cuban publisher for whom I had done occasional illustrative work. His name was José Ramirez, and he looked like an extremely overfed version of a burlesque seducer—that is to say, he had a waxed mustache which he had dyed such a flagrant, shiny black that it actually seemed to be cut out of a piece of patent leather. Because he was so immensely overweight, he naturally perspired very freely, and he always wiped himself with a highly perfumed handkerchief, held in unbelievably jewel-encrusted fingers. A real type.

At any rate, Ramirez had brought Señora Inclan to my studio because he was planning to publish some of her husband's manuscripts, he told me, and it had occurred to him that a few of my pen-and-ink sketches might perhaps help along in the eventual salability of this work. I looked quickly through a few of the typewritten pages they had brought to my house, and it seemed to me, at first glance, that this opus needed a hell of a lot more than just illustrations to make it appeal to anyone, excepting, maybe, the author and his immediate family. And the publisher, of course. And that's where I struck a puzzler, right off—because Ramirez was nothing if not an old shrewdy, and it seemed incredible to me that he could possibly see a shred of merit in any of this long-winded, autobiographical drivel. However, in about half an hour I realized that my publisher friend had simply cast a lewd and bloodshot eye at his author's wife, and that he was only just stringing her along, to keep her in good humor. Understanding this made my relations with them much simpler, of course, and, after I'd served up a couple of brandies, they finally took off. I thought I'd never hear any more about this nonsense, but, no more than a month later, Inez called on me again, and this time she even brought along some printed proofs of the great work.

"Does Mr. Ramirez expect to publish this in Cuba or in America?" I asked her.

"In both places at the same time," she said. "It will become the rallying flag of revolution everywhere. There will be a Spanish and an English edition, and the date of its appearance will mark the end of tyranny in this entire hemisphere."

"Great!" I said. "I didn't know Ramirez published anything of this sort. The stuff of his that I've seen so far was mostly comic-style books—magazines, really—and once, about a year ago, he showed me the manuscript for a children's story."

"Señor Ramirez is a man with heart," she said. "He can no longer find peace wasting his life with trifles. We need strong, ringing sentences to lead our people into the light—and no man with a conscience can remain aloof from the struggle any more. That is why I am here. I think we need a powerful title page that will summarize, in a few lines, the whole meaning of our program."

And so on and so on.

It made no sense, of course, and, after she'd gone, I tried to read those galleys she left behind, and I can assure you that I actually fell asleep over them. Remember, I'm the kind of man who, in an emergency, can read a timetable with interest —so, the fact that Diego's little rallying cry acted as a soporific on me is no mean compliment to his stupefying powers, if nothing else. Meanwhile, that good man went right on teaching school.

So, once more I proceeded on the assumption that this was going to be the last of it all—until, less than two weeks later, that dizzy woman turned up again. She had more proofs, this time, and she told me she was planning to meet Ramirez later that afternoon at his hotel, somewhere near the Plaza. "We'll settle everything then," she said.

I must say she looked great. She was powdered and perfumed and curled and lacquered like a carrousel horse, and her fine dark eyes simply sparkled with revolutionary zeal, and with disarranged hormones. An hour after she was gone, my place still smelled like a house of assignation, and, for the first time in our acquaintance, I suddenly began to feel rather sorry for the dumb broad.

With reason, too, as it turned out, because the day after her visit she called me on the phone, and her voice sounded so choked with grief and unshed tears I nearly asked her to go out and take dinner with me.

Ramirez had gone back to Cuba without having established any definite publishing date. She was absolutely crushed by this setback—particularly since everything had been agreed upon just a few hours before she'd gone to visit him at his hotel. Now, suddenly, he had been called away, and only a quarter of the manuscript had, so far, been set in type. The whole epoch-making struggle had been thrown off schedule, and she was completely shattered.

"Well, that's the end of it at last," I thought. "That wily sweat gland has gotten what he wanted out of her, and now she joins ranks with Ariadne and her ball of mildewed fishing twine."

Wrong again!

I had another call from her before the month was out. A Señor Reni Herbal, a junior partner in the Ramirez publishing business, was coming to New York to continue the negotiations. A couple of days later she dragged this bundle of cheap connivance up to my place, too, and he really looked like the proverbial *maquereau* that French cartoonists, many years ago, had made popular in the less savory comic papers of Paris. He was such a travesty of a man that only an utterly self-de-

306

ceived woman could possibly have been fooled by him. But she *was* fooled just the same—and yet—I must say this in his favor—he was barely able to look me in the eye, all through the longish time they stayed at my studio. He tried to drag her out of there, every ten minutes or so, but she would have none of it. She was aflame with libertarian fervor, and, when they finally left, she was obviously so beholden to that revolting clown I realized that the only place where she could finally ratify her gratitude properly was in his hotel room.

And then, prescient as I am, I suddenly foresaw the whole tragic comedy of all her oncoming years. I foresaw how endless other members of the Ramirez firm were going to make periodic pilgrimages to New York, and how each of these successive entrepreneurs was going to sacrifice her connubial devotion on the slimy altar of his conscienceless lechery.

It happened just like that, too. I eventually met seven of those publishing rodents, and, after the third one had departed, I finally even graduated to the role of the great consoler in her life. There was no longer any shame or double talk between us, and yet, no matter how thoroughly convinced she became of the duplicity of all these characters, she was quite incapable of resisting the blandishments of the next one that happened to come along.

Also, it eventually occurred to me that she was rather enjoying herself. I couldn't help noticing that, with each new arrival, she positively blossomed out in more shining blouses— in longer earrings—and such new, bewildering clouds of pungent perfumes that the effect of all these enticing devices had an undeniably rejuvenating influence on her entire organism.

She meant *well* and did *ill*, and the results, I must say, were, by and large, rather salutary. Remember that her conscience, after all, was quite clear. She was doing what she did out of sheer love for her husband—and what was of particular pride to her, and what greatly sustained her in all her travail, was the fact that that good man, busy with his teaching chores, never once suspected what stupendous sacrifices she had made —and was still willing to go on making—in his behalf.

As a matter of fact, I wouldn't be at all surprised if, in the most secret recesses of her heart, she considered herself rather suitable material—for incipient sainthood.

CHAPTER NINETEEN

VALENTINA WILL SURELY COME. So will Victor. Valentina and Victor—the Veevees, we used to playfully call them—look like animated illustrations by Cruikshank. She is enormously fat, and he is proportionately lean, as if a great share of her monstrous bulk had, for her sole benefit, been mysteriously drained right out of *him*. She is wall-eyed, bushy-browed and Levantine in her entombment of mobile grease. He is aquiline, nutmeg-colored and absolutely insect-like in the overarticulation of his bony substructure. Also, Victor has an Adam's apple that simply cannot be ignored. When you are supposed to look into his eyes, your attention is bound to stray to that luridly prominent, almost constantly active, protuberance, which seems to have a highly volatile life of its own. I have often wondered whether this barometric nubbin was not really the central nucleus around which all

309

the other parts of the *foetus Victor* had later, willy-nilly, added themselves, just a short time before the infant had finally come to birth.

The surprising thing is that all of these strange bodily disfigurements have really become so extravagantly acute only in the last ten years. That is to say, Valentina had always been just a trifle overweight, and Victor was certainly, from the very beginning, somewhat on the lean side—but their emergence as living caricatures dates, definitely, to the year in which their son Randall went off to Buenos Aires and Victor joined Alcoholics Anonymous.

In short, if this were a scientific work—instead of a lovingly poised mirror of memories by a man with instant extinction constantly on his mind—I could now give you a substantially documented account on the behavioristic pattern of a most successfully matched, thoroughly mismated, couple.

In the beginning, as I said before, the Veevees looked reasonably average and certainly would have attracted little attention by the mere fact that, shortly after their marriage, they got on very badly together. But then, just before a separation seemed inevitable, Valentina became pregnant. She had a very tough time of it, and Victor's anxieties about her condition drove all thoughts of a separation completely from his mind. Indeed, I clearly recall that they had never been fonder and more devoted to each other than during this critical period of gestation.

The final fruit of all this agony became their son Randall, whose childhood ailments were a fantastic litany of clinical complexities. He nearly died every Tuesday and Thursday, and on the days in between his fever charts were the consternation and despair of his devoted begetters. Later on, Randall hardly ever went to school, and when he did he was so powerful a disruptive force in every classroom he attended that the physicians who had successfully managed to save his life had frequent occasion to wonder whether their efforts in his behalf might not have served a more socially constructive purpose.

At any rate, I think it was just about then that Victor began to drink rather heavily. He certainly had a plethora of extenuating circumstances, for, among other things, Randall, starting at the age of fifteen, had begun to appear rather frequently on the defendant's side of various police blotters around town, and at least half-a-dozen of his sundry escapades were even reported in the daily press. It is noteworthy, I think, that his trespasses against the public peace seemed to tie the Veevees into anxious bonds of almost unbelievable domestic felicity. They were constantly on the run to some lawyer or bondsman to arrange for proper legal representation or to obtain suitable bail for their erring child, and, if one accidentally happened to encounter them snatching a quick bite near a magistrates' court or a house of detention somewhere, there was something understandably furtive but, nevertheless, rather cozily jovial in their grieving togetherness, too.

And then a very curious thing happened. At the age of twenty-one, Randall fell in love with a girl from Argentina who was paying a short visit to some relatives in this country. At first, of course, everyone expected the worst, but within two months it became plain that love had wrought a true miracle. The headstrong, undisciplined boy quietly and eagerly apprenticed himself to this girl's uncle, a man reputed to be of considerable puissance in the export and import business. Indeed, it was this man who eventually astonished the Veevees to the point of speechlessness by announcing to them that their son had an absolutely uncanny gift for this highly complex form of commercial endeavor.

Suffice it to say that when the momentous significance of this pronouncement had finally sunk in, and when, further, Randall, under the influence of his exotic fiancée and the sponsorship of the redoubtable satrap, her uncle, had emerged as a sober and solvent citizen, the loud cries of joy which issued from the home of his parents could easily have been heard in the local precinct police station, more than six blocks away.

Two days after Randall, accompanied by his brand-new bride, had gone off to South America, I happened to run into the Veevees somewhere on the lower end of Sixth Avenue. I noticed at once that they seemed quite abnormally and certainly most unreasonably depressed by the separation from their so recently reformed offspring. I took dinner with them at a nearby Italian restaurant and, in the course of the evening, it became perfectly clear to me that their marriage, which had for years been solidly anchored to their relentless worries about the boy, was suddenly finding itself at loose ends without that focal center of mutual concern.

I remember that they were both deeply in the dumps when I finally left them, and I wondered how long they could possibly continue together in their emotionally amorphous condition.

Luckily, Valentina, at this late point of their lives, suddenly discovered Victor's excessive drinking. Their friends had known all about it for years, of course, and everyone gave off a joint sigh of relief when she at last persuaded him to join Alcoholics Anonymous. There were many ups and downs in the beginning of his weaning period, but Valentina stood bravely by and served as a shining example of truly devoted wifehood. I think I was the only one among the people who knew them who wondered what would happen to their marriage pattern when the compulsive drunkard actually did learn to shed his mania for poisonous tipple.

Within less than a year, I knew. He started to shrivel, and she proceeded to blow up. He became a violent health-food faddist, and she a compulsive eater. Naturally, they quarreled

constantly and venomously about their divergent predilections, but, even so, they didn't separate because they were so
used to each other's vile habits that they couldn't really bother
to develop fresh patterns of rancor for any newcomers in their
lives. In short, the various points of high irritation which
they were constantly inflaming in one another had, after a
while, become like so many familiar landmarks in an otherwise
pointless journey.

Having them around for an evening eventually became a
truly nerve-racking experience. I am convinced, however,
that if either one of them were to get leukemia tomorrow,
their bankrupt marriage would instantly be revivified. All
they need to be happy again is just a good, mountainous
anxiety of some sort—and then their almost total incapacity
for love would be adequately disguised into a passionately
selfless concern for the critically damaged member of their
domestic setup.

If you wonder why I bother to write about such people at
all, I must point out to you that I hope to make this testament
of mine into a minor moral epic which will forevermore
bring a certain sense of uneasiness to the hearts of people who
triumphantly attend funerals. I want them to be aware, or, at
least, I want them to suspect, that the corpse lying cold, and
seemingly helpless, in his coffin is really just quietly sneering
at them.

All through my life I've had something of a gift for amiable
disparagement anyway, and so I like to think that, at my very
last public session down here, a good many of the *noodnicks*
who have so unconsciously entertained me, during the years,
will manage to come by for a final look-see at my ultimately
amused remains.

High up on any list of such particular characters I would
place Wanda Yarmas, a Hungarian lady, who once got a very
good friend of mine into quite a bit of a jam. His name is

Aladar Halasz, and he has for many years been a successful set designer out in Hollywood.

Halasz, like most of the Hungarians I know, fancies himself a great lover, and, although he is enormously fat, bald and rather short, I must confess he has had some undeniably astonishing conquests to enter on the plus side of his amorous scoreboard. Even so, he is a terrible show-off, and he once astonished me no end when I happened to room with him out in Santa Monica some years ago.

The occasion was the following. Aladar was planning to go away to some resort place for a short vacation, and the day before he took off he asked me to stop at a drugstore and to pick up an extra-large tube of contraceptive paste for him, since he planned to take this prophylactic emulsion along in his luggage—just in case! As he was only expecting to remain away two weeks altogether, I was rather amused by his optimism in commissioning me to buy him a giant-size issue of this comfort, since the quantity involved would easily have served a normally endowed man for the better part of three, and even, possibly, six months. Well, I had the tactlessness to remark on this megalomanic project to one of Aladar's closest friends, and I can only tell you that a couple of days after he had gone that mad Hungarian sent me a special-delivery letter asking me to forward three additional tubes, by express, return mail.

That'll give you a pretty good idea, I think.

Since Hollywood is also the sort of place where you may completely lose track of people who have moved half a mile away from you, I didn't get to see Aladar for quite a spell after I had found a house of my own. As a matter of fact, nearly two years passed before we started to get clubby again, and that came about mainly because we were accidentally involved at nearly opposite ends of the same job at one of the major movie studios. We fell into the pleasant habit of driving one another home, and occasionally we would take dinner together at some favorite restaurant of ours.

It was then that I first met Wanda Yarmas and her husband, Ernie. They had been friends of Aladar's for many years and, when I came to know them, the three of them used to go off on rather lengthy weekends together.

Wanda must have been about thirty-three or thirty-four at that time, and Ernie was at least ten years older—that is to say, he was just about Aladar's age. In the beginning I had the feeling that they had a sort of *ménage à trois* arrangement going between them, but when I became a little more familiar with the Yarmas household I realized that Aladar was nothing but a true friend of the family—and this was so despite the fact that the lady in question was undoubtedly of a rather easily accessible nature.

I once talked to Aladar about her. "You are quite right," he said. "Wanda is an incorrigible flirt. Not that I hold this against her. What makes her completely uninteresting for me is the fact that I've seen too many of her metamorphoses. You see, in Budapest she was a pretty, rather plumpish young girl with vivacious eyes and shiny, dark ringlets, and *I*, along with half-a-dozen other young men, paid a lot of attention to her. She married one of my friends, and when she came back from her honeymoon she was a thinnish blonde with sophisticated airs and much too much eye shadow. I lost sight of her for a few years—and during this time she was divorced and married Yarmas; when I met them here, in Hollywood, she was, as you see her now, redheaded and, I think, a little desperate in her seductiveness. She vamps everything around her—every messenger boy, every elevator man, every doorknob—and she even ogles every bridge lamp—without the slightest sense of discrimination. It is just a little too hysterically nymphomanic for my taste."

"How does Ernie feel about all this?" I said.

"He pretends it is all just a joke. Actually I think he's very much in love with Wanda—but he just doesn't quite know how to assert himself. I think if he ever does get sore—it will be quite a mess."

These were truly prophetic words. Six months later, Ernie sued Wanda for a divorce and named my friend Aladar as the corespondent. And, what is more, by a curious set of circumstances, *I* was called in to testify for the defendant.

The scene of the crime was supposed to have been Aladar's house, near the beach, and the complainant maintained that Wanda had gone there on a certain specified date for purposes obviously libidinous. The plaintiff even produced two photographs purporting to represent his wife in a bikini on the back porch of the said domicile, and he further testified that Aladar, not visible in the picture, had flitted around the house, at that same period of time, in a state of almost complete undress.

Although these assertions were generally true enough, it just happened that I was there, too, and I could truthfully say that nothing indicated in the complaint had actually taken place that afternoon. It was a very hot day, and if anyone had bothered to investigate thoroughly, he would have discovered that I myself was wearing nothing but a little pair of ordinary shorts during the entire lengthy tenure of Wanda's visit.

So, the case was thrown out—and when the lady, in her turn, a month later, sued Ernie for a divorce, it was not only granted—she even received a substantial share in her husband's estate and was authorized to collect a handsome monthly allowance besides.

So far so good.

Of course, Wanda, from thenceforth, became my bosom pal—and I mean *bosom* in its most literal, but still quite platonic, sense—while Aladar, that aging *flâneur*, flitted off to seek greener pastures somewhere else. Before he departed, I did manage to interrogate him, however, on *l'affaire Wanda*, since I was convinced beyond the shadow of a doubt, at this point, that he had, after all, been quite definitely involved with that highly available lady. Not on the afternoon of my visit, but surely before, and perhaps even after, that critical date in their lives.

"Yes," he admitted, "I finally succumbed to the siren, and despite all reason and logic, too, I mingled my confusion with hers, before sanity again prevailed."

"Nonsense!" I said. "The *divorce proceedings* prevailed, and I'm not sure you weren't monkeying with her even after that."

"You are right," he said. "It was an error compounded by recklessness. But, I'm afraid, such is the sad condition of the human animal."

"Anyway, the human animal called *Aladar*," I said. "How come you suddenly changed your mind about her? I thought she wasn't your type at all. She'd transformed herself far too often to suit your particularly exacting tastes, and, sexually, she hadn't the slightest interest for you. Remember?"

"That is true, too," he said, "but, you see, my dear Alexander, I have a great secret to disclose to you: what makes a woman attractive very often depends entirely on *where* it happens."

"What sort of balderdash is that?" I said.

"It is a fatal fact—and, what's more, I will at once proceed to demonstrate it to you. Do you remember when Ernie and Wanda and myself were going off to this hunting lodge in the hills, over the Easter holidays?"

"Yes," I said. "And, as I recall it, Ernie couldn't make it until two days later—but you and Wanda and six other people from the studio went off together that Friday night."

"Quite right," he said. "Well, you may believe me that

this entire trip had only the most blameless intentions. We were surrounded by friends—we ate—we drank—we laughed together—and about midnight, when we all went to bed, I can assure you that nothing was further from my mind than the seduction of Wanda. As it happens, we did have adjoining rooms on the second floor, but I never even gave this a thought. It was a real California hunting lodge, with huge glass-brick fireplaces and plastic woodbark all over the outside of the building—but, nevertheless, a certain rustic quality did manage to assert itself. Also, there was a birchwood balcony that ran all along the side of the building, but this I didn't discover until later on. Well, I'd had an exhausting day, and I went to bed immediately. I didn't even read *The Hollywood Reporter;* I just turned right in. Of course, I'd had a couple of brandies, and so, while I was lying there listening to the fountain splashing outside—I suddenly heard a faint scratching—on the wall—right next to my bed. I tell you, Alex, that sound was absolutely uncanny. I'd never heard anything like it before in all of my life."

"You never heard any scratching before?" I said.

"Never! Not like that. It was like the sound of dawning awareness scratching at the eggshell of life. It was like the beginning of creation trying to find a crack in the wall of primordial inertia. It was—"

"It was *Wanda*," I said.

"Yes, it *was* Wanda. But she was like the blind tool of all the mating forces that were swishing around this world when everything was still dark and blind in the atavistic ooze of primitive existence."

"I'm sure she was scratching with a highly manicured nail," I said, "and maybe even with just a nail *file*, for all we'll ever know."

"I'm sorry," he said, "but you can't reduce the sound that I heard from its high and noble origins by just making a lot

318

of cheap wisecracks about it. That sound, at that hour of the night—in the fabulous forest stillness that surrounded us—"

"With the illuminated fountain splashing in front of the building?"

"The fountain is turned off at one o'clock," he said. "All I can tell you is that I got up very quietly—almost without volition—like a somnambulist—and put on my bathrobe. I didn't turn on the light—I just automatically walked to the French doors that led out to the balcony—and I stepped out into the moonlight like a man in a trance. I took two steps—and then I realized that I was somehow failing that intuitive voice that had so gently called me; so, I went back into my room, lay down on the bed again, and I started to scratch on the wall, too. I tell you, it was sheer enchantment. We were like two entombed egos searching for responsive identities. I don't know how long we went on like that—until, at last, I heard the bed creaking in the next room, and then I got up again and went back into the moonlight. Wanda was standing a few feet away from me, and she seemed absolutely enveloped in a gossamer cocoon. She was like a magical creature waiting to be kissed into reality."

"And you kissed her."

"I did. I have never known such a night. All I can tell you is that she completely enraptured me. It was as if my whole destiny had been nothing but a blind stumbling about—until this blissful moment of enrichment had come into my life. I don't remember what happened the next day—I can only recall that, somehow, the time passed until midnight came again—and—with it—the scratching on the wall started once more. I was living in a dream—and then—the following morning—Ernie arrived. It was a bitter awakening for me. I was trapped in a fabric of pure magic, and I simply couldn't let go. You can understand that, can't you?"

"And what happened after that?" I asked. "Did you both

319

go on scratching on all the walls of every hotel room you used to meet her in—or what?"

"Go on with your little jokes," he said. "Just go on making fun of a howling tragedy."

"What tragedy?"

"The tragedy of trying, hopelessly, to repossess a precious moment—a moment forever lost and never to be recaptured again. Don't you see, you insensitive scribbler, that we were just fumbling about—like two lost children who had been be-hexed by a sound and who were vainly searching to recapture that first blissful moment of their bewitchment."

"Well, one of these bewitched children has finally managed to settle for some substantial alimony," I said, "and I think the other child had better stop fooling with the walls around here before any of these stinking buildings comes tumbling down about his ears. Remember, this Hollywood architecture was just meant to be *looked* at, and not be *scratched!*"

"You are an incorrigible cynic," he said, "and, I can see, you will end up by marrying an heiress. There is no real hope for you. If you had been present on the day of creation, you would have scoffed because God modeled man only out of mud. I'm sure you could have done a better job out of spumoni ice cream. All I can say is, it's certainly very lucky, for all of us, that you *weren't* there. *Vale,* my unhappy friend! *Vale!*"

An old Negro woman, Vanessa Slade, who phones to inquire about my state of health every few months or so, will stop by to quietly press Margie's hand, when the time for sympathetic consolation finally comes around. I've fallen into possession of this woman's friendship through a girl called Marie

320

Randall, who once worked in my household many, many years ago.

What I am doing here, now, is writing a long overdue panegyric to Marie, who was greatly loved by my whole family—and even nowadays, whenever my sons come to visit with me, they hardly ever fail to mention her name most affectionately.

In these strange times when most human beings employed in any form of domestic service are actually ashamed of their occupations, it must seem deplorably patronizing for me to chant the praises of a cook and housekeeper who lived with us more than a quarter of a century back. Well, then, let me tell you—that I have sometimes had a deep and lasting regard for some of these people who worked for me, and that at least three of them were as truly devoted to us as any friend or relative we've ever had.

Marie was the outstanding one among those three. She had originally come to the United States from the Virgin Islands, and, as an immigrant, somewhat looked down upon even in the bitter slums of Harlem, she seemed to have acquired an extra tendon of pride to sustain her in her precarious posture of hard-won self-assurance. She had great humor, too, and when I first hired her I realized at once that she was a person of considerable character. She was very tall and exceptionally thin, with beautifully slender hands and feet. Also, she was a thirty-three-year-old spinster. I once heard her laughingly say to my wife, "I'm a virgin from the Virgin Islands—and they don't generally have enough of them around for export."

I cannot tell you how affectionately she eventually came to care for, and even to gently tyrannize over, our household, and how clearly it was understood between us that she was indeed an integral part of our lives.

I say all this to give honor to the years of her service with us, but I would also like to recall at least one occasion which would perhaps partially demonstrate the delicately pivoted balance of the emotional and social relationship between us. Perhaps I had better tell you about the time when my house was robbed.

I was living with my family on East Thirty-seventh Street during those years, but we also owned a good-sized log cabin up in Kent Cliffs, New York, where we generally spent most of our summers while the children were still rather young. Well, it was this place in the country that had suddenly been invaded by some local marauders in the middle of winter, and one day a deputy sheriff, or some other sort of legal *shamus*, came to town to alert us about this piece of vandalism. Frankly, I was rather reluctant to go to Kent Cliffs to inspect the amount of the damage since we had nothing at all in the house that was worth seriously bothering about. Outside of the furniture, we only had left some boxes of canned goods on the kitchen shelves, and I couldn't quite imagine what sort of desperate character had decided to invade a boarded-up log cabin standing up to its high porches in hard-frozen snow.

But the arm of the law was flexed, and I just had to get dressed like a polar explorer to go into the wilderness and assess the injury done to my property. It was truly idiotic, and I was simply furious. On the way up to the country, the legal minion gave me the low-down on the situation.

"It's dem kids," he said. "Dem kids have broken into a half-a-dozen places on the Cliffs, and dey spilled a lot of dried peas and rice all over de floors. Dey shot off one of Judge Langley's guns, too—dat's why we gotta prosecute—see?"

In other words, some of the local farm boys, snowed in over the winter and bored to the point of acute stupefaction, had broken into the homes of a few summer residents and, finding nothing that was worth the taking, had finally, out of pure frustration, I suppose, dribbled a lot of boxed cereals

322

all around those icy premises. As I've already indicated, the whole hullabaloo was really quite silly—but those foolish youngsters had committed one pretty serious crime (a crime against common sense): they had also feloniously entered the home of Judge Alfred Langley, a retired Tammany hack—a man afflicted by a sense of megalomanic self-importance and capable of pretty formidable and sustained rancor. They had, as it turned out, perpetrated no sort of damage to his goods and chattels, either—they had, however, fired several shots out of one of his hunting rifles. I was told that, after discharging these aimless blasts, the intruders had even carefully replaced the weapon to its proper place on the gunrack; but what drove the irascible jurist to absolute frenzy was the fact that they had failed to clean out and properly polish the barrel of the gun, after firing.

In my house I found that the invaders had lifted a couple of cans of embalmed frankfurters, and, aside from the damage to the front-door lock, I couldn't discover anything else amiss. At any rate, that afternoon I appeared before the local grand jury to give my testimony. This conscripted body of law was composed of local farmers, of course, all of whom I knew, and I testified to the effect that if *I* had been snowed in over the winter at the age of sixteen—the least I would do would be to break open all the sealed-up summer cottages in the neighborhood. I claimed to have suffered no injury worth mentioning and earnestly appealed to those tobacco-chewing worthies to forget the whole thing. I understand that Judge Langley, who followed me with his testimony, was a good deal less amiable about this whole matter—but since the children suspected of having perpetrated this nuisance were, all of them, in one way or another, related to the grand jurors—the verdict was to find *no fault,* and the charges were, at once, summarily dismissed.

When I came back to New York, I told my family all about

the case, and only Marie, our moral balance wheel, seemed quite put out by the way I had reacted to this whole situation.

"You want those children to grow up to be housebreakers?" she asked me.

"Of course not," I said. "It was just foolish mischief on their part, and I'm sure they didn't mean any real harm at all. After all, how would you like to be snowed in all winter, in the country, with not a damned thing to do?"

"There's always plenty to do around a farm, summer or winter," she said. "I just think that some day those parents of those children will not give you thanks for what you did to-day. You should have made it plain to those boys that to break a lock on another man's door is a serious thing. I think it's too bad Judge Langley was mixed up in it, because he is just an old curmudgeon who should have lived three hundred years ago. But you were at fault, too—because there is a road of right that leads straight between the Langleys and the Kings that those children had better learn to walk on. I don't think that much of God's work was accomplished by any of you this day. Not much."

That was her unshakable opinion, and nobody was able to talk her out of it.

The following summer, after we'd moved out into the country again, I was stopped on the road one afternoon by one of my neighbors, a farmer by the name of Herman Goff. "It was my son Steven who was the ringleader of that gang of kids last winter," he said. "He broke into your house, too, and I heard that it was your words to the jury that finally squashed the case. Mr. King, I'm really very thankful to you."

"It's nothing," I said. "After all, we were all young and foolish once, and I'm sure he'll never do such a thing again."

"I hope you're right," said Goff. "All I can say is that he's always been a very good boy till now, and I want you to know that he's a first-rate mechanic for his age—and if there's ever anything wrong with your car, or any of the other machinery around your place, he'll come around and straighten it out for you in a minute. That's the least he can do for you. Matter of fact, I'll send him around next Saturday, and you let him look over your motor; he's a real whiz with motors."

"Oh, that isn't at all necessary, Mr. Goff," I said. "Steven doesn't owe me a thing."

"I think he does," said Goff. "I think he ought to show his appreciation and be of some service to you. Don't think any more about it, Mr. King. He'll be glad to drop by every once in a while and look things over in your garage."

When I got home for luncheon I told the family about my talk with Mr. Goff. "Steve is probably going to come over Saturday," I said, "and see how the car is doing. I think the station wagon needs new brake linings, anyway. Maybe he'll drive it down to the village and have it attended to."

I noticed that, all through my discourse, Marie's face was as buttoned up as a priest's cassock. She served the meal without a word, and I had no way of knowing how she was taking the news about Mr. Goff's offer on behalf of his son.

On Saturday I found out.

The kids and I were playing croquet on the lawn behind our cabin, and about two o'clock Marie came out on the porch and waved significantly to us.

"What is it, Marie?" I asked.

"Mr. King," she said, "your *burglar* is here!!!"

She said it quite seriously.

After all, I was a man of some means. I had a maid, a country home; I had a man who looked after our garden; and now I even had my own burglar.

Later, when Steve had washed up and was ready to leave, Marie called him over to the kitchen window. "I've got a cherry pie here, for your father," she said. "Your father is a good man who knows what's right and what's wrong. Not like *some* people around here. You can have a slice too, and don't forget to bring the pie plate back—when you come again next Saturday."

That was our Marie.

Some years after Marie had died, I visited her home grounds, the Virgin Islands, and I even talked to some of her relatives about her. I was cruising pretty extensively in the Caribbean at the time, doing some sort of photo-reportage job with a cameraman for one of the news magazines. It was in the early forties, I think, and when I happened to contract a pretty serious infection in one of my hands I finally stopped off at Haiti to have one of the Austrian refugee doctors there look after it for me. This was Dr. Erich Wohlheim, whom I had come to know rather well in Paris some years before all these events took place.

I installed myself in the Oloffson Hotel, up on the hill, and, after a couple of days, I became rather curious about one of my fellow guests, an American lady named Sandra Palmer. She was a tall, blue-eyed, blond-haired woman in her late thirties, or early forties, perhaps, and she looked like the female guardian principle celebrated in carved effigies on the prows of ancient ships. She could readily have posed for Freya, the great Norse goddess, and she certainly carried herself proudly and beautifully, as hardly any women ever do nowadays. She wore her hair in a wide braid around her head, and her clothes, even in Haiti, had a certain heroically Icelandic cut about them. She didn't live in the main structure of the hotel at all—she had, instead, rented a small cottage on the premises and only took two meals a day along with the other guests on the main terrace.

In the tropics it is, of course, quite inevitable that you meet all the other outlanders, and by the end of the week I had even visited Sandra Palmer's cottage. She had it attrac-

326

tively embellished with certain easily available local handicrafts, and when the time came she served me some truly delicious Chinese tea.

It was at once apparent to me that she was a person of considerable intellectual attainments, and, as a matter of fact, she talked to me at great length about art and archaeology, with particular emphasis on Etruscan sculpture. Now real Etruscan art is very rare, and not very much is known about the Etruscans. Indeed, that whole period in human history is pretty well shrouded by the mists of scholarly conjecture, and I can't tell you how fascinated I was by my hostess' gently modulated erudition.

"Have you been to Tuscany?" I asked her. "And have you seen the tombs and watched the diggings yourself?"

"Yes," she said. "I've spent almost three years with some of the archaeologists there, and I plan to go back again next May."

"Is this just a hobby of yours," I said, "or are you actively engaged in some serious researches of your own?"

"Both," she said. "Would you like another cup of tea, Mr. King?"

And that's about as far as I got with her.

However, the following day, when I went to have the dressing on my hand changed, I asked Dr. Wohlheim about her.

"Actually, she is a five-hundred-page novel by D. H. Lawrence," he said.

"Wasn't *he* pretty interested in the Etruscans, too?" I asked.

"He was. But he would have been even more interested in her. She is one of his natural, unwritten heroines."

"Do you know her?" I said.

"I do, but, better still, my wife used to be an intimate friend of hers, and she even visited with us several times in Europe."

I must tell you at this point that Dr. Wohlheim's wife, who

had but recently died, had originally been an American girl whom he had encountered for the first time while she had been doing some postgraduate medical work in Vienna.

"So you know all about her," I said.

"Nobody ever knows *all* about anybody else. The best you can do is make an enlightened and, I hope, amiable guess as to what makes people tick."

"How come she knows so much about the Etruscans?" I said.

"That's all she lives for," he said. "At least, that's all she's *been* living for during these past ten years. You see, she was a very brilliant student. My wife told me that really great things were expected of Sandra Palmer."

"So what happened?"

"She got married, while still very young, to a man named Llewellyn Rawford."

"Rawford?" I said. "Isn't that some kind of a great art expert or something?"

"That's *Louis* Rawford, his father, you're thinking of."

"So what if she got married?" I said. "Nowadays women pretty well manage to follow their natural inclinations just the same—don't they?"

"It isn't always easy," said Dr. Wohlheim. "You see, Llewellyn Rawford was the son of a very famous man. You know perfectly well that that is one of the greatest hardships any human being can possibly bear."

"Yes," I said. "I've known some of the children of distinguished people, and most of them were just howling disasters."

"Just so," he said. "Llewellyn was in a particularly unfortunate position because he actually did have some of his father's great endowments. Sometimes that even works out. The Brueghels, the Van Eycks, the Adamses, and the Huxleys managed very well, despite close propinquity to greatness—but those are very exceptional cases. Llewellyn was an only son who specialized in art *expertise,* too, and there just didn't seem to be enough room for two Rawfords in the same business at the same time. I think it's damned lucky Bernard Berenson never had any sons."

"So what happened?"

"First of all, Sandra became pregnant. There weren't ever any financial worries, because the old man was earning enough for everybody, of course, and, in a little while, they moved to Paris. I think even their first child was born there. At any rate, from the way *she* tells it, the marriage didn't really work well from the very start. Llewellyn had a great deal too much free time on his hands, and so he spent most of it at home, with her, doing some desultory research, some spasmodic writing, and a lot of griping about the world in general and about the art world in particular. She claims she would never have gotten involved with him if she had ever properly surmised his vast aimlessness. What had brought them together had been their joint passion for painting and sculpture and, of course, their obviously great physical attractions. Llewellyn is six feet two and looks like a Russian ballet dancer. He is dark-haired, rather taciturn, athletic, and really remarkably intelligent. Sandra you have seen. Eighteen years ago—she is forty now—she was absolutely ravishing. Of course, the one figure who completely overshadowed their lives was Llewellyn's father. Somehow or other, Sandra had never managed to meet him. He was always off somewhere writing—lecturing—giving cast-iron opinions on various art objects—and during most of the early years of her marriage he was in Tuscany, working with some archaeologists in their diggings."

"Aha!" I said. "I'm beginning to smell an Etruscan!"

"Not yet," said Dr. Wohlheim. "After they had their second child, Llewellyn decided to go to Persia. It was at least a field his father had never touched. So, off they went, and stayed for about a year and a half before Llewellyn discovered that it had been so thoroughly gone over by experts that there was really no place for him to sink his eyeteeth into. And then, while he went back to America, she and her two little boys returned to Paris. Shortly after she'd gotten herself settled out in Neuilly somewhere, old man Rawford suddenly announced that he was coming to France to see his grandchildren. And that's when Sandra finally met him, for the first time. It proved to be the great, joyous and catastrophic event of her life. She fell instantly in love with him. He was as handsome or handsomer than Llewellyn. Indeed, Llewellyn suddenly seemed like a mere childish travesty of his rugged and grizzled father. He was a man with a mission; he was a man with passion—he was a man who radiated personality and glamour. A real, honest-to-God thunderclap."

"What about *him?*" I said. "The old man, I mean. Did he fall for her, too?"

"Who knows? We can only conjecture. The chances are he did. He had been a widower for nearly a decade, and Sandra, with her looks, could have upset a fire hydrant. When Llewellyn came back from America, he found that his wife insisted on having a bedroom of her own, and, what's more, she didn't really ever want him to come in there, either. Llewellyn had no trouble imagining what had happened—the only thing he was sure of was that the old man would never make a false move. In this dreadful *hate-love* relationship which he had developed toward his father over the years, he was still unable to accredit him with just the ordinary vices of common men. So, he did the only thing he could do, considering the peculiar dilemma he found himself in. He began to cast doubts and aspersions on his father's artistic and scientific judgments. Strange, anonymous articles began to appear in the various public prints in which Louis Rawford's opinions and dicta on various aesthetic matters were being seriously questioned. The old man had aroused enough envious conjectures during his overly active life, and so these scurrilous pieces were not only happily welcomed in certain quarters but were joyously commented on by many of his frustrated colleagues. After a while there was a real tide of calumny that began to engulf his name, and the one point where the most headway was being made was on the subject of his Etruscan authentications. You see, Louis Rawford had managed to collect a great many Etruscan bronzes and terra-cotta pieces from the very best period of that civilization—about 600 B.C., I think—and, finally, somebody even produced an Italian sculptor, Carlo Sonati, by name, who claimed that he was really the author of a good many of those supposedly antique figures."

"I remember something about that," I said. "Sonati disappeared all of a sudden, didn't he? I remember reading about it at the time."

"You are quite right," said Dr. Wohlheim. "Sandra, as soon as she found out who was actually behind that whole campaign of slander, of course, instantly began to sue Llewellyn for a divorce. That's ten years ago now, and the battle between her and Llewellyn has never ceased. However, it came to a real head three years ago when the old man fell into one of those digging pits and instantly died. You see, when his will was probated it was disclosed that Louis Rawford had left his entire Etruscan collection to his ex-daughter-in-law, Sandra Palmer. I don't know how many lawyers in various countries are making a fat living, even now, trying to break that will. Of course, to Sandra it was not only a great triumph, it was a post-mortem verification that the old man had loved her just as much as she had loved him. I remember seeing her a few times, just about then, and I can tell you she looked like Niobe —like Isolde—and quite a bit like a goddess of vengeance, too. She spends all of her time since his death to authenticate, beyond the shadow of a doubt, all of his archaeological and aesthetic judgments. She has two of the greatest scholars in that field preparing an enormous work on her Etruscan collection, and that is, incidentally, the reason she is here in Haiti right now. Dr. Ehrenfeld, one of her experts, is waiting here for his visa to go to America, where the work will finally be completed and published. After publication, she will very likely house all these works of art in some special wing of a great museum, or perhaps in some university building to be particularly set aside for these treasures. You simply cannot imagine how many art people are after her to move all this stuff into their bailiwicks."

"And what about Llewellyn?" I said.

"Last anybody heard of him, he's in a sanatorium up in Connecticut, somewhere, and he only seems to emerge, from time to time, to hire new attorneys—and to devise new methods of attack against his father's last will and testament. However, a lawyer-patient of mine, from America, who knows quite a bit about the matter, told me just recently that Llewellyn is actually running out of courts that will further bother even to consider his case. It seems, also, that he has practically impoverished his share of the estate with all those costly legal fees. I, personally, think that Sandra is just waiting for him to go completely broke, so that she can offer him the job as curator of her Etruscan collection when it finally goes on exhibition before the public. She is a woman of truly noble proportions, and I think her passions are designed along equally classical lines."

"Tell me just one thing," I said. "How was it possible for Louis to gather all these art works together? Doesn't the Italian government forbid the export of such national treasures?"

"I think he made a deal with them," said the doctor. "I think they let him keep one out of every so many—in full return for his expert services. That's another thing Llewellyn accused him of—he claimed that the old man had given the authorities a lot of freshly made junk, while he kept all the good things for himself. But Sandra shipped the whole collection off to Italy and let the government experts examine everything for themselves. I really don't think poor Llewellyn has a chance. He is just up against a fierce natural force that is totally, and unequivocally, committed to a dead man."

"I really must look up the Etruscans when I get back home again," I said. "I never suspected they might become the springboard for such a fascinating story."

"You won't find out much about them," said Dr. Wohlheim. "You see, they are one of the few peoples who ever lived on this earth whose alphabet nobody has as yet been able to decipher completely. We do know certain things about them, of course. We know they had the most elaborately painted women, the most fiercely visaged warriors, and the very gayest burial tombs. They wrestled and fought in the open arena with wolves, bears, bulls and lions, and they seemed to love music on all occasions and above all things. I'm sure they were quite a rascally and mischievous lot, too, and I think they would have been utterly enchanted with Sandra Palmer."

Sandra has stayed in my mind throughout the years, but, then, a great many women whose emotional antennae were not even vaguely pointed in my direction seem to have haunted my memory far more persistently than a good many of the ladies who eventually became rather intimately involved with me. For nearly half a century I have been under the spell of a little girl whose puppetlike face and figure first enraptured my childish imagination at the age of twelve.

Her name was Lisl Gandolfi, and she was the youngest daughter of an acrobatic family collectively known as the Flying Gandolfis. They performed predominantly on the medium-high trapeze, and after I had lost my heart to Lisl as the topmost pinnacle of a structure consisting of her incredibly agile siblings, sturdily sustained by her sensationally muscled begetters, I finally decided to do something about it. I had saved a little money at the time, and so I bought an enormous bouquet of rather loose-lipped roses, and, encumbered with this gargantuan nosegay, I installed myself in a seat that was nearly on eye level with the diminutive Lisl when the grand finale of the Gandolfi performance reached its apex. I think I ought to mention that those enormous overripe blooms of mine were held together by a network of supporting wire that could easily have supplied the inner structures of at least seven ordinary umbrellas. In short, before I had ever landed in my highly strategic post I was already bleeding from half-a-dozen cuts and scratches that I had managed to acquire while conveying my floral tribute up to my front-row seat in the first balcony.

When the Flying Gandolfis finally reached the end of their vertiginous performance—that is to say, they were all six of them, in diminutional proportions, standing on top of one another—I suddenly hurled my horticultural time bomb directly at the midriff of that unsuspecting child, and a loud cry of sudden dismay rose like an oceanic roar from the assembled spectators in that arena. Fortunately, the fantastic, catlike agility of those combined ambidexterites successfully prevented what might easily have become a major disaster. Indeed, Gandolfi *père* managed to snatch the fluttering Lisl away from imminent disaster only a mere second before her doll-like skull was about to crack open on the tanbark.

I will draw a discreet veil over most of the events which ensued immediately after my little amorous tribute had managed to achieve its target. I will only tell you that I was instantly grabbed by some very powerful men and that, eventually, a deeply irate judge lectured my shattered parents for fifteen solid minutes about the proper way to bring up children. His Honor concluded with a rather sinister prognosis on the subject of my rather doubtful future, but, in view of my tender age and certain mitigating testimonials from several of my teachers, I was, at last, remanded in custody of my attorney, who, very fortunately for all of us, happened to be a blood relation of the officiating justice.

Six weeks after my little serenade of mayhem had run its course, a much-puzzled policeman arrived at my house and handed me a picture post card originating in Copenhagen and addressed to my name in care of the local magistrates' court.

It was a greeting from Lisl.

"Dear Bullcalf," she said. "I forgive you because I think you didn't really mean any harm. Copenhagen is beautiful. They have cookies here called Kreutzerkeks. They are the best. Your friend, Lisl."

You can't imagine how many dreary circus performances I have sat through, and how many hackneyed vaudeville acts I inspected throughout the following years—just on the mere outside chance that I might find my Lisl again.

I never did.

At another time, when I had just turned thirteen, my mother and I happened to be shopping in a Viennese department store not too far from where we lived when a strange girl, who spoke only halting German, suddenly accosted us. She turned out to be a teen-age emigrant, en route from Russia to America, and she only wanted my mother to direct her to a public bathhouse of some sort, where she might clean herself up, and where she could conveniently manage to change into some fresh clothing.

I cannot tell you how much the wild beauty of that pale girl, as well as her outlandish accent, affected my already highly inflamed imagination.

Her name was Ileana Iswolski.

My mother, without hesitating for a moment, at once invited her to our home, of course. Ileana blushed and made

335

becomingly polite noises about not wanting to intrude on us, but, in the end, she seemed happy enough to come along. On the way to our home she made us understand that she was traveling in the company of twenty-three other people and that the transportation agent who was responsible for their tour had been treating the lot of them just as so much cattle. There had been no bathing facilities for nearly five days, she said, and, since they were stopping off at Vienna for about four hours, she had decided to break away from the group and to find some means of getting herself properly spruced up.

My mother behaved throughout all this talk as if she were listening to the most ordinary sort of routine conversation. Later she did admit her bewilderment to me, but while it lasted she couldn't possibly have been playing it any cooler. When we got to the house, she instantly ran a tub of water— produced her fluffiest towels—and offered up her most delicately scented soaps on the altar of hospitality.

I was so spellbound by Ileana that, every once in a while, I found myself literally gasping for air. I think that, for moments on end, I simply forgot to breathe altogether. At any rate, while my mother went out to the kitchen to talk to our girl about preparing a small snack of some sort for our transient angel, I plumped myself down on my mother's bed—with my eyes hynotically riveted onto that bathroom door, behind which Ileana was performing her sacred ablutions.

And then, after a little while, a wonderfully unbelievable thing happened. Ileana opened the door and stood before me in all of her ravishing nudity.

I had seen completely naked women before, of course. For more than two years I had been a regular pupil at the Secession Art School, where live models posed for our classes at least twice a week. But never during those two years had I seen *such* a figure—a figure shrinking away in infinite grace

336

the moment she became aware of my unexpected presence. Although she was obviously in a state of acute surprise when she discovered that she was not alone, there was no excessive show of female fugitiveness in her manner at all. With the immemorial self-assurance of all true beauty, she merely made a small, almost demure, concession to the commonly accepted statutes of civilized modesty and withdrew herself from my sight, like a quickly waning moon.

"I'm terribly sorry," she said, "but I forgot my fresh clothes out on the wicker basket in your hallway. Would you please get them for me?"

With burning cheeks I went to fetch her sacred belongings, and when she reached out to take them from me she gave me a smile of such sweet conspiratorial communion that I have been carrying the image of it in my heart for nearly fifty years—that, as well as the whiteness of her skin, the slenderness of her limbs, and the dark triangular hummock that shadowed the delta of her ultimate womanly vulnerability.

Ileana passed out of our lives that very afternoon, but I have continued to search for her—for almost half a century.

Of such, and suchlike, is made up the secret kingdom of a man's imaginative life, and in the seraglio of my mind these shadowy figures will continue to be enthroned as long as a single thought is still left rambling around inside my head.

I will tell you about another one of my frustrated romances, and this one concerns a young art student whom I came to know, very briefly, at the Metropolitan Museum of Art in New York City some time in 1915. Her name was Nancy Stanhope, and she used to come to the museum five times a week to copy a small Gerard Dou. It was a painting full of minute and meticulously delineated details showing a Dutch cavalier gazing out of a vine-covered window. I couldn't imagine why that dear girl had ever come to bother with that extremely difficult and rather trivial problem; and yet, I was myself involved, at the time, with an equally foolish and even more complicated and painstaking opus of my own. I was making a large pen-and-ink drawing of the Rheims cathedral. This great Christian monument had been bombed by the Germans during their first invasion of Belgium—and—I daresay I fancied that—somewhere—some day—someone would pay me a huge sum for this unique work. There were about twelve hundred statues strewn about the façade of this edifice, and, believe me, I rendered these figures with as much careful attention as the original sculptors had probably showered upon them in the Middle Ages.

A really nutty piece of business.

Well, one day, while I was taking a little breather out in the corridor, I noticed a dark-haired, very sleepy-eyed girl tiptoeing up to my library table and taking a look at my work. I had seen her before, in one of the upstairs galleries, painting away at her meaningless Gerard Dou, and even during that short glimpse of her I had been deeply touched by a certain waiflike, almost otherwordly, forlornness in her pallid face. Her half-closed eyes had a fairy-tale quality of drowsiness in them which at once touched me to the heart. "She is Sleeping Beauty who doesn't ever want to wake up," I said to myself. Indeed, I was so eager to keep intact all my lovely illusions toward her that I even decided to sacrifice any of the pleasures her acquaintance might possibly bring me to the infinitely more seductive imaginings that I had fancied about her.

But when she stopped to inspect my handiwork that day I finally decided to speak to her.

"Silly, isn't it?" I said. "But I began it sort of halfheartedly about three months ago, and now I don't seem to be able to stop myself from going on."

"It is beautiful," she said, and I realized, with a shiver of joy, that she not only had submarine eyes but that she also had the *voice* of Undine. "I envy you," she continued, "because you'll never get done with it."

"Is that why you are copying the Gerard Dou?" I said.

The faintest trace of blood crept into her high cheekbones. "Yes," she said. "I like to work on projects whose end can't be foreseen. I daresay it's like being snowed in up to the eaves. I can't quite explain it—but that's the sort of problem that especially appeals to me."

We said a few other things, too, but you can easily guess that after that short conversation the spell of her enchantment was even more firmly knit across my wildly romantic faculties. Nevertheless, I managed to remain true to my original purpose, which was to avoid her as much as possible. I drew great comfort from the mere fact that five days a week she was alive in the same building with me, and that I could, at will, climb two flights of pseudoclassical stairs and find myself in her magical presence.

An acquaintance of mine, a boy called Vance Donner, was copying some paintings at the museum, too, and, as was quite inevitable, this lad was, after a while, also quite struck by the evasive beauty of my little nixie. "I wish I had a decent studio," he said to me one day. "I'd like to invite her up to pose for me."

"Why don't you leave her alone?" I said. "You've *got* a girl, haven't you?"

"As a matter of fact, I'm planning to get married next year," he said. "But that doesn't mean that I don't have eyes left for something special."

"She's like a visitor from another planet," I said. "I'm really surprised she speaks English."

"Sometimes she looks like a delicate plant," he said. "Maybe you're right about her; after all, you don't really have to handle every primrose or tear hunks out of every lilac bush you pass—do you?"

You see, he was really quite a nice guy. He read Stendhal and Keats, and even the most subtle emotions of the human heart were quite accessible to him. Until—!

After four and a half decades I still hate to bring back to mind what eventually happened between us.

One day I came to the museum, and when I got to the subterranean room where we generally stored our work I found Nancy packing her half-finished canvas into an ordinary brown paper bag.

"You'll just ruin that picture," I said. "You ought to nail four corks into the corners of the stretcher and get a large cardboard to put across the front of it before you put any paper around it."

"I know," she said, looking at me, quite distraught, "but I haven't the time. I'm leaving for India this afternoon, and I have a million things still left to do before we start out."

"India?" I said as my heart was suddenly turned to cement and a taste of sand came into my mouth. "How long will you be gone?"

"For many years," she said. "You see, I'm an orphan, and my father's brother has sent for me to live with him in Hyderabad. It's all just like a dream, isn't it? I haven't really realized it all completely—because if I did—I suppose I'd just lie down on the ground and do nothing. It's just too much for my small brain to cope with. So, I just put one foot in front of the other and pretend I'm only going up to Larchmont for the weekend."

I said nothing, but with burning eyes I methodically proceeded to properly wrap that painting of hers. When it was finally done, I helped her carry her paintbox and her canvas out into the street, where she ran on ahead of me to hail a taxi. I helped to stow her various belongings into the cab, and my sense of loss and of stupefaction so completely flooded my whole being that for a moment I hardly reacted when she suddenly put her arms around me. But I finally did wake up, long enough to cling to her, desperately, for a moment, like a lost soul.

"I shall always remember you," she said; "you and your cathedral." And then she kissed me on the mouth. "Please have it photographed and send me a print of it. Don't wait until it is done—do it tomorrow!"

"Where shall I write to you?" I said.

"Write care of Gerald Stanhope, Government House, Hyderabad," she said.

And then she was gone.

There is an ancient obelisk stationed right in back of the museum, and often before, in past bouts with misery, I had climbed the small hill on which it is located and had plunked myself down in its shadow. I did it again that afternoon, and I cannot tell you how, or why, but the mere presence of that antique stone helped to calm my frantically churned up spirits into at least a socially negotiable state of torpor.

After a while I decided to go back into the museum store-room to collect my picture, and when I got there the little old woman who was employed as caretaker of our treasures seemed to be in a state of unusual fluster.

"Evvybody's movin' today!" she said. "I never seen sech goin's on. Dey storm in here demandin' paper and string, like dis wuz a stationery store or sumpin'. I don't mind bein' helpful to folks, but dey's a limit to what dey has a right to expeck, after all."

"What happened?" I said. "Who else moved this afternoon besides Miss Stanhope?"

"Dat friend o' yours—what's his name?—Vance—I tink. De one dat's doin' dat fat Eyetalian woman wid de shawl. Vance Donner, dat's who I mean."

"Vance is moving, too?" I said.

"He moved already," she said. "Went troo here like a

tornadoo—dat's what he did. Here—! He leff dis envelope for you, too, an' I ain't gonna be no servant an' no post office for nobody. Dat's not my job!"

She handed me a large Manila envelope, and when I opened it I found it to be full of scraps of torn paper. It was my Rheims cathedral. Vance had shredded my drawing into tiny bits, and when I turned the envelope completely upside down I found among those tattered fragments a scribbled note written with a brush. It said:

> I saw everything! In certain places, under certain conditions, this might cost someone his life. You have deliberately and foully betrayed a sacred trust, and I am destroying the lie you are working on merely as a memorial to your treason. May your life with her be one long misery.
>
> VANCE

It was more than likely that he had observed the two of us on the street in front of the museum, and when he had seen her put her arms around my neck—and even kiss me—he must have concluded that our relationship had finally matured to a point of public intimacy. In a flash of blinding fury he had probably felt himself ultimately betrayed; had felt that I had eliminated him as a rival by the most flagrantly heartless of devious devices—by having fraudulently imposed on his poetic imagination—and by having appealed to his spontaneous chivalry as an artist—while I myself had secretly managed to pursue my own revoltingly lecherous ends.

I tell you all this without the slightest warrant of any authority. I just *imagine* that that's what really happened that afternoon at the museum. I shall never know for certain what actually did take place—since, for the rest of my whole, long life, I never again laid eyes on Vance Donner.

342

But the earliest betrayal of my own existence actually happened in Vienna shortly after my eleventh birthday. I had a cousin on my mother's side, whose name was Laura Breuer, who suddenly erupted into my life like a shimmering fountain of the purest radiance. She was just eighteen at the time, and this age discrepancy alone would surely have been enough to discourage any reasonable human imagination, excepting only my own, of course. I fell desperately in love with her gray, deeply shadowed eyes; her beautiful, dark, soft brown hair; and her exquisitely modeled neck and hands.

And now comes the hazel-hatchery part. This ravishing girl seemed, quite deliberately, to encourage my advances, and, what is more, she never spoke to me, even before other people, as if she were merely addressing a child. There was never the sound of trivial, grown-up condescension in her manner toward me, and if we ever happened to go out walking together she invariably deferred to me in various small and yet significant matters, as if I had been her logical, and carefully chosen, cavalier.

I remember going with her to the various museums and public parks around the city, and spending many hours in elaborately voluble communion with her, and never once during those rapturous journeys did she ever betray the slightest sense of adult patronage toward me. If we ever took tea together in any of the *Konditoreis* that were strewn about Vienna, *I* was always the one who did the ordering for both of us, and *I* was the one who paid the check, and appropriately tipped the waiter, afterward.

Well, this dream of unadulterated bliss lasted for an entire winter, and I lived altogether in such a state of tremulous ecstasy that I simply marveled at the blindness of the people all around us—who never once suspected the feverishly enraptured state of my emotions.

And then one day we had a visitor at our house, a Dr.

Arnim Wilmer from Prague, who had come to spend part of his vacation in Vienna. He was a nice enough looking young chap—dark-haired and a little nearsighted, perhaps—but let me tell you that even at that early period when this character showed up for the first time at our dinner table I at once recognized a truly shocking change in the behavior of my adored Laura.

She became—suddenly—almost cute.

I mean, she positively fidgeted and grew kittenish in the presence of that myopic disaster, and her manner toward me, throughout that soul-shattering séance, was absolutely revolting. Her hypocritical tone seemed to have been derived from those nauseating juvenile books which people were constantly giving me for Christmas, and, indeed, it was more like a line of verbiage that had been especially derived from the manual of a nursing home for retarded children.

Halfway through that disastrous meal I pleaded a violent headache and went instantly to my room and to bed. I cannot tell you what a tempest of chagrin was raging in my soul, and I finally did fall asleep, because I literally wept myself out of my painful bewilderment into a state of complete exhaustion.

The next day, Laura and I had been planning to go to the zoo in Schoenbrunn, but, since the previous night's celebration had concluded at a rather late hour, she begged to be excused until the following day. So I went off to the park by myself, and you can believe me that I found the whole world suddenly transformed into a totally burnt out cinder pile. I remember sitting down on a bench opposite a large aviary, and my eyes filled with uncontrollable tears as I watched those playfully chattering birds leaping and flying about that enormous cage with seemingly not an anxious thought beneath their carefree feathers.

I realized, of course, that I had to learn to master myself.

344

The perceptive eyes of my mother would require constant self-control and elaborate forms of deception on my part, and I made many secret vows to carry my grief with becoming manly dignity.

One thing I must tell you—that although nothing actually overt had as yet taken place between Laura and Dr. Wilmer during their first meeting—my heart knew as if it had been written in large letters of fire across the sky—that deep, un-namable sorrows were brewing for me somewhere in the womb of time. I absolutely dreaded to wake up in the morning —because I had the feeling that some bitterly inevitable proc-ess had been set into motion that would forever banish all further joy from my life.

During the following days, Dr. Wilmer came to our house with constantly increasing frequency, and as the relationship between him and Laura became more and more relaxed, her manner toward me finally turned into one of somewhat self-conscious, almost formal, friendliness. All our little secrets, the wonderful thoughts we had expressed to one another during our long, enchanting walks through the city, were just as if they had never been. I had, obviously, been brutally and relentlessly betrayed by just a common flirt.

I began to lose weight, and my mother suddenly became quite worried about me. I had foreseen and feared just such a contingency, and I did my childish utmost to present a brave front to hide my desperately lonely ordeal.

I used to conceal myself behind curtains and doorways for long, long periods of time, just to study, to analyze, the me-diocre physical presence and the small intellectual endow-ments of my rival. I couldn't, for the life of me, understand how a brilliant and beautiful girl like Laura was able to see any merit in that awkward, ill-spoken oaf. His hairline, which, despite his young years, was already beginning to recede, looked as if a flock of halfhearted mice had been nibbling away at its outer periphery, and his large, translucent ears were so absurdly pink that I sometimes had difficulty not to laugh directly into his face.

Meanwhile, "the wheels of destiny ground relentlessly on," and one apocalyptic afternoon I heard my mother say to my father, "I think they ought not to get married until next year. It is much too soon after his mother's death even to announce the engagement right now."

No names were mentioned, but my prescient heart knew only too well what final disaster was now impending. I became so desperate in my unuttered misery that, for the first time in my life, I decided to leave home. I couldn't possibly face the unavoidable prenuptial festivities with any sort of reasonable human composure, and I seriously planned to run off to my dear friend, Nandor, in Hungary, until all these disastrous events had finally passed into history.

And then I became very seriously ill. I contracted double pneumonia and was far too feeble in my misery to remain very acutely aware of what was going on around me. For weeks on end I lay in bed, surrounded by the loving and frightened concern of my family, and when Laura occasionally dropped into my sickroom to offer me her sympathetic, wide-eyed stare I thought I even recognized traces of a certain shameful agony in *her* pale face that were not altogether caused by her worries over my illness alone.

Eventually, after I had recovered, I went off with my mother to convalesce on the beautiful shores of the upper Danube. My dear, dear mother, a woman of almost unbelievable awareness, never once mentioned Laura's name to me throughout that whole summer. Luckily, recuperation from severe illness is a totally magical and completely absorbing process. It is as if the organism which had come so close to extinction were slowly and yet ever so eagerly rediscovering all the wonders of God's great world. My body healed, and so did my mind, and one day, shortly before we returned to Vienna, I said to my mother, "When is Laura's wedding going to take place?"

"In two months," my mother said. "They are going to be married in Prague, where most of his family lives, and where his medical practice is located, too. We are not planning to go to Prague. I'm going to give them my mother's four silver candlesticks for a wedding present. They are over a hundred years old, and Laura has always admired them so much. And now we had better go indoors, because at this time of day the wind is getting just a little too cool for sitting around in the shadow of these huge trees. Yes, the summer is almost over, and everything—everything—eventually passes; doesn't it, my darling?"

"Yes, Mother," I said. "It does."

CHAPTER TWENTY

_____

As I THINK BACK upon all the people I have written about in this book, it comes to me what a great number of
them have been valuable human beings, intelligent and well-
intentioned, and how many of them have enriched and even
loved me. As for those men and women who touched me
deeply on our way toward death—I should have kissed them
more, too, before it was too late. Actually, most of them never
really knew the true nature of my esteem for them, and I am
sure that this was wrong, since I don't believe I shall ever have
a chance to rectify this grievous lapse—in any Elysian fields
—hereafter.

And, to those people who would console me with hopes of
immortality, I can only say, "Thanks, folks—thanks a lot—I
take it very kindly of you. I do, indeed."

Believe me, I _am_ consoled. I had a rich and colorful life—

loaded with undeserved rewards—and I was always ready to accept the world most thankfully—just as I was able to perceive it. That's quite something—isn't it? It was always enough for *me*.

Two thousand years ago, a Chinese king wrote this about his dead mistress:

> *The rustle of her silken skirts*
> *Has ceased on the marble pavement.*
> *The gray dust has grown deep.*
> *Her empty rooms are cold and still.*
> *The fallen leaves*
> *Are piled high against her door.*

This unknown woman, ennobled by an emperor's grief, has become as immortal as ever *I* aspire to be.